D1616650

JANE'S LIGHT TANKS AND ARMOURED CARS

JANE'S LIGHT TANKS AND ARMOURED CARS

Christopher F. Foss

JANE'S

Copyright © Christopher F Foss 1984

First published in the United Kingdom in 1984 by
Jane's Publishing Company Limited
238 City road, London EC1V 2PU

ISBN 0 7106 0322 3

All rights reserved. No part of this publication may be reproduced,
stored in a retrieval system, transmitted in any form by any means
electrical, mechanical or photocopied, recorded ot otherwise without
prior permission of the publisher.

Typesetting by D. P. Media Limited, Hitchin, Hertfordshire

Printed in the United Kingdom by
Biddles Ltd, Guildford, Surrey

Distributed in the Philippines and the USA and its
dependencies by
Jane's Publishing Inc
135 West 50th Street
New York, NY 10020

Introduction

While Main Battle Tanks are the backbone of all the European countries as well as many countries in the Middle East and elsewhere, light tanks and armoured cars play a vital role in providing the Main Battle Tanks with detailed information on the strength, position and future direction of movement of enemy forces so that friendly units can be used to their best advantage. In NATO some of the roles traditionally undertaken by light tanks and armoured cars are now being supplemented by other surveillance systems such as helicopters, remotely piloted vehicles (RPVs), long-range radars and other sensors (both ground and air), satellites, electronic intelligence and so on. But as these are in some cases susceptible to enemy countermeasures, light tanks and armoured cars still have a vital role to play both now and in the future.

There are considerable differences within NATO on the types and role of reconnaissance vehicles. For example the West German Army uses the Luchs (8 × 8) amphibious vehicle which is armed with a 20 mm cannon while the United Kingdom and Belgium both use the Alvis Scorpion CVR(T) with a 76 mm gun. The French use both the Panhard AML-90 light armoured car and the EBR (8 × 8) heavy armoured car, both of which have a 90 mm gun. The EBR, whose design can be traced back to before the Second World War, is now being replaced by the AMX-10RC (6 × 6) amphibious vehicle with a 105 mm gun and an advanced fire control system incorporating a laser rangefinder, computer and low light level television similar to that being fitted to the latest production AMX-30 B2 Main Battle Tanks. The United States used the M114 command and reconnaissance carrier and the M551 Sheridan light tank in the reconnaissance role. The former has now been withdrawn from service while the latter remains in service with only one battalion based in the United States and attached to the 82nd Airborne Division. In place of the M114 and M551, M60 series MBTs and M113 APCs have been used, although a modified version of the M2 Bradley Infantry Fighting Vehicle, the M3 Cavalry Fighting Vehicle, is now being produced for the cavalry scout role.

In the Soviet Union the PT-76 light amphibious tank has been replaced in many units by specialised versions of the BMP-1 MICV but the BRDM-2 (4 × 4) armoured amphibious scout car is still widely used for reconnaissance. The chassis of the BRDM-2 has also become the basis for a complete family of specialised versions including anti-tank guided missile carriers, command vehicles, the SA-9 Gaskin surface-to-air missile system and a NBC reconnaissance vehicle. A new scout car/armoured car is expected to enter service in the future and this will probably be a 6 × 6 model with greater mobility than the current BRDM-2.

As mentioned previously, the light tank has almost faded away in the United States Army but the formation of the Rapid Deployment Force (now Central Command) has once again awakened interest in this type of vehicle as the M1 Abrams MBT is too heavy to be quickly airlifted to trouble spots in the Middle East and elsewhere in the required numbers. None of these light tanks are yet in service although

information and photographs of some of the vehicles under consideration are given in the text where this information has been released.

This book provides a detailed description of each light tank and armoured car and its variants, full technical specification, list of user countries, current status and manufacturer. Each vehicle is, where possible, also provided with a side drawing (all to a scale of 1/76th), selection of photographs of the basic vehicle and where applicable, some of the variants as well.

In addition to describing the light tanks and reconnaissance vehicles that are already in service, coverage is also given of some of the future vehicles under study or development where this information has been released.

Light tanks and armoured cars that were developed during the Second World War and are still in service today, such as the American M3 light tank and the M8/M20 light armoured car have been excluded. There is however an entry on the M24 Chaffee light tank as this has been modernised by Norway and this conversion is still being offered.

In recent years there has been a trend to design vehicles that can be used for a number of different roles such as armoured car and/or armoured personnel carrier, although in some cases the end result has been a vehicle that can effectively carry out neither of these conflicting requirements. In this volume only the multi-mission Arrowpointe Dragoon 300 (4 × 4) and the Cadillac Gage V-150 (4 × 4) and V-300 (6 × 6) Commando series have been included.

Some of the vehicles included in this volume, such as the British Alvis Scorpion Combat Vehicle Reconnaissance (Tracked) and Fox Combat Vehicle Reconnaissance (Wheeled) have been developed specifically to meet the requirements of the national army. Others, for example the Cadillac Gage V-150 and V-300, Panhard ERC and Renault VBC-90 have been developed with company funds specifically for the export market, although in some cases the home army has ended up adopting these vehicles to meet a special requirement that has risen over a short period of time and where insufficient funding has been available to design a new vehicle from scratch.

In the 1950s and 1960s most armoured cars were armed with a relatively small calibre weapon such as a 20 mm cannon or heavier weapons in the 76 to 90 mm range that fired HEAT or HE ammunition. In the last few years however there has been dramatic advances in both gun and ammunition technology and new generation 90 mm weapons, such as the French GIAT Super 90 and the even newer Cockerill Mk VII can fire armour-piercing fin-stabilised discarding sabot (APFSDS) that is capable of defeating the armour of first generation tanks and penetrating the sides and rear of second generation tanks as well. The American ARES 75 mm cannon, now in its final stages of development has already been installed in the AAI Rapid Deployment Force Light Tank and the High Survivability Test Vehicle (Lightweight) can fire at the rate of one round a second until its ammunition is exhausted and inflict severe damage on tanks.

The West German Rheinmetall 105 mm Super Low Recoil gun and the new Royal Ordnance Factory Nottingham L7 105 mm with new recoil system, neither of which are in production yet, can fire standard 105 mm tank gun ammunition, including APFSDS rounds that are capable of knocking out all but the latest MBTs and these weapons can be installed on vehicles with a combat weight of 20 tonnes or under. Such a vehicle, for example the MOWAG Shark would have the same firepower as the Leopard 1, M60, M1 and AMX-30 MBTs but have better mobility because of its higher power-to-weight ratio, greater strategic mobility because it is wheeled rather than tracked, but of course thinner armour protection. Most people would agree that the latter, to some extent at least, is offset by its mobility.

There have also been major advances in fire control systems and night vision equipment. Most light tanks and armoured cars today are available with very simple fire control systems right up to more complex systems with a computer, laser rangefinder, powered controls and a stabilisation system enabling them to engage both stationary and moving targets with a high first round hit probability.

In most cases the basic chassis of the armoured car, or its automotive components, can be adopted for a wide range of other roles so enabling the user to have a complete family of vehicles all using common components with substantial savings in training, spare parts and operating costs. Many companies have designed armoured cars that have common components with armoured personnel carriers, for example the Panhard AML armoured car shares 95 per cent of its automotive components with M3 APC, the ENGESA EE-9 Cascavel armoured car shares many components with the EE-11 Urutu armoured personnel carrier and the Renault VBC-90 armoured car shares many common components with the VAB family originally developed to meet the requirements of the French Army.

Virtually all current light tanks and armoured cars are available with wide range of optional equipment such as passive night vision equipment, air conditioning system, NBC kit, amphibious capability, navigation system and various armament installations to name but a few. These all help to keep the price of the basic vehicle as low as possible and at the same time enable the customer to select only that optional equipment that he really needs. Often this equipment is refitted at a later date. Vehicles can also be upgunned to meet a changing threat, for example the Alvis Scorpion was originally introduced with a 76 mm gun but is now available with the more potent 90 mm Cockerill Mk III weapon. The M41 light tank was originally armed with a 76 mm gun but more recently AAI have developed APFSDS ammunition for this weapon while Cockerill can offer their 90 mm Mk IV gun as a retrofit package.

The author would like to take this opportunity of thanking the many companies, armies and individuals who have provided material for this book. Information and photographs for revised editions should be forwarded to the author via the publisher.

Christopher F Foss
May 1984

ARGENTINA

Vehiculo de Apoyo y Exploración

The French companies of Panhard and Renault have each built prototypes of a 6 × 6 armoured vehicle to meet the requirements of the Argentinian Army under the designation of the Vehiculo de Apoyo y Exploración (VAPE). Both of these were fitted with a French SAMM TTB 190 turret armed with a GIAT 90 mm CS 90 F4 gun with a coaxial 7.62 mm machine gun. The weapons have an elevation of +15 degrees and a depression of −8 degrees with turret traverse a full 360 degrees. Three types of turret power drive can be fitted, electric, hydraulic or electro-hydraulic. A total of 23 rounds of 90 mm and 2000 rounds of 7.62 mm ammunition are carried. Optional equipment includes replacement of the co-axial 7.62 mm machine gun by a 12.7 mm machine gun, installation of a 7.62 mm anti-aircraft machine gun, various fire control systems, laser rangefinder and night vision equipment.

It is believed that the prototype selected for production will be manufactured under licence in Argentina. Using the same components both companies have also designed an armoured personnel carrier designated the Vehiculo Armado Exploración (VAE).

SAMM TTB 190 90 mm two-man turret armed with GIAT TS 90 mm CS 90 F4 gun which fires the same ammunition as the GIAT TS 90 turret fitted to the Panhard ERC 90 F4 Sagaie armoured car

Status: Prototypes.

AUSTRIA

Jagdpanzer SK 105 Light Tank/Tank Destroyer

Development

The Jagdpanzer SK 105, also nicknamed the Kürassier, was developed from 1965 by Saurer-Werke which was taken over in 1970 by the Steyr-Daimler-Puch company, and is based on a redesigned chassis of the Saurer APC. The SK 105 was developed to provide the Austrian Army with an independent anti-tank weapon for difficult terrain.

The first prototype was completed in 1967 with the second following in 1969. Five pre-production vehicles were completed in 1971 and since then 150 production vehicles have been built for the Austrian Army and over 250 for export to seven countries.

Description

The hull of the SK 105 is welded steel and is divided into three compartments: driver's at the front, fighting in the centre and the engine at the rear. The SK 105 is immune to 20 mm armour-piercing rounds over its frontal arc.

The driver is seated at the front of the vehicle on the left and is provided with a single-piece hatch cover that opens to the left. There are three periscopes forward of his hatch cover and in wet weather a small windscreen with a wiper can be fitted. Ammunition and the vehicle's batteries are stowed to the right of the driver.

The Steyr turret JT 1 mounted in the centre of the vehicle is derived from the FL-12 built by Fives-Cail Babcock of France and assembled in Austria with a number of improvements. The oscillating turret is similar to that fitted to some mem-

bers of the AMX-13 light tank family and the Brazilian ENGESA EE-17 Sucuri (6 × 6) tank destroyer. The commander is seated on the left of the turret and the gunner on the right. The commander is provided with seven periscopes, a periscopic sight with alternatively ×1.6 magnification and a 28-degree field of view or a ×7.5 magnification and a 9-degree field of view, and a single-piece hatch cover that swivels to open. The gunner has two observation periscopes, a telescopic sight with a magnification of ×8 and an 8.5-degree field of view and a one-piece lifting and swivelling hatch cover. Due to the design of the oscillating turret all sights are always linked to the main and secondary armament. For engaging targets at night an infra-red periscopic sight with a magnification of ×6 and a 7-degree field of view is provided for the commander. A TCV 29 laser rangefinder (range of 400 to 5000 metres) mounted on the roof of the turret is surmounted by an XSW-30-U 950-watt infra-red/white light searchlight. A fixed fan in the turret draws out fumes when the main or secondary armament is fired.

The engine and transmission are at the rear of the vehicle and the engine compartment is fitted with a fire extinguisher which can be operated by hand or automatically. When flames enter the suction part the intake pipe is closed and air is then drawn in from the crew compartment.

The engine permanently drives an oil pump with a variable output linked to a hydraulic motor acting on the differential which controls the tracks. By acting on the steering gear and the speed of the engine the driver can continuously adjust the speed ratio of both tracks. All turning radii can thus be obtained until pivoting on the spot occurs with both tracks turning in an opposite direction at the same speed. Since this system needs no action from the brakes, the whole

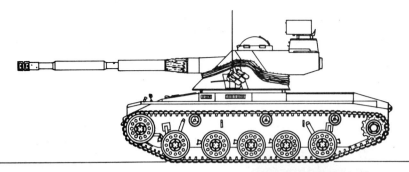

Jagdpanzer SK 105 light tank/tank destroyer

power produced by the engine is constantly available at the tracks. The main brakes of the SK 105 are hydraulic, foot-operated.

The torsion bar suspension consists of five dual rubber-tyred road wheels with the drive sprocket at the rear and the idler at the front. There are three track return rollers and the first and last road wheel stations have hydraulic shock absorbers. The vehicle has tracks with rubber blocks, each track having 78 links. Steel spikes can be fitted for operations in ice and snow.

The SK 105 has individual NBC protection and a diesel oil heater is fitted as standard on all models. The SK 105 is not amphibious but can ford to a depth of one metre.

The 105 mm gun, designated the CN-105-57, fires the following types of spin-stabilised fixed ammunition: HE with the complete round weighing 18.5 kg with a muzzle velocity of 700 metres per second; HEAT with the complete round weighing 17.3 kg with a muzzle velocity of 800 metres per second and a maximum effective range of 2700 metres which will penetrate 360 mm of armour at an incidence of 0 degrees or 150 mm of armour at an incidence of 65 degrees, and smoke with the complete round weighing 19.1 kg and a muzzle velocity of 695 metres per second. As the projectiles are identical to those of the AMX-30 MBT the SK 105 therefore has the same kill probability. The SK 105 has also been tested with the West German Lemstar tank fire-control system.

The 105 mm gun is fed from two revolver type magazines in the turret bustle, one in either side and each holding six rounds of ammunition. Once the gun is fired the empty cartridge cases are ejected out of the rear of the turret through a trapdoor hinged on the left. A rate of fire of one round every five seconds can be achieved until the two magazines are empty. Once empty the magazines have to be refilled by hand from outside the tank. A gun barrel travelling lock is fitted at the front of the hull and this folds back onto the glacis plate when not in use.

Mounted coaxially to the right of the main armament is a 7.62 mm MG 74 (Steyr) machine gun and fitted on either side of the turret are three smoke dischargers.

Variants

Kürassier II
In 1978 Steyr-Daimler-Puch completed the prototype of the Kürassier II which has a fully stabilised upper turret including the seats for the commander and gunner, ballistic calculator with sensors for air pressure, humidity, cross wind, temperature of propellant and barrel wear. Ballistic data for two types of ammunition can be inserted into the computer

Jagdpanzer SK 105 light tank/tank destroyer with laser rangefinder and infra-red/white searchlight

Jagdpanzer SK 105 with turret hatches open (Christopher F Foss)

and the laser rangefinder will automatically provide data for the computer. Mounted externally above the 105 mm gun is a passive night vision camera with a tv screen connected to the calculator to indicate the aiming point on the screen with the lateral speed of the target taken from the traverse speed of the turret. The turret front has improved ballistic protection. Overall height of the Kürassier II is 2.514 metres and firing height is 1.95 metres.

Greif Armoured Recovery Vehicle
The first prototype of the Greif ARV was completed in 1974 with production beginning in 1976/77. The chassis is identical to the SK 105 but a new superstructure has been built at

Jagdpanzer SK 105 with spent 105 mm cartridge case being ejected from turret bustle

Greif armoured recovery vehicle in travelling configuration (Austrian Army)

Prototype of Kürassier II showing redesigned turret front and passive tv camera above main armament

SPECIFICATIONS

CREW	3	MAX RANGE	520 km	AMMUNITION	
COMBAT WEIGHT	17 500 kg	FORDING	1 m	(main)	44
POWER-TO-WEIGHT		GRADIENT	75%	(coaxial)	2000
RATIO	18.28 hp/tonne	SIDE SLOPE	40%	FIRE-CONTROL SYSTEM	
GROUND PRESSURE	0.68 kg/cm²	VERTICAL OBSTACLE	0.8 m	Turret power control	hydraulic/manual
LENGTH GUN		TRENCH	2.41 m	By commander	yes
FORWARDS	7.763 m	TURNING RADIUS	8.5 m in 1st gear	By gunner	yes
LENGTH HULL	5.582 m	ENGINE	Steyr 7FA 6-cylinder	Max rate power	
WIDTH	2.5 m		liquid-cooled 4-stroke	traverse	360° in 12–15 s
WIDTH OVER TRACKS	2.5 m		turbo-charged diesel	Gun elevation/depression	+12°/−8°
HEIGHT			developing 320 hp	Maximum power elevation/	
(to top of commander's			at 2300 rpm	depression	4.5° to 5°
cupola)	2.529 m	AUXILIARY ENGINE	none		second
(to hull top)	1.413 m	TRANSMISSION	ZF manual with 6	Commander's override	yes
FIRING HEIGHT	1.965 m		forward and 1 reverse	Commander's fire-	
GROUND CLEARANCE	0.4 m		gears	control override	yes
TRACK	2.12 m	STEERING	hydrostatic split	Gun stabiliser	
TRACK WIDTH	380 mm		torque type	(vertical)	no
LENGTH OF TRACK		CLUTCH	F and S single	(horizontal)	no
ON GROUND	3.037 m		dry-plate	ARMOUR	
MAX SPEED		SUSPENSION	torsion bar	Hull front	25 mm
1st gear	6.82 km/h	ELECTRICAL SYSTEM	24 V	Hull sides	15 mm
2nd gear	11.96 km/h	BATTERIES	2 × 12 V, 180 Ah	Hull top	8 mm
3rd gear	19.09 km/h	ARMAMENT		Hull rear	15 mm
4th gear	29.93 km/h	(main)	1 × 105 mm	Turret front	40 mm
5th gear	46.39 km/h	(coaxial)	1 × 7.62 mm MG	Turret sides	20 mm
6th gear	65.34 km/h	SMOKE-LAYING		Turret top	10 mm
reverse	7.36 km/h	EQUIPMENT	3 smoke dischargers		
FUEL CAPACITY	400 litres		either side of turret		

Status: In production. In service in Argentina (in 1978–79 70 SK 105s were delivered. In mid-1981 the Austrian government approved an export licence for the sale of 57 SK 105s worth, with spare parts and ammunition, about £90 million. In 1982 it was reported that Argentina had placed an order for an additional 225 vehicles), Austria, Bolivia, Morocco, and Tunisia. Chile placed an order for the SK 105 but this was subsequently stopped by the Austrian Government.

Manufacturer: Steyr-Daimler-Puch AG, Werke Wien, A-1111 Vienna, Austria.

Engineer Tank 4KH7FA-Pi in travelling configuration with dozer blade raised and hydraulic arm with bucket stowed to rear

Training version of Jagdpanzer SK 105, the FA (Fahrschulpanzer)

Pionier Engineer Vehicle

The Pionier vehicle is designated the Engineer Tank 4KH7FA – Pi (Pionier panzer) and has the same hull and chassis as the Greif ARV. It has a new winch with a capacity of 8000 kg and is fitted with a larger dozer blade at the front of the hull. On the right side of the hull, where the crane on the ARV is situated, is a hydraulically operated excavator. At present this vehicle is at the prototype stage. Loaded weight is 19 000 kg and it has a crew of four.

Driver Training Vehicle

This is called the 4KH7FA – FA (Fahrschulpanzer) and is based on the chassis of the SK 105. Each SK 105 is convertible into a driver training vehicle within two hours.

ÖAF Armoured Car

Development/Description

ÖAF and Graf and Stift have developed to the prototype stage a 6 × 6 amphibious reconnaissance vehicle which is based on the chassis and automotive components of the ÖAF Type 20.320 (6 × 6) 10 000 kg cargo truck, 350 have been delivered to the Austrian Army.

The hull of the vehicle is of all-welded steel construction with the driver at the front, fighting compartment in the centre and the engine and transmission at the rear. An entry door is provided in each side of the vehicle between the first and second axles.

The armour provides protection from 20 mm projectiles over its frontal arc and 12.7 mm projectiles on its sides. The prototype is however of mild steel.

the front of the vehicle to the right of which is mounted a hydraulic crane with a maximum lifting capacity of 6000 kg. The crane is provided with 42 metres of cable and its jib can be extended from its normal length of 3 metres to 3.9 metres. The main winch, with a capacity of 20 000 kg, is mounted in the lower part of the hull and is led out through the front. Mounted at the front of the hull is a hydraulically-operated blade which can be used for dozing or stabilising the vehicle when the winch is being used. Full designation of this vehicle is the Armoured Recovery Vehicle 4K-7FA, SB 20 (Bergepanzer Greif). Loaded weight is 19 800 kg and it has a crew of four: driver, commander and two mechanics.

The five-man crew consists of the driver, commander, gunner and two infantrymen who can dismount from the vehicle to carry out their reconnaissance duties.

The prototype has been fitted with an Oerlikon two-man GDD-BOE power operated turret armed with a 35 mm Oerlikon KOE automatic cannon, 7.62 mm coaxial machine gun and smoke dischargers.

The vehicle is fully amphibious being propelled in the water by two propellers at the rear of the hull. Before entering the water a trim vane is erected at the front of the vehicle, this folds back onto the glacis plate when not required.

Variants

Command Vehicle

(4 × 4) with a maximum crew of six armed with a 12.7 mm machine gun.

Armoured Personnel Carrier

(6 × 6) with a total crew of ten armed with a 12.7 mm machine gun.

Engineer Vehicle

(6 × 6) fitted with an Oerlikon 20 mm turret model GAD-AOA, maximum crew of 8 and a rope winch with a capacity of 8000 kg. This model would be fully amphibious.

Reconnaissance Vehicle

(6 × 6) with a total crew of five, fitted with various turrets including the Oerlikon-Bührle GDD-BOE 35 mm or a two-man turret armed with a 90 mm gun and a rope winch with a capacity of 8000 kg. This model would be fully amphibious. An 8 × 8 model is also projected.

BRIEF SPECIFICATIONS	4 × 4 model	6 × 6 model	8 × 8 model
COMBAT WEIGHT	14 000 kg	18 000 kg	28 000 kg
MILITARY PAYLOAD	2500 kg	5000 kg	12 000 kg
ENGINE	MAN D 2538 MT V-8 diesel developing 320 bhp at 2500 rpm		
MAXIMUM SPEED	90 to 110 km/h	90 to 110 km/h	90 to 110 km/h
GRADIENT	adhesion limit up to 70%		

Status: Prototype.

Manufacturers: Graf and Stift AG, Brünner Strasse 72, A-1211 Vienna, Austria. ÖAF AG, Brünner Strasse 72, A-1211, Vienna, Austria.

Prototype of ÖAF (6 × 6) armoured car fitted with Oerlikon GDD-BOE two-man turret

FN 4RM/62F AB Light Armoured Car

Development

The FN 4RM/62F AB light armoured car was developed by Fabrique Nationale of Herstal to meet the requirements of the Belgian Gendarmerie and is based on the chassis of the FN 4RM/62 Ardennes (4 × 4) 1500 kg truck. The first prototype was completed in 1962 with the second following in 1965. Between 1971 and 1972 62 production vehicles were built. Fabrique Nationale is no longer involved in the development or production of armoured vehicles or trucks.

Description

The hull of the vehicle is all-welded steel with the driver seated at the front in the centre. The driver is provided with a single-piece hatch cover that opens upwards, in the top of which are three periscopes and in the lower part a bullet-proof window with an armoured cover. There is a single door in each side of the hull; the door on the right is fitted with a rectangular observation port.

The all-welded turret is in the centre of the hull with the gunner on the left and the commander, who also acts as loader, on the right. Both the commander and gunner are provided with a single-piece hatch cover that opens to the

rear. The commander has eight periscopes and the gunner has three plus an optical sight linked to the main armament. Turret traverse is electric, two-speed (fast and slow) with manual controls for emergency use.

The engine compartment at the rear of the hull is equipped with an automatic fire-extinguishing system. Standard

Machine gun and mortar model of FN 4RM/62F AB light armoured car

90 mm gun model of FN 4RM/62F AB light armoured car with driver's hatch open

equipment includes an NBC system, searchlights for both the commander and gunner, and channels for crossing ditches carried on the rear of the turret (on 90 mm gun model only). The vehicle has no night vision equipment and has no amphibious capability.

Variants

90 mm Gun Model

This variant is armed with a 90 mm CATI gun which fires two types of ammunition, HEAT and shrapnel. The HEAT round weighs 3.5 kg and has a muzzle velocity of 640 metres a second and an effective range of 1000 metres. The shrapnel round weighs 5.1 kg, has a muzzle velocity of 330 metres a

second and a maximum effective range of 1800 metres. A 7.62 mm MAG machine gun is mounted coaxially to the right of the main armament and a similar weapon pintle-mounted in front of the commander's cupola is used for anti-aircraft defence. Mounted on either side of the turret at the rear are six electrically-operated smoke dischargers.

Machine Gun and Mortar Model

This model is armed with twin 7.62 mm MAG machine guns and a 60 mm breech-loaded mortar which can be elevated separately or in parallel. It is not fitted with an anti-aircraft machine gun and the smoke dischargers are towards the front rather than the rear of the turret as in the case of the 90 mm gun model.

SPECIFICATIONS (data in brackets relate to 90 mm gun model where this differs from the machine gun model)					
CREW	3	FORDING	1.1 m	SMOKE-LAYING	
CONFIGURATION	4 × 4	GRADIENT	60%	EQUIPMENT	2 × 6 smoke
LOADED WEIGHT	8800 kg (8000 kg)	TURNING RADIUS	6 m		dischargers
WEIGHT ON FRONT		ENGINE	FN 652 6-cylinder in-line	AMMUNITION	
AXLE (loaded)	3800 kg (3350 kg)		OHV petrol developing	(main)	46 (40)
WEIGHT ON REAR			130 hp at 3500 rpm	(machine gun)	4830 (3680)
AXLE (loaded)	5000 kg (4650 kg)	TRANSMISSION	manual with 4 forward and 1	(smoke grenades)	36
POWER-TO-WEIGHT			reverse gears	FIRE-CONTROL SYSTEM	
RATIO	14.77 hp/tonne	TRANSFER CASE	2-speed	Turret power control	electric/manual
	(16.25 hp/tonne)	STEERING	worm and twin finger	By commander	yes (fast only)
LENGTH GUN		CLUTCH	single dry plate	By gunner	yes
FORWARDS	4.5 m (5.42 m)	SUSPENSION	longitudinal leaf springs with	Gun elevation/	
LENGTH HULL	4.5 m		double-action hydraulic	depression	+55° (MGs)/−10°
WIDTH	2.26 m		shock absorbers front and		(+27°/−12°)
HEIGHT (overall)	2.37 m (2.52 m)		rear		+75° (mortar)/−10°
GROUND CLEARANCE	0.324 m	TYRES	9.00 × 20	Gun stabiliser	
TRACK	1.62 m	BRAKES		(vertical)	no
WHEELBASE	2.45 m	(main)	drum on all wheels, dual	(horizontal)	no
ANGLE OF APPROACH/			circuit, servo-assisted	ARMOUR	6.5–13 mm
DEPARTURE	50°/37°	(parking)	handbrake acting on		
MAX SPEED (road)	110 km/h		propeller shaft		
ACCELERATION		ELECTRICAL SYSTEM	24 V		
(0 – 80 km/h)	65 s	BATTERIES	4 × 12 V, 50 Ah		
FUEL CAPACITY	180 litres	ARMAMENT			
MAX ROAD RANGE		(main)	1 × 60 mm (1 × 90 mm)		
(at 80 km/h)	600 km	(coaxial)	2 × 7.62 mm MG (1 × 7.62 mm MG)		
		(anti-aircraft)	none (1 × 7.62 mm MG)		

Status: Production complete. In service only with the Belgian Gendarmerie. It is reported the Uruguay has taken delivery of a small number of FN 4RM/62 AB light armoured cars.

Manufacturer: Fabrique Nationale Herstal SA, B–4400 Herstal, Belgium.

BRAZIL

X1A1 Light Tank

Development

In the early 1970s the Bernardini company of São Paulo rebuilt two M3A1 light tanks for the Brazilian Army. Technical control of the project was under the direction of the Brazilian Army Research and Development Centre. The modifications included replacing the armour above the tracks by new sloped armour provided by the Biselli company, replacement of the original American petrol engine by a six-cylinder Saab-Scania diesel developing 280 bhp, new volute suspension designed by the Novatracao company, new turret with a French DEFA D-921A 90 F1 90 mm gun as fitted to the Panhard AML (4 × 4) and other light AFVs,

and a fire-control system designed by the D F Vasconcelos company.

Following trials with the two prototypes the Brazilian Army placed an order for 80 M3A1 Stuart light tanks to be rebuilt to the new standard, which were subsequently delivered to the Cavalry Regiments under the designation X1A. The vehicle weighs 15 000 kg, has a road range of 450 km and can ford to a depth of one metre without preparation.

The X1A was followed by the Carcara, or X1A1. This is essentially a stretched X1A with an additional volute spring suspension group, additional return wheel and a new tension wheel each side. Engine and turret are the same as fitted to the earlier X1A tank.

Trials with the X1A1 were completed in 1977/78 but the

X1A light tanks awaiting delivery to Brazilian Army

X1A light tank, essentially rebuilt M3A1 Stuart

Brazilian Army did not place an order for the vehicle and further development resulted in the X1A2 which is based on a new chassis rather than a rebuild of an M3A1 chassis.

XLP-10 AVLB

Following trials with prototype vehicles based on the X1A chassis, the Brazilian Army ordered ten production models based on the X1A1 chassis. The aluminium and steel bridge is launched over the front of the vehicle, weighs 2750 kg, can span a gap of up to ten metres and take a maximum load of 20 000 kg.

XLF-40 Rocket Launcher

This is based on the X1A1 chassis and carries three ready-to-launch XLF-40 surface-to-surface rockets which have a solid propellant motor giving a maximum range of 25 000 metres. For travelling the missiles point towards the front and on arrival at the firing position the hydraulic stabilisers are lowered at the front and rear of the chassis. The launcher itself has a traverse of about 90 degrees left and right.

SPECIFICATIONS (X1A1)	
CREW	4
WEIGHT	17 000 kg
GROUND PRESSURE	0.55 kg/cm²
LENGTH GUN	
FORWARDS	6.36 m
LENGTH HULL	5.3 m
WIDTH	2.4 m
HEIGHT	2.45 m
(to hull top)	1.63 m
GROUND CLEARANCE	0.5 m
MAX SPEED	60 km/h
FUEL CONSUMPTION	1.7 km/litre
RANGE ROAD	520 km
FORDING	1.3 m
GRADIENT	60%
VERTICAL OBSTACLE	0.8 m
ENGINE	Saab-Scania diesel developing 280 hp
ARMAMENT	
(main)	1 × 90 mm
(coaxial)	1 × 7.62 mm MG
(anti-aircraft)	1 × 12.7 mm MG

Status: X1A in service with the Brazilian Army. X1A1 production as required for export only.

Manufacturer: Bernardini S/A Indústria e Comércio, Rua Hipólito Soares No 79, 04201 São Paulo, SP, Brazil.

Prototype of XLP-10 AVLB in travelling configuration showing stabilising blade under vehicle's nose (Ronaldo S Olive)

XLF-40 rocket launcher with stabilisers lowered front and rear

X1A2 Light Tank

Development
Following development of the X1A light tank, essentially a modernised M3A1 Stuart light tank, Bernardini rebuilt two vehicles to a new standard known as the X1A1 which is basically an X1A with an additional volute spring suspension group, additional return wheel and a new tension wheel either side. Engine and turret are the same as the X1A's.

The Brazilian Army did not adopt this model but development continued and resulted in the X1A2 which is similar to the X1A1 but is based on a new chassis instead of a rebuilt M3A1 Stuart and is now in production for the Brazilian Army as well as being offered for export.

Description
The hull of the X1A2 is all welded with the driver's compartment at the front, fighting compartment in the centre and the engine at the rear.

The driver is seated at the front of the hull on the left and is provided with a single-piece hatch cover that opens to the left. Mounted in front of the hatch cover are three periscopes for observation when the hatch cover is closed.

The all-welded turret is in the centre of the hull with the commander, who also acts as the loader, on the left and the gunner on the right. Both are provided with a single-piece cover that opens to the rear. The commander's cupola has five observation periscopes and the gunner has three and a telescope linked to the main armament.

The vertical volute suspension has three bogies each side each with two road wheels, with the drive sprocket at the front, idler at the rear and two track return rollers. There is a

X1A2 light tank from rear showing turret bustle

X1A2 light tank at speed with all hatches in open position with commander manning 12.7 mm M2 HB machine gun

possibility that later vehicles will be fitted with torsion bar suspension to improve cross-country mobility.

Optional equipment includes a laser rangefinder for the main armament, full range of night vision equipment and an air-conditioning system.

Prototype X1A2s had a French D-921 gun as fitted to the Panhard AML-90 (4 × 4) armoured car and early production ENGESA (6 × 6) Cascavel armoured cars but production vehicles have a 90 mm Cockerill gun made under licence in Brazil by ENGESA which is also now fitted to current production Cascavel armoured cars. A 7.62 mm machine gun is mounted coaxially with the main armament and a 12.7 mm machine gun is mounted externally at the commander's position for anti-aircraft use. Three electrically operated smoke dischargers are mounted either side of the turret at the front.

X1A2 light tank fitted with ENGESA-built 90 mm Cockerill gun

SPECIFICATIONS

CREW	3	FUEL CONSUMPTION	1 litre/km	ARMAMENT	
COMBAT WEIGHT	19 000 kg	FORDING	1.3 m	(main)	1 × 90 mm
POWER-TO-WEIGHT		GRADIENT	70%	(coaxial)	1 × 7.62 mm MG
RATIO	15.78 hp/tonne	SIDE SLOPE	30%	(anti-aircraft)	1 × 12.7 mm MG
GROUND PRESSURE	0.63 kg/cm²	VERTICAL OBSTACLE	0.7 m	SMOKE-LAYING	
LENGTH GUN		TRENCH	2.1 m	EQUIPMENT	3 smoke dischargers
FORWARDS	7.1 m	TURNING RADIUS	7 m		either side of turret
LENGTH HULL	6.5 m	ENGINE	Saab-Scania model DS-11	AMMUNITION	
WIDTH	2.6 m		6-cylinder water-cooled	(main)	66
HEIGHT			turbo-charged diesel	(coaxial)	2500
(to turret top)	2.45 m		developing 300 hp at 2200	(anti-aircraft)	750
GROUND CLEARANCE	0.5 m		rpm	FIRE-CONTROL SYSTEM	
TRACK WIDTH	460 mm	TRANSMISSION	manual with 2 forward	Turret power control	hydraulic/manual
MAX SPEED			and 1 reverse gears	By commander	manual
(road, forwards)	55 km/h	STEERING	controlled differential,	By gunner	hydraulic
(road, reverse)	15 km/h		manual operated by	Max rate power	
(cross-country)	30 km/h		hydraulic system	traverse	360° in 12 s
FUEL CAPACITY	600 litres	SUSPENSION	vertical volute	Gun elevation/	
MAX RANGE		ELECTRICAL SYSTEM	24 V	depression	+17°/−8°
(road)	600 km	BATTERIES	2 × 12 V	Gun stabiliser	
(cross-country)	350 km			(vertical)	no
				(horizontal)	no

Status: In production. In service with the Brazilian Army.

Manufacturer: Bernardini S/A Indústria e Comércio, Rua Hipólito Soares, No 79,04201, São Paulo, SP, Brazil.

ENGESA EE-9 Cascavel Armoured Car

Development

The EE-9 Cascavel was designed by ENGESA (Engesa Engenheiros Especializados) to meet the requirements of the Brazilian Army. Design work began in July 1970 after the company had completed design work on the EE-11 armoured personnel carrier, with the first prototype being completed in November 1970. Following trials with prototype vehicles a pre-production order was placed by the Brazilian Army, which named the vehicle the CRR (Carro de Reconhecimento Sobre Rodas), for ten vehicles which were delivered between 1972 and 1973.

Production of the EE-9 began at a new plant at Sao José dos Campos in 1974 with the first production vehicles being delivered the same year. The production vehicles were slightly longer and wider than the prototypes and had a different wheelbase. First production vehicles delivered to the Brazilian Army were fitted with a turret armed with 37 mm guns removed from old American-supplied M3 Stuart light tanks, but first production vehicles for export were fitted with a French CNMP-Berthiez (now Hispano-Suiza) H 90 turret. Current production vehicles have a new turret of Brazilian design mounting a Brazilian 90 mm gun.

The EE-9 Cascavel shares many components with the EE-11 Urutu (6 × 6) armoured personnel carrier and many automotive components used in both vehicles are standard commercial parts available world-wide.

The EE-9 Cascavel (6 × 6) armoured car has been used in combat by the Iraqi Army during the recent fighting with Iran where it has carried out the traditional role of armoured reconnaissance as well as direct and indirect fire support and flank guard for tank units. During the invasion of Chad by Libyian backed guerillas in 1983 numbers of the early model of the EE-9 Cascavel fitted with the French H 90 turret armed with a 90 mm gun were captured by the Chad Army. These were supplied to the guerillas by Libya.

Description

The all-welded hull of the EE-9 has dual hardness armour which was developed by ENGESA's Research Department with the co-operation of the University of São Paulo and consists of an outer layer of hard steel and an inner layer of softer steel roll-bonded and heat-treated to give maximum ballistic protection. Increased protection is given over the frontal arc and special emphasis has been given to protect the vehicle against attack from booby traps, grenades and molotov cocktails.

The driver is seated at the front of the hull on the left side and is provided with a hatch cover opening to the right. There are three periscopes in the top part of the glacis plate giving the driver a 120-degree view. The driver is also provided with a small windscreen and wiper, which folds forward onto the glacis plate when not in use. The driver's seat and steering wheel are both adjustable.

Initial production vehicles were fitted with a French H 90 turret armed with a 90 mm D 921 gun but current production vehicles have an ENGESA ET-90 turret armed with an ENGESA EC-90 gun. The commander is seated on the left side of the turret and the gunner on the right, both with a single-piece hatch cover that opens to the rear and four periscopes. The gunner has a telescopic sight linked to the main armament with a magnification of ×6.

The engine compartment is at the rear of the vehicle and access to the engine is via two hatches in the hull roof. Power is transmitted from the engine to the gearbox (either a Clark manual with five forward and one reverse gears or a Detroit Diesel Allison MT 643 with four forward and one reverse gears) to the two-speed ENGESA transfer box, which splits the drive between the front and rear differentials. The front differential is bolted to the hull with the power being transmitted to the front axle by shafts, and the rear differential forms part of the ENGESA Boomerang walking beam suspension. The latter, which is also used on ENGESA 6 × 6 trucks, consists of a rigid axle connected to the hull by double leaf springs and telescopic dampers which holds two lateral walking beams. Power is taken from the drive shaft to the four

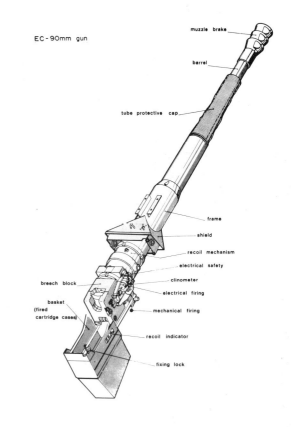

ENGESA EC-90 90 mm gun as fitted to current production models of the ENGESA EE-9 Cascavel (6 × 6) armoured car

Brazilian Army ENGESA EE-9 Cascavel armoured car showing large vertical wheel travel made possible by walking-beam rear suspension

ENGESA EE-9 Cascavel armoured car fitted with laser rangefinder over 90 mm gun and commander's cupola with externally-mounted 12.7 mm M2 HB machine gun

A summary of the various models of the ENGESA Cascavel armoured car already produced is given below:

Mark I

First production model armed with a 37 mm gun, Mercedes-Benz diesel engine, manual transmission, 12-volt (hull) and 24-volt (turret) electrical system, no central tyre-pressure regulation system. These were built only for the Brazilian Army and most have now been rebuilt with the new ENGESA ET-90 turret.

Mark II

First production model for export, Mercedes-Benz diesel, automatic transmission, 12-volt (hull) and 24-volt (turret) electrical system, no central tyre-pressure regulation system and fitted with French Hispano-Suiza H 90 turret with 90 mm gun. No longer in production.

rear wheels by gears inside the walking beam, which can rotate freely around the central hub. The design of the rear suspension allows up to a maximum of 0.9 metre of vertical wheel travel and ensures that all four rear wheels are in contact with the ground at all times. The run-flat tyres enable the vehicle to travel for more than 100 km after being completely deflated. The Cascavel has a double 24 V electrical system; a battery set is used for vehicle operations and turret while a second set is used purely for engine start to avoid lack of power after long still radio operations. The Cascavel is also equipped with disc brakes and an automatic tyre inflation system.

Optional equipment includes an air-conditioning system, heater, laser rangefinder, automatic fire extinguisher and passive or active night vision equipment. A fire-control system is under development.

The gun is called the EC-90-III and is mounted in an ET-90 turret. The rifled-bore gun fires the following types of ammunition: HE (muzzle velocity 700 metres a second), HEAT (muzzle velocity 900 metres a second), HESH (muzzle velocity 800 metres a second), Smoke White Phosphorus (Smoke WP-T) with a muzzle velocity of 690 metres a second and HEAT Target Practice with a muzzle velocity of 900 metres a second. Of 44 rounds of 90 mm ammunition carried, 24 are in the turret and 20 in the hull. ENGESA has also developed a commander's cupola for the EE-9 which can be traversed through 360 degrees and has vision blocks for all-round observation and a 12.7 mm (0.50) machine gun mounted externally on a bracket forward of the commander's single-piece hatch cover that opens to the rear.

A 7.62 mm machine gun is mounted to the left of the main armament and a similar weapon, or a 12.7 mm (0.50) Browning M2 HB machine gun, can be mounted on the turret roof for anti-aircraft defence. Three smoke dischargers are mounted either side of the turret and are electrically fired from within the vehicle.

Recent production vehicles for Iraq have a traverse indicator, clinometer, improved seating, laser rangefinder integrated into sight which is protected by a shutter when the main armament is fired, and a 12.7 mm FN M2 HB machine gun on an anti-aircraft mount which is similar in design to that used by the Soviet Union with its 12.7 mm DShKM machine guns.

ENGESA EE-9 Mark IV Cascavel armoured car of the Gabon Army with pintle-mounted 7.62 mm MAG general-purpose machine gun for anti-aircraft defence

Latest production ENGESA EE-9 Cascavel armoured car with ENGESA ET-90 turret with ENGESA EC-90 90 mm gun, laser rangefinder over main armament, commander's cupola with remote controlled 7.62 mm machine gun, ARGUS day/night sight and six (2 × 3) electrically operated smoke grenade launchers

ENGESA EE-9 Mark II Cascavel armoured car fitted with original Hispano-Suiza H 90 turret armed with 90 mm gun. Some of this model were captured by Chad Army units during the invasion of the country by Libyian backed guerillas in 1983

Mark III

First production models completed in 1977 and fitted with ENGESA ET-90 turret with ENGESA EC-90 gun, Mercedes-Benz diesel, automatic transmission, 12-volt (hull) and 24-volt (turret) electrical system, no central tyre-pressure regulation system.

Mark IV

Powered by General Motors Detroit Diesel model 6V-53 diesel developing 212 hp at 2800 rpm, automatic transmission, 24-volt (hull and turret) electrical system, disc brakes, central tyre-pressure regulation system and ENGESA ET-90 turret.

Mark V

As Mark IV but powered by a Mercedes-Benz OM 352 A diesel developing 190 hp at 2800 rpm.

Variants

There are no variants of the EE-9 apart from the different armament installations described above.

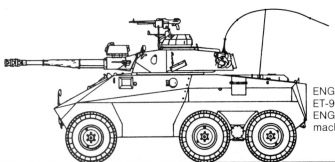

ENGESA EE-9 Cascavel (6 × 6) armoured car with ENGESA ET-90 turrfet armed with ENGESA EC-90 turret armed with ENGESA EC-90 gun, commander's internally-mounted 7.62 mm machine gun cupola and laser rangefinder over main armament

SPECIFICATIONS (Mark IV)				
CREW	3	ENGINE	Detroit Diesel 6V-53N 6-cylinder water-cooled diesel developing 212 hp at 2800 rpm (other engines can also be installed)	(parking)	mechanical on transfer case output
CONFIGURATION	6 × 6			ELECTRICAL SYSTEM	24 V (4 batteries)
COMBAT WEIGHT	12 000 kg				
UNLOADED WEIGHT	10 800 kg				
POWER-TO-WEIGHT RATIO	17.5 hp/tonne	TRANSMISSION	Detroit Diesel Allison MT 643 automatic with 4 forward, 1 reverse gears (or Clark manual with 5 forward and 1 reverse gears)	ARMAMENT	
				(main)	1 × 90 mm
LENGTH GUN FORWARDS	6.29 m			(coaxial)	1 × 7.62 mm MG
LENGTH HULL	5.25 m			(anti-aircraft)	1 × 7.62 mm or 12.7 mm MG (optional)
WIDTH	2.59 m				
HEIGHT		TRANSFER CASE	ENGESA 2-speed	SMOKE-LAYING EQUIPMENT	2 or 3 smoke dischargers either side of turret
(top of commander's cupola)	2.60 m	STEERING	ZF integral hydraulic		
(to turret roof)	2.29 m	CLUTCH	single dry plate manual transmission only	AMMUNITION	
(to hull top)	1.75 m			(main)	44
GROUND CLEARANCE		SUSPENSION		(coaxial)	2400
(front axle)	0.375 m	(front)	independent with helical springs and double action shock absorbers	FIRE-CONTROL SYSTEM	
(hull centre)	0.52 m			Turret power control	manual
TRACK	2.1 m			By gunner	yes
WHEELBASE	2.343 m + 1.414 m	(rear)	as front but with ENGESA Boomerang with walking beams and differential blockage system	Max rate of traverse	360° in 25 s
ANGLE OF APPROACH/ DEPARTURE	70°/75°			Gun elevation/ depression	+15°/−8°
MAX SPEED (road)	100 km/h			Gun stabiliser	
FUEL CAPACITY	360 litres	TYRES	12.00 × 20	(vertical)	no
MAX RANGE (cruising)	750 km	BRAKES		(horizontal)	no
FORDING	1 m	(main)	air over hydraulic, dual circuit, disc brakes	ARMOUR	8.25–16 mm
GRADIENT	60%				
SIDE SLOPE	30%				
VERTICAL OBSTACLE	0.6 m				

Status: In production. In service with Bolivia, Brazil (Army and Marines), Chile, Colombia, Cyprus, Gabon, Iraq, Libya, Tunisia, Uruguay, Zimbabwe and other undisclosed countries.

Manufacturer: Engesa Engenheiros Especializados SA, Avenue das Nacões Unidas, 22.833 (Santo Amaro), CEP 04795, PO Box 12.705 (CEP 01000), São Paulo, SP, Brazil.

ENGESA EE-3 Jararaca Scout Car

Development

The EE-3 Jararaca scout car was originally designed specifically for the export market and complements the other vehicles in the ENGESA range of armoured vehicles which include the EE-11 Urutu (6 × 6) armoured personnel carrier and the EE-9 Cascavel (6 × 6) armoured car. All vehicles in the ENGESA range use standard automotive components. The production model of the EE-3 Jararaca, to which the description and specifications relate, is slightly different in layout and appearance from the prototype in that the door is now on the right side of the hull and the driver's and commander's hatches have been redesigned.

Description

The all-welded hull of the EE-3 consists of an outer layer of hard steel and an inner layer of softer steel roll-bonded and heat-treated to give the maximum ballistic protection. The armour is similar to that used on other members of the ENGESA family of armoured vehicles.

The driver is seated towards the front of the hull, slightly to the left of the vehicle's centre line and has a single-piece hatch cover that lifts and swings to the right to open. There are three periscopes for forward observation immediately in front of the driver. A windscreen and wiper which can be fitted in front of the driver's position for use in wet weather folds forward onto the glacis plate when not in use. The machine gunner is seated behind the driver on the right side of the hull and has a circular mounting which can be traversed through 360 degrees and a single-piece hatch cover that opens to the rear. A standard 12.7 mm (0.50) M2 HB machine gun is pintle-mounted on the forward part of the circular mounting, but there is no provision for aiming the weapon from inside the vehicle. There are vision blocks in both sides of the hull.

The three-man crew enters and leaves the EE-3 by a door in the right side of the hull that opens forward. Immediately behind the door is a single vision block under which is a firing port. The commander is seated on the left side of the hull to the rear and has a hatch cover that opens to the rear.

The engine is at the rear of the hull and access to it is by two large hatches in the roof. The suspension, front and rear, consists of semi-elliptical springs and hydraulic shock absorbers. The axles have hypoid gears. The wheels of the EE-3 are not within the armoured part of the vehicle as the light sheet steel covering over the top of each wheel will blow away if the vehicle hits a mine. The Jararaca is fitted with an automatic tyre inflation system as standard.

The standard 12.7 mm (0.50) M2 HB pintle-mounted machine gun can be replaced by a 7.62 mm machine gun or a 20 mm cannon. Other armament installations currently available include a 60 mm breech-loaded mortar, a Euromissile MILAN launcher and a cupola with internally operated 7.62 mm machine guns.

The EE-3 has no amphibious capability. Optional equipment includes passive night vision equipment and various radios with an intercom system. The EE-3 can be fitted with an NBC system.

ENGESA EE-3 Jararaca (4 × 4) scout car from front with all hatches closed

ENGESA EE-3 Jararaca (4 × 4) scout car fitted with 12.7 mm MG with both roof hatches closed

Variants

Apart from the NBC reconnaissance version illustrated on the right and the different armament installations mentioned previously there are no variants of the EE-3 Jararaca.

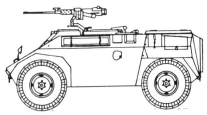

ENGESA EE-3 Jararaca scout car with 12.7 mm MG

ENGESA EE-3 Jararaca (4 × 4) NBC reconnaissance vehicle fitted with commander's internally operated 7.62 mm machine gun cupola and four smoke dischargers

ENGESA EE-3 Jararaca (4 × 4) scout car, armed with pintle-mounted 12.7 mm (0.50) Browning M2 HB machine gun, showing door in right side of hull

SPECIFICATIONS

CREW	3	MAX RANGE (road)	750 km	SUSPENSION	semi-elliptical springs and hydraulic shock absorbers, both have hypoid gears and tapered gear, single reduction differential
CONFIGURATION	4 × 4	FUEL	135 litres		
COMBAT WEIGHT	5500 kg	FORDING	0.8 m		
POWER-TO-WEIGHT		GRADIENT	60%		
RATIO	21.8 hp/tonne	SIDE SLOPE	30%	TYRES	11.00 × 20
LENGTH	4.125 m	VERTICAL OBSTACLE	0.4 m	BRAKES	
WIDTH	2.13 m	ENGINE	Mercedes-Benz OM 314A turbo-charged, 4-cylinder water-cooled diesel developing 120 hp at 2800 rpm	(main)	drum, air-assisted
HEIGHT (without				(parking)	drum, acting on transfer case
armament)	1.56 m			ELECTRICAL SYSTEM	double 24 V system
(top of 12.7 mm MG		TRANSMISSION	manual with 5 forward and 1 reverse gears	ARMAMENT	1 × 12.7 mm MG
mount)	1.97 m				
GROUND CLEARANCE	0.315 m	TRANSFER CASE	ENGESA 2-speed		
TRACK	1.71 m	TURNING RADIUS	7.2 m		
WHEELBASE	2.6 m	STEERING	ZF integral hydraulic		
ANGLE OF APPROACH/		CLUTCH	single dry plate hydraulically operated		
DEPARTURE	65°/58°				
MAX SPEED (road)	100 km/h				

Status: In production. In service with Gabon, Tunisia and Uruguay.

Engesa Engenheiros Especializados SA, Avenue das Nações Unidas, 22.833 (Santo Amaro), CEP 04795, PO Box 12.705 (CEP 01000), Sao Paulo, SP, Brazil.

Light Armored Vehicle

Between 1979 and 1983 the Diesel Division of General Motors Canada built a total of 419 Armoured Vehicle General Purpose (AVGP) for the Canadian Armed Forces. These were based on the Swiss MOWAG Piranha (6 × 6) design and built in three versions:

Cougar 76 mm Wheeled Fire Support Vehicle (WFSV)
Grizzly Wheeled Armoured Personnel Carrier (WAPC)
Husky Wheeled Maintenance and Recovery Vehicle (WMRV)

Following a competition with vehicles submitted by Alvis (Scorpion 90 and Stormer), Cadillac Gage (Command V-300 and V-150) and General Motors Canada (WFSV) the US Marine Corps selected the General Motors Canada in an 8 × 8 configuration to meet its requirement for a Light Armored Vehicle (LAV). The US Marine Corps has a requirement for 289 vehicles while the US Army has a requirement for 680 vehicles, subject to Congressional action and changes in requirements. The first year buy of 60 vehicles valued at $29.9 million was for the US Marine Corps with the first production vehicles being delivered in October 1983. The Marines call the vehicle the LAV-25 while the the US Army designation is the LAV-25(A) or M1047. Main difference between the two vehicles is that the US Marine Corps model has a three man crew consisting of commander, gunner and driver and can carry six troops while the US Army vehicles have a similar crew but do not carry any troops. Variants required by the US Marine Corps and Army include an anti-tank vehicle with same launcher and M901 Improved TOW Vehicle, logistics support, mortar carrier and recovery vehicle. A detailed description of the LAV-25 is not given in this book as it was originally designed as an armoured personnel carrier and will be used in that role by the US Marine Corps.

Prototype of the LAV-25 fitted with two-man Arrowpointe turret armed with 25 mm M242 cannon and coaxial 7.62 mm machine gun

(LAV-25 Basic Specifications relate to USMC model, those in brackets relate to the US Army model where this differs)

CREW	3 + 6 (3 + 0)	TRANSMISSION	Allison MT-653 DR automatic, 5 forward and 1 reverse gears	(anti-aircraft, optional)	1 × 7.62 mm M60 or 1 × 12.7 mm M2 HB machine gun
CONFIGURATION	8 × 8	TRANSFER CASE		(smoke dischargers)	2 × 4 (M257)
COMBAT WEIGHT	12 882 kg (12 700 kg)	STEERING	Rockwell AG-VST (modified) power assisted on front two axles	AMMUNITION (ready use)	
UNLOADED WEIGHT	11 067 kg (11 113 kg)			(25 mm)	210
LENGTH	6.388 m			(7.62 mm)	400
WIDTH	2.499 m	SUSPENSION		AMMUNITION (reserve)	
HEIGHT OVERALL	2.692 m	(Front four wheels)	independent coil springs and shock absorbers	(25 mm)	420 (990)
HEIGHT REDUCED	2.565 m			(7.62 mm)	1200 (2200)
MAXIMUM ROAD SPEED	100 km/h	(Rear four wheels)	independent torson bars and shock absorbers	FIRE-CONTROL SYSTEM	
MAXIMUM WATER SPEED	10.46 km/h	BRAKES		Turret power control	hydraulic/manual
MAXIMUM RANGE	668 km	(main)	8-wheel dual air hydraulic drum brake	Elevation/depression	+60°/−10°
GRADIENT	70%			Turret traverse	360°
VERTICAL OBSTACLE	0.5 m	(parking)	transmission brake and transfer case lock	Gun stabiliser	
TRENCH	2.057 m			(vertical)	yes
ENGINE	GM Detroit Diesel model 6V-53T, 6-cylinder diesel developing 275 hp at 2800 rpm	TYRES	11.00 × 16 with Hutchinson run-flat inserts	(horizontal)	yes
				Periscopes	7 × M27
		ARMAMENT		Sights	2 × M36E1
		(main)	1 × 25 mm M242 cannon		
		(coaxial)	1 × 7.62 mm M240 MG		

Status: LAV-25 is in production and in service with US Marine Corps. In January 1984 it was announced that funding for the US Army was being cancelled from FY 1985.

Manufacturer: Diesel Division, General Motors Canada Limited, PO Box 5160 London, Ontario M6A 4N5, Canada.

CHINA, PEOPLE'S REPUBLIC

Type 63 Light Tank

Development

In the late 1950s China received several batches of Soviet PT-76 light amphibious tanks. There is a possibility that this tank was built in China in a slightly modified version under the designation Type 60, as a number of Chinese PT-76 tanks have been observed with provision for mounting a 12.7 mm anti-aircraft machine gun on one of two pintle type mounts on the turret roof.

This was followed by the redesigned version of the Type 60 known as the Type 63 which had the same armament and certain other automotive components as the Type 62. The Type 63 was used in combat in Viet-Nam by the North Vietnamese Army and during the 1971 Indo-Pakistan war by Pakistan. During the later stages of the fighting in South Viet-Nam the North Vietnamese used the Type 63 in

armoured cavalry battalions of one tank company of seven to ten Type 63s to two companies of BTR-60PA or Type 531 (previously K-63) armoured personnel carriers. It is issued in the Chinese Army on the scale of four tanks in the reconnaissance platoon of each armoured regiment and ten in the reconnaissance company of each armoured division.

Description

The hull of the Type 63 is welded rolled steel and is divided into three compartments: driver's at the front, fighting in the centre and engine at the rear. The glacis plate of the Type 63 is much shallower than on the Type 60 or PT-76. The driver is seated at the front of the hull on the left and is provided with a single-piece hatch cover that swings to the left and three periscopes forward.

The turret is in cast sections with the commander and gunner seated on the left of the turret and the loader on the right. The commander's hatch opens forward and the

Type 63 light amphibious tank (provisional drawing)

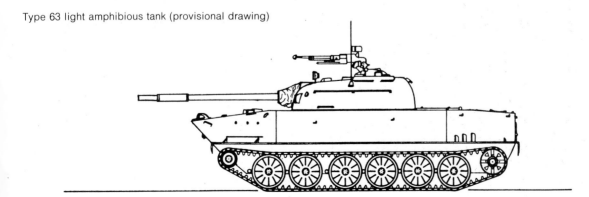

Type 63 light tank on display in South Korea without 12.7 mm anti-aircraft machine gun fitted on turret roof (Paul Handel)

loader's to the rear. A dome-shaped ventilator is mounted in the turret roof to the rear of the commander's and gunner's hatches. The engine and transmission are at the rear of the hull and additional fuel tanks can be fitted on top of the hull to increase operational range. The engine of the Type 63 is the same as in the Type 59 MBT.

The torsion bar suspension consists of six large rubber-tyred road wheels similar to those on the Soviet PT-76, with the drive sprocket at the rear and the idler at the front. There are no track return rollers.

Main armament of the Type 63 is an 85 mm gun, probably

Type 63 light amphibious tank showing turret detail (DIA)

Type 63 light amphibious tank from rear showing covers for water jet propulsion system (DIA)

identical to that installed in the Type 62 light tank, which fires ammunition of the fixed type including AP, APHE, HE, HEAT and smoke. The 85 mm gun could be a modification of the 85 mm Type 55 anti-tank gun which is a Chinese copy of Soviet D-44 weapon. If so, the gun fires the following types of ammunition:

TYPE	APHE	HE	HVAP
WEIGHT OF PROJECTILE	9.3 kg	9.5 kg	5 kg
MUZZLE VELOCITY	792 m/s	792 m/s	1030 m/s
PENETRATION (0°/1000 m)	102 mm	n/app	130 mm

It has been reported that some vehicles have been fitted with a laser rangefinder over the main armament similar to that fitted to the Type 59 MBT.

SPECIFICATIONS (provisional)
(Note: in some cases differing specifications have recently become available from US sources, these are given in brackets)

CREW	4	LENGTH OF TRACK ON GROUND	4.08 (4.55) m	ARMAMENT (main)	1 × 85 mm
COMBAT WEIGHT	18 000 kg	MAX SPEED		(coaxial)	1 × 7.62 mm MG
POWER-TO-WEIGHT		(road)	50 km/h	(anti-aircraft)	1 × 12.7 mm MG
RATIO	28.9 bhp/tonne	(water)	9 km/h	AMMUNITION	
GROUND PRESSURE	0.5 kg/cm²	FUEL CAPACITY	545 litres	(main)	56
LENGTH GUN		MAX RANGE	240 km	(12.7 mm)	1200
FORWARDS	8.27 m	FORDING	amphibious	(7.62 mm)	3000
LENGTH HULL	6.91 (7.16) m	GRADIENT	60%	GUN ELEVATION/	
WIDTH	3.25 m	VERTICAL OBSTACLE	1 m	DEPRESSION	+18°/−5°
HEIGHT TO TURRET		TRENCH	2.8 (3.00) m	ARMOUR	
TOP (excluding AA MG)	2.19 m	ENGINE	V-12 liquid-	Hull front (max)	11 mm at 80°
(including AA MG)	2.46 m		cooled diesel	Hull sides upper	14 mm
GROUND CLEARANCE	0.37 (0.4) m		developing	Hull top	10 mm
TRACK	2.74 (2.6) m		520 hp/2000 rpm	Hull floor	10 mm
TRACK WIDTH	360 (450) mm	TRANSMISSION	manual, 5 forward	Hull rear	10 mm
			and 1 reverse gears	Turret mantlet	11 mm
		ELECTRICAL SYSTEM	24 V		

Status: Probably still in production. In service with China, Pakistan, Sudan, Tanzania and Viet-Nam.

Manufacturer: Chinese state arsenals.

Type 63 light amphibious tank (left) compared with Type 59 MBT (right), both on display in South Korea (Paul Handel)

A 7.62 mm machine gun is mounted coaxially to the right of the main armament and a Type 54 heavy machine gun is mounted at the loader's station for anti-aircraft defence. The Type 54 is the Soviet M1938/46 DShKM manufactured in China.

The tank is fully amphibious being propelled in the water by two water jets of Soviet design. Before entering the water a trim board is erected at the front of the hull; when travelling this folds back onto the glacis plate. As far as it is known the Type 63 has no NBC system or night vision equipment.

Type 62 Light Tank

Description

The Type 62 light tank is virtually a scaled down Type 59 MBT and weighs about 21 000 kg. It is believed that the tank is used in place of the Type 59 in rugged terrain such as that

encountered in Southern China. The layout of the tank is identical to the Type 59 with the driver seated at the front of the hull on the left and the other three crew members in the turret. The commander and gunner are seated on the left of the turret with the loader on the right. The engine and transmission are at the rear of the hull. The torsion bar suspension consists of five road wheels with a distinct gap between the first and second wheels. The drive sprocket is at the rear and the idler at the front. Main armament is an 85 mm gun, probably identical to that on the Type 63 light amphibious tank, which fires fixed ammunition including AP, APHE, HE, HEAT and smoke. A total of 47 rounds of ammunition are carried. The 85 mm gun could be a modification of the 85 mm Type 55 anti-tank gun which is a Chinese copy of the Soviet D-44 weapon. If so, the gun fires the following types of ammunition: APHE with the projectile weighing 9.3 kg, muzzle velocity of 792 metres per second, which will penetrate 102 mm of armour at 0 degrees at a

27

range of 1000 metres; HE with the projectile weighing 9.5 kg and a muzzle velocity of 792 metres per second; HVAP with the projectile weighing 5 kg, muzzle velocity of 1030 metres per second, which will penetrate 130 mm of armour at a range of 1000 metres.

A 7.62 mm machine gun is mounted coaxially to the right of the main armament and a 12.7 mm Type 54 heavy machine gun is mounted at the loader's position for anti-aircraft use. The Type 54 is the Soviet M1938/46 DShKM manufactured in China.

The Type 62 is not amphibious, has no NBC system and has not been observed with any infra-red night vision equipment.

The Type 62 was used in combat in Angola by Zaïrean forces and by Tanzania against Uganda in their 1978 October–November border war.

Type 62 light tank

SPECIFICATIONS (provisional)

CREW	4	MAX SPEED		ELECTRICAL SYSTEM	24 V
COMBAT WEIGHT	21 000 kg	(road)	60 km/h	ARMAMENT	
POWER-TO-WEIGHT		FUEL CAPACITY	730 litres	(main)	1 × 85 mm
RATIO	18 hp/tonne	MAX RANGE		(coaxial)	1 × 7.62 mm MG
GROUND PRESSURE	0.71 kg/cm²	(road)	500 km	(anti-aircraft)	1 × 12.7 mm MG
LENGTH		FORDING	1.3 m	AMMUNITION	
(gun forwards)	7.9 m	GRADIENT	60%	(main)	47
(hull)	5.55 m	VERTICAL OBSTACLE	0.7 m	(coaxial)	1750
WIDTH	2.86 m	TRENCH	2.55 m	(anti-aircraft)	1250
HEIGHT	2.55 m	ENGINE	liquid-cooled diesel	GUN ELEVATION/	
GROUND CLEARANCE	0.42 m		developing 380 hp at	DEPRESSION	+20°/−4°
TRACK	2.39 m		1800 rpm		
TRACK WIDTH	380 mm	TRANSMISSION	manual, 4 forward		
LENGTH OF TRACK			and 1 reverse gears		
ON GROUND	3.53 m	SUSPENSION	torsion bar		

Status: Probably still in production. In service with Albania, Congo, China, North Korea, Mali, Sudan, Tanzania and Zaïre.

Manufacturer: Chinese state arsenals.

FRANCE

AMX-13 Light Tank

Development

Shortly after the end of the Second World War the French Army issued a requirement for three armoured vehicles: a heavy armoured car (which Panhard developed as the EBR from their pre-war AMR 201), a light tank (the AMX-13) and a heavy tank (the AMX-50). The AMX-50 was built only to the prototype stage and not placed in production as the USA supplied the French Army with a large number of M47 medium tanks under the Mutual Aid Program.

Design work on the AMX-13 began in 1946 at the Atelier de Construction d'Issy-les-Moulineaux and the first proto-type was completed two years later. Production was under-taken at the Atelier de Construction Roanne (ARE) from 1952 with the first production tanks being completed the following year. At one time production of the tank was run-ning at 45 units per month but in the early 1960s production of the whole family was transferred to the civilian company of Creusot-Loire at Châlon sur Saône as the ARE was tooling

up for production of the AMX-30 MBT. The basic chassis has been used for a wide range of vehicles including the AMX VCI mechanised infantry combat vehicle, 105 mm self-propelled howitzer, 155 mm self-propelled gun Mk F3 and twin 30 mm DCA self-propelled anti-aircraft gun system.

The AMX-13 is still used on a large scale by the French Army and although the basic design is over 30 years old no announcement has been made on a new design to replace it. By early 1982 total production of the AMX-13 light tank had amounted to over 3000 vehicles.

Description

The hull of the AMX-13 is all welded and is divided into three compartments with the driver's and engine compart-ment at the front and the turret mounted at the rear. The driver is seated at the front of the vehicle on the left side with the engine compartment to his right and the differential in front of him. The driver is provided with a single-piece hatch cover that opens to the left and three periscopes, the centre

FL-10 turret showing ammunition resupply hatches in roof at turret rear and empty cartridge case ejection port in turret rear

road wheels with the drive sprocket at the front and the idler at the rear. There are three (or two in some cases) track return rollers which support the inside of the track only. The first and last road wheel stations have hydraulic shock absorbers. The steel tracks have 85 links per side and can be fitted with rubber pads if required.

The AMX-13 does not have an NBC system, cannot be fitted for deep wading and as built was not fitted with any night fighting equipment although a number of armies have fitted their vehicles with some: for example, a Fives-Cail Babcock infra-red searchlight to the rear of the gunner's position and an infra-red sight for the gunner. More recently, the AMX-13 has been offered fitted with passive night firing and night driving equipment, laser rangefinder and automatic display of the battle sight.

Variants

Model 51 with 75 mm gun

This was the first model of the AMX-13 to enter service and is fitted with the FL-10 turret armed with a 75 mm gun with a single baffle muzzle brake. The weapon is fed from two revolver type magazines in the turret bustle, one either side, each magazine holding six rounds. Once the gun has fired the empty cartridge case is ejected out of the rear of the turret through a trapdoor hinged on the left. A rate of fire of one round every five seconds can be achieved until the two magazines are empty. Once empty the magazines have to be refilled by hand from outside the tank. The gun fires two main types of ammunition:

one of which can be replaced by an infra-red or image-intensification periscope for night driving.

The oscillating turret, manufactured by Fives-Cail Babcock, is mounted at the rear of the hull and the type of turret depends on the model of the tank and its armament. All turrets are oscillating and the commander is seated on the left of the turret and the gunner on the right. The tank commander is provided with a domed hatch cover that opens to the rear and eight periscopes. The gunner has a single-piece hatch cover that opens to the rear and two periscopes.

The torsion bar suspension consists of five rubber-tyred

AMX-13 Model 51 light tank in Singapore

AMX-13 Model 51 with 75 mm gun showing cartridge case ejection door in turret bustle (E C P Armées)

AMX-13 with 90 mm gun and infra-red searchlight stowed on right side of turret at rear (P Touzin)

AMX-13 with 90 mm gun

This entered service in the early 1960s and is still in production. It is armed with a 90 mm gun in an FL-10 turret and the barrel is fitted with a thermal sleeve and a single baffle muzzle brake. The gun fires the following types of fin-stabilised ammunition:

Type	Canister	HE	HEAT	Smoke
WEIGHT OF CARTRIDGE	10.4 kg	10.4 kg	8.9 kg	10.6 kg
WEIGHT OF PROJECTILE	5.28 kg	5.27 kg	3.65 kg	5.4 kg
MUZZLE VELOCITY	750 m/s	750 m/s	950 m/s	744 m/s
ARMOUR PENETRATION	n/app	n/app	320 mm/0°	n/app
			120 mm/65°	

Now in production by GIAT is an APFSDS round with a muzzle velocity of 1300 m/s which will penetrate a triple target (10/25/60 mm) at an incidence of 60° at a range of 2000 metres.

AMX-13 light tank fitted with FN 7.62 mm anti-aircraft GPMG

Type	HE	APC
WEIGHT OF COMPLETE ROUND	12.5 kg	14.4 kg
MUZZLE VELOCITY	750 m/s	1000 m/s
ARMOUR PENETRATION	n/app	170 mm/2000 m

Note: The APC round is designated the 75 POT 51 A. The 75 PCOT 51 P projectile will penetrate 170 mm of armour at 0 degrees at 1000 metres, and 40 mm of armour at an incidence of 60 degrees at the same range.

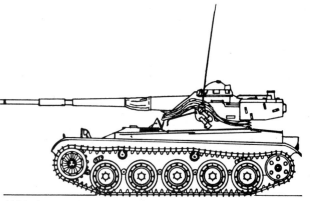

AMX-13 armed with 90 mm gun

A 7.5 mm or 7.62 mm machine gun is mounted coaxially to the right of the main armament and a similar weapon is often mounted externally at the commander's position. Thirty-seven rounds of 75 mm and 3600 rounds (in belts of 200) of machine gun ammunition are carried. In addition there are two electrically operated smoke dischargers either side of the turret.

The turret also has a coaxial machine gun and a similar weapon can be mounted at the commander's position. Thirty-four rounds of 90 mm ammunition are carried of which 21 are in the turret (12 in the magazines) and 13 in the hull, plus 3600 rounds of machine gun ammunition.

AMX-13 with 105 mm gun

This was developed specifically for export and has an FL-12 turret armed with a 105 mm gun which fires the same non-rotating rounds as the AMX-30 MBT. This turret is also

AMX-13 with 105 mm gun of Netherlands Army with infra-red searchlight to right of turret (Royal Netherlands Army)

fitted to the Austrian SK 105 tank destroyers used by Argentina, Austria, Bolivia, Morocco and Tunisia. The gun can fire the following types of ammunition:

Type	HEAT	HE	Smoke
WEIGHT OF COMPLETE ROUND	17·7 kg	18·4 kg	19·1 kg
WEIGHT OF PROJECTILE	10·95 kg	12·1 kg	12·8 kg
MUZZLE VELOCITY	800 m/s	700 m/s	695 m/s
ARMOUR PENETRATION	360 mm/0° 150 mm/65°	n/app	n/app

75 mm Gun in FL-11 Turret
This model of the AMX-13 was developed in the 1950s for use in North Africa and has an FL-11 turret, also fitted to some models of the Panhard EBR armoured car, equipped with a manually-loaded 75 mm gun. This model can be distinguished from the basic AMX-13 as its turret has no overhang at the rear.

Model 51 with 75 mm Gun and SS-11 Missiles
This is the standard model with two Aérospatiale SS-11 wire-guided anti-tank missiles mounted each side of the main armament. This missile weighs 30 kg, has a minimum range of 350 metres and a maximum range of 3000 metres and its warhead will penetrate 600 mm of armour. This model is in service with the French Army.

Model 51 with 75 mm Gun and HOT Missiles
In the 1960s a number of AMX-13s were fitted with three launcher boxes either side of the turret for three Euromissile HOT ATGW systems. This model has not been adopted by the French Army but is being offered for export.

AMX-13 with Diesel Engine
Shown for the first time at the 1979 Satory Exhibition of Military Equipment was a Creusot-Loire AMX-13 light tank with its original SOFAM petrol engine replaced by a General Motors 6V-53T diesel developing 280 hp at 2800 rpm. This version, which had completed over 6000 km of trials by mid-1979, has a maximum road speed of 64 km/h and a road fuel consumption of 1 litre per km, giving it a road range of about 500 km compared with 350 to 400 km for the original

petrol-engined version. In addition to installing the new engine the cooling system has been improved by Creusot-Loire. At the same time as the engine is being replaced the AMX-13 can also be up-gunned to 90 mm or 105 mm and a laser rangefinder and night vision equipment installed. It is believed that Singapore is considering refitting its AMX-13 tank fleet with a new powerpack. The diesel conversion proposal is applicable to other members of the AMX family such as the APC/MICV and the SPGs. This model is now in production.

For trials purposes an AMX-13 light tank has had its original petrol engine replaced by a Poyaud 520 4LCS25 four-cylinder diesel developing 265 hp at 2600 rpm. In 1983 Baudouin announced that it was offering its model 6 F 11 SRY six-cylinder diesel developing 280 hp at 3200 rpm as a replacement for the original SOFAM petrol engine.

AMX-13 Model 51 fitted with four Aerospatiale SS-11 wire-guided ATGWs

AMX-13 light tank fitted with General Motors V6 diesel engine

AMX-13 with Laser Rangefinder

The French company of Compagnie Industrielle des Lasers has developed the TCV 29 laser rangefinder for installation on the AMX-13 and similar tanks. This has a range of between 400 and 10 000 metres and is mounted externally behind the gunner's position. This system has already been adopted by the Austrian Army for their Jagdpanzer SK 105 tank destroyers.

AMX-13 Armoured Recovery Vehicle

The AMX-13 ARV (Char de Dépannage Model 55) is used to recover other members of the AMX-13 family as well as changing major components such as turrets and engines. Equipment fitted includes a front-mounted A-frame, 15 000 kg capacity winch with 50 metres of 25 mm diameter cable, secondary winch with 120 metres of 6 mm diameter cable, four spades at the rear of the hull and tools and other equipment. The vehicle has a crew of three consisting of commander, driver and winch operator and weighs 15 300 kg. Armament consists of an externally-mounted 7.5 mm or 7.62 mm machine gun and smoke dischargers.

AMX-13 Bridgelayer

The AMX-13 bridgelayer (Char Poseur de Pont AMX-13) is fitted with a folding class 25 bridge which has an unfolded length of 14.01 metres. The bridge is launched over the rear of

AMX-13 bridgelayer laying its bridge in position (E C P Armées)

the vehicle and two stabilisers steady the vehicle when the bridge is being positioned. The vehicle has a loaded weight of 19 700 kg and without the bridge weighs 15 000 kg.

AMX-13 Driver Training Tank

This is simply the standard tank with the turret removed.

SPECIFICATIONS (90 mm version)

CREW	3
COMBAT WEIGHT	15 000 kg
UNLOADED WEIGHT	13 000 kg
POWER-TO-WEIGHT RATIO	16.66 bhp/tonne
GROUND PRESSURE	0.76 kg/cm²
LENGTH GUN FORWARDS	6.36 m (6.5 m for 105 mm version)
LENGTH HULL	4.88 m
WIDTH	2.5 m
HEIGHT (to top of commander's hatch)	2.3 m
GROUND CLEARANCE	0.37 m
TRACK	2.159 m
TRACK WIDTH	350 mm
LENGTH OF TRACK ON GROUND	2.997 m
MAX ROAD SPEED	60 km/h
FUEL CAPACITY	480 litres
MAX RANGE ROAD	350–400 km
FORDING	0.6 m
GRADIENT	60%
VERTICAL OBSTACLE (forwards)	0.65 m
(reverse)	0.45 m
TRENCH	1.6 m
TURNING RADIUS	skid turns
ENGINE	SOFAM Model 8Gxb 8-cylinder water-cooled petrol developing 250 hp at 3200 rpm
AUXILIARY ENGINE	none
TRANSMISSION	manual with 5 forward and 1 reverse gears
STEERING	Cleveland type differential
CLUTCH	single-disc
SUSPENSION	torsion bar
ELECTRICAL SYSTEM	24 V
BATTERIES	4 × 12 V, 190 Ah
ARMAMENT	
(main)	1 × 90 mm gun
(coaxial)	1 × 7.5 mm or 7.62 mm MG
(anti-aircraft)	1 × 7.5 mm or 7.62 mm MG (optional)

SMOKE-LAYING EQUIPMENT	2 smoke dischargers either side of turret
AMMUNITION	
(main)	32
(MG)	4000
SMOKE CANISTERS	12
FIRE-CONTROL SYSTEM	
Turret power control	hydraulic with manual for emergency
By commander	yes
By gunner	yes
Max rate of power traverse	360°/12 s
Max rate of power elevation	5° in 1s
Gun elevation/ depression	+12.5°/−5°
Commander's override	yes
Gun stabiliser	
(vertical)	no
(horizontal)	no
Commander's sight	telescope L961 with ×1.5 and ×6 magnification
Gunner's sight	telescope L862 with ×7.5 magnification
ARMOUR	
Hull front	15 mm at 55° (equal to 40 mm)
Hull sides	20 mm
Hull top	10 mm
Hull rear	15 mm
Turret front	25 mm at 45° (equal to 40 mm)
Turret sides	25 mm
Turret top	10 mm

SPECIFICATIONS (105 mm version)
As 90 mm version apart from the following

LENGTH GUN FORWARDS	6.5 m
HEIGHT	1.495 m
GROUND CLEARANCE	0.47 m

LENGTH OF TRACK ON GROUND	2.80 m
MAX ROAD SPEED	
(petrol engine)	60 km/h
(diesel engine)	64 km/h
MAX RANGE ROAD	
(petrol engine)	350–400 km
(diesel engine)	500–550 km
ENGINE	
(petrol)	SOFAM Model 8Gxb 8-cylinder water-cooled petrol developing 250 hp at 3200 rpm
(diesel)	General Motors Detroit Diesel 6V-53T turbo-charged, 6-cylinder water-cooled diesel developing 280 hp at 2800 rpm
TRANSMISSION	manual with 5 forward (4 synchronised) and 1 reverse gears
FIRE-CONTROL SYSTEM	
Turret power control	elevating and traversing gear controls (1). either by means of pistol grips and hydraulic motor (gunner and commander, the latter over-riding the former) (2). or by means of a crank handle (gunner)
Commander's sight	M212 telescope with ×1.5 and ×6 magnification
Gunner's sight	M213 telescope with ×7.5 magnification

Status: In production. In service with Algeria, Argentina (was also assembled in the country), Chile, Dominican Republic, Ecuador, France, El Salvador, India, Indonesia, Ivory Coast, Jibuti, Lebanon (recent delivery), Morocco, Netherlands, Nepal (from Israel), Peru, Singapore (from Israel), Tunisia and Venezuela.

Manufacturer: Creusot-Loire at Châlon sur Saône.

Enquiries to Creusot-Loire, Armament Department, 15 rue Pasquier, 75383 Paris Cedex 08, France.

AMX-13 armoured recovery vehicle with A frame in operating position

AMX-10RC Reconnaissance Vehicle

Development

The AMX-10RC reconnaissance vehicle was designed from September 1970 at the Atelier de Construction d'Issy-les-Molineaux to meet a French Army requirement for a vehicle to replace the Panhard EBR heavy armoured car. The first of three prototypes was completed in June 1971 and by late 1977 the three had completed some 60 000 km and 3000 hours of trials under a wide range of operational environments. Four TK turrets were built and between them fired over 2000 rounds of ammunition during trials. Many of the automotive components of the AMX-10RC are identical to those used in the tracked AMX-10P IFV.

The AMX-10RC will equip the reconnaissance regiments of the corps of the French Army as well as the cavalry regiments of the infantry divisions. The first unit to be equip-

ped with the vehicle was the 9e Régiment de Hussards based at Provins, which received its complement of vehicles late in 1979. The first orders for the French Army were placed in 1976 when 20 vehicles were ordered; a further ten vehicles were ordered in 1977, followed by 40 in 1978, 60 in 1979 and 50 in 1981. Forty-seven were ordered in 1982 but later cancel-

AMX-10RC (6 × 6) reconnaissance vehicle (GIAT) **(1)** M504 telescope **(2)** gunner's tv monitor **(3)** gunner's panel **(4)** traversing box **(5)** commander's tv monitor **(6)** commander's panel **(7)** position indicator **(8)** slant sensor **(9)** M389 telescope **(10)** radio set **(11)** M389 telescope electronics **(12)** ventilation **(13)** NBC protection **(14)** smoke dischargers **(15)** tachymetry **(16)** commander's seat **(17)** radio-loader's seat **(18)** transmission assembly **(19)** overriding aiming control **(20)** elevation sensor **(21)** gunner's seat **(22)** road wheel arm **(23)** suspension jack **(24)** driver's seat **(25)** tv camera **(26)** gunner's control station **(27)** gun sight mirror

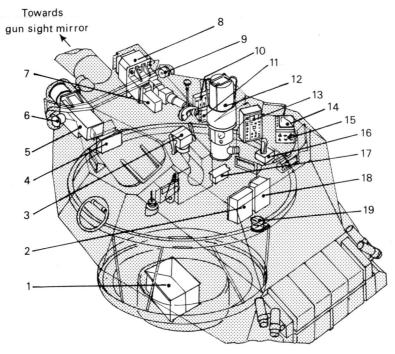

Towards gun sight mirror

TK 105 turret as installed on AMX-10RC (6 × 6) reconnaissance vehicle **(1)** junction box including logic system, hydraulic electronic supply, deviation computer, tachometry electronics **(2)** tv channel box **(3)** gunner's control station **(4)** loader's panel **(5)** TVBNL analysis box **(6)** fire-control unit elevation sensor **(7)** M550 laser rangefinder **(8)** M504 telescope with optical compensator and automatic bore sighting unit **(9)** M389 sensor **(10)** gunner's panel **(11)** gunner's tv monitor **(12)** M389 commander's telescope **(13)** commander's panel **(14)** commander's tv monitor **(15)** tv control box **(16)** commander's control station **(17)** slant sensor **(18)** M389 commander's telescope **(19)** fire-control unit bearing sensor (GIAT)

led for financial reasons. The 1983 order is for 44 vehicles. The only known overseas sale of the AMX-10RC is to Morocco who ordered 108 vehicles, with the first of these being delivered in 1981.

Description

The all-welded aluminium hull and turret provides the crew with protection from small arms fire, flash burns and shell splinters. The driver is seated at the front of the vehicle on the left side and is provided with an adjustable seat and a large single-piece hatch cover that opens to his right with three periscopes, the centre one of which can be replaced by a passive OB-31-A periscope for night driving.

The turret is in the centre of the vehicle with the commander and gunner seated on the right and the loader, who also acts as the radio operator, seated on the left. Both the commander and the loader are provided with a single-piece hatch cover that opens to the rear and the loader has three periscopes, one to his front, one to his left and one to his rear.

The vehicle commander has six periscopes for all-round observation and a periscope and panoramic M389 telescope with a magnification of ×2 and ×8 which has full contra-rotation and enables the commander to observe the target regardless of the position of the turret. The M389 can be elevated from −12 degrees to +24 degrees and has automatic projection of reticles, ×2 for MG and ×8 for 105 mm gun. The commander also has overriding controls enabling him to lay the gun onto the target. The gunner has two periscopes and an M504 telescope manufactured by SOPELEM and Compagnie Industrielle des Lasers (CILAS) which is the main part of the fire-control system. The M504 has a magnification of ×10 and is combined with an optical compensator with control electronics for automatic input of fire corrections, M550 laser rangefinder and an M553 bore-sight unit which corrects for any abnormal droop or accidental misalignment of the main armament.

The complete COTAC fire-control system comprises various sensors which provide the computer with the following data: target distance as measured by the laser rangefinder

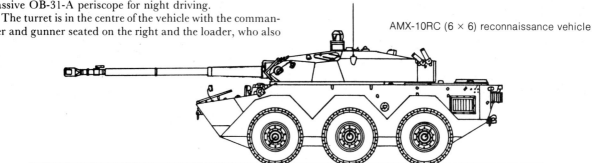

AMX-10RC (6 × 6) reconnaissance vehicle

with an accuracy of ± 7 mils between 400 and 10 000 metres; horizontal and vertical speed of the target; angle of cant of the vehicle and windspeed, altitude and outside temperature, which is fed into the computer manually.

In a typical target engagement the gunner aligns his sight with the target, tracks the target and depresses the measuring button for two or three seconds, the time taken for the target information to be fed into the computer. The introduction of fire correction data takes only 1½ seconds and the gunner opens fire.

For night engagements the AMX-10RC is fitted with a Thomson-CSF model DIVT 13 LLLTV. The system consists of a television camera mounted in the mantlet to the left of the main armament, electronics unit, control unit and two television screens, one for the commander and the other for the gunner. An aiming reticle is generated electronically and superimposes itself on the monitor screen. The deviation computer of the COTAC fire-control system then introduces fire correction data and shifts this aiming reticle by the required value under the same conditions as for the day reticle.

The integrated test system of the modular fire-control system enables any fault to be quickly located and the defective unit replaced. A test kit makes it possible to locate within a unit the defective sub-assembly which is then replaced.

The engine at the rear of the hull is identical to that of the tracked AMX-10P vehicle with which it also has many automotive components in common. The engine is coupled to the gearbox through a hydraulic-torque converter with a cut-out clutch. The gearbox has two functions: pre-selection through four gear ratios in both directions with an auxiliary drive for the two water-jets, and steering, with outlet epicyclic gears and hydraulically-actuated disc brakes. The AMX-10RC is skid-steered in a similar manner to the tracked AMX-10P.

In 1983 it was confirmed that the last two production batches of AMX-10RC vehicles for the French Army will be fitted with the Baudouin model 6 F 11 SRX diesel engine which develops 300 hp at 3300 rpm in place of the standard Renault HS 115 diesel developing 280 hp at 3000 rpm. In addition to being a more powerful engine the Baudouin is more fuel-efficient which will give the vehicle a larger operating range. It is expected that earlier vehicles will be retrofitted with the new engine.

The hydro-pneumatic suspension system, designed and manufactured by Messier Auto-Industrie, can be quickly adjusted by the driver to suit the type of ground being crossed. The minimum ground clearance is 210 mm, but for road travel 350 mm is normal, for cross-country travel 470 mm and for amphibious operations 600 mm.

AMX-10RC with suspension lowered to give ground clearance of 0.6 metre (GIAT)

AMX-10RC with suspension raised for minimum ground clearance (GIAT)

AMX-10RC with suspension on right side raised and left side lowered (GIAT)

AMX-10 RAC (6 × 6) reconnaissance vehicle (GIAT)

The suspension at each wheel station consists of a road wheel arm, suspension assembly (link rod, level and cylinder) with the cylinder acting as spring and shock absorber and allowing the height to be adjusted. A centralised lubrication unit facilitates maintenance of the suspension system. The tyre pressure can be adjusted to suit the type of ground being crossed.

The AMX-10RC is fully amphibious being propelled in the water by two water-jets either side of the rear of the hull. Before entering the water a trim vane is erected at the front of the vehicle, with a transparent window in the left side to allow the driver to see ahead when afloat. The vehicles delivered to Morocco were not fitted with waterjets.

The NBC system is mounted in the rear of the turret and maintains a slight overpressure in the fighting compartment. For use in cold climates an auxiliary heater is installed.

Main armament of the AMX-10RC is a 105 mm semi-automatic gun with a vertical wedge breech-block and a barrel with a thermal jacket and a two-stage muzzle brake. The gun itself is 48 calibres long without the muzzle brake and has a recoil length of 600 mm and a recoil force of about 13 tonnes. The recoil mechanism comprises a brake on the left side and a counter-recoil mechanism on the right side of the gun. The gun fires three types of ammunition, HEAT, HE and practice.

The fin-stabilised HEAT round will penetrate 350 mm of armour at an incidence of 0 degrees or 150 mm of armour at 60 degrees. Both this and the practice round are fitted with a tracer in the rear of the projectile. The anti-tank round has an effective range of 1250 metres. Basic details of the ammunition are as follows:

Of 38 rounds of 105 mm ammunition carried 12 are for ready use in the turret. A 7.62 mm machine gun is mounted coaxially to the left of the main armament. Two smoke dischargers mounted either side of the turret towards the rear are electrically fired from within the vehicle. An APFSDS 105 mm round is currently being developed by GIAT for the weapon fitted to the AMX-10RC.

The turret is equipped with a SAMM CH49 electro-hydraulic control system consisting of a servo-controlled cylinder, flow dividing unit, servo-motor, hydraulic power source, electronics box, twin handles for the gunner and a single handle for the commander.

If required the AMX-10RC can be delivered without the air conditioning system, heater, NBC system, night fire-control equipment, navigation system and amphibious capability.

Variants

In 1971 a prototype of a wheeled (6 × 6) APC called the AMX-10RP was shown for the first time but it has not been placed in production. A tracked version of the AMX-10RC developed to the prototype stage is known as the AMX-10C but has not yet been placed in production.

Model of AMX-10 RAA twin 30 mm self-propelled anti-aircraft gun (GIAT)

Type	HEAT	HE	Smoke
DESIGNATION	OCC 105 F3	OE 105 F3	OFUM 105 F3
WEIGHT OF CARTRIDGE	13.85 kg	13.7 kg	13.7 kg
WEIGHT OF PROJECTILE	5.65 kg	7.2 kg	7.2 kg
WEIGHT OF EXPLOSIVE	0.92 kg	1.74 kg	1.50 kg (composition)
LENGTH OF CARTRIDGE	838 mm	888 mm	888 mm
MUZZLE VELOCITY	1120 m/s	800 m/s	800 m/s

Note: Training version of HEAT is BSCC 105 F3 and has a muzzle velocity of 1120 metres a second. All rounds are fin stabilised.

AMX-10 RAC

This is essentially the AMX-10RC with its original turret replaced by the GIAT TS 90 turret which is fully described in the entry for the Panhard ERC 90 F4 Sagaie armoured car later in this book. The vehicle has a loaded weight of 14 800 kg with the three-man crew consisting of commander/loader, gunner and driver. The turret has manual traverse but can be fitted with power traverse if required. A total of 37 rounds of 90 mm and 3200 rounds of 7.62 mm machine gun ammunition are carried.

AMX-10 RAA

Shown in model form at the 1981 Satory Exhibition of Military Equipment was the AMX-10 RAA. This is essentially the AMX-10RC with its original turret replaced by the Thomson-CSF/SAMM SABRE turret armed with twin 30 mm cannon.

AMX-10 RTT

In 1983 GIAT announced that the prototype of a wheeled armoured personnel carrier version of the AMX-10RC had been built under the designation of the AMX-10 RTT (Roues Transporteur de Troupes). This has a similar suspension to the AMX-10RC but with the driver at the front of the hull on the left and the engine compartment to his right. The troop compartment is at the rear of the hull with periscopes giving observation to the sides. Over the top of the troop compartment is a GIAT CIBI 12.7 mm weapon station armed with a 12.7 mm M2 HB machine gun. The three-man crew consists of commander, gunner and driver and it can carry 10 fully equipped infantrymen.

SPECIFICATIONS (with 0.3 m ground clearance)

CREW	4			SMOKE-LAYING		
CONFIGURATION	6 × 6			EQUIPMENT	2 smoke dischargers	
COMBAT WEIGHT	15 800 kg	MAX RANGE (road)	800 km		either side of turret	
UNLOADED WEIGHT	14 900 kg	FORDING	amphibious			
POWER-TO-WEIGHT		GRADIENT	60%	AMMUNITION		
RATIO	16.45 hp/tonne	SIDE SLOPE	40%	(main)	38	
LENGTH GUN		VERTICAL OBSTACLE	0.7 m	(coaxial)	4000	
FORWARDS	9.15 m	TRENCH	1.15 m	(smoke grenades)	16	
LENGTH HULL	6.35 m	ENGINE	Hispano-Suiza HS-115	FIRE-CONTROL SYSTEM		
WIDTH	2.95 m		super-charged	Turret power control	electro-hydraulic/	
HEIGHT			water-cooled 8-cylin-		manual	
(overall)	2.68 m		der diesel developing	By commander	yes	
(to turret top)	2.215 m		260 hp at 3000 rpm	By gunner	yes	
(to hull top)	1.565 m	TRANSMISSION	preselective with 4	Gun elevation/		
GROUND CLEARANCE			forward and 4 reverse	depression	+20°/−8°	
(normal)	0.35 m (adjustable		gears	Gun stabiliser		
	from 0.2 – 0.6 m)	SUSPENSION	hydro-pneumatic	(vertical)	no	
TRACK	2.425 m	ELECTRICAL SYSTEM	24 V	(horizontal)	no	
WHEELBASE	1.550 m + 1.550 m	BATTERIES	6 × 12 V, 100 Ah			
MAX SPEED		ARMAMENT				
(road)	85 km/h	(main)	1 × 105 mm			
(water)	7.2 km/h	(coaxial)	1 × 7.62 mm MG			

Status: In production. In service with the French Army and Morocco.

Manufacturer: Atelier de Construction Roanne (ARE). Enquiries to Groupement Industriel des Armements Terrestres, 10 place G Clemenceau, 92211 Saint Cloud, France.

Panhard EBR Heavy Armoured Car

Development

In 1937 Panhard started design work on a new armoured car for the French Army called the AMR 201, which was to have better cross-country mobility than armoured cars used by the French Army at the time, such as the Panhard AMD (4 × 4). Design of the AMR 201 (Auto-Mitrailleuse de Reconnaissance) was completed within a year and construction of the first prototype began in 1938 and was completed by December 1939. The prototype had a crew of three and was fitted with a turret armed with a 25 mm gun and a 7.5 mm coaxial machine gun. Its eight-wheel drive gave it excellent cross-country mobility. When travelling on roads the four centre wheels were raised off the ground as they had steel ribs which would bite into the surface of the road. The four centre (or intermediate) wheels were lowered when the vehicle was crossing rough country. When the Second World War broke out the AMR 201 was taken to North Africa where it was subsequently lost.

Shortly after the end of the Second World War the French Army issued a requirement for three new armoured vehicles: a heavy armoured car (which eventually became the Panhard EBR 75), a light tank (which became the AMX-13) and a heavy tank (which became the AMX-50 but was never placed in production).

Panhard EBR with FL-10 turret armed with 75 mm gun (E C P Armées)

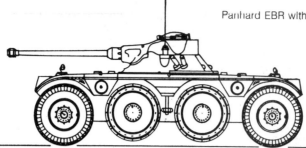

To meet the requirement for a heavy armoured car four French companies submitted proposals, Hotchkiss (6 × 6), Latil (8 × 8), Lorraine (6 × 6) and Panhard (8 × 8). Panhard completed its design early in 1946 and was awarded a contract to build two prototype vehicles which were completed by July 1948. After trials with the Panhard and Hotchkiss designs, the former was accepted for service, with modifications, in December 1949. Production began early in 1950 and the first production vehicles were completed in late 1950. By the time production had been completed in 1960 1200 EBRs (Engin Blindé de Reconnaissance) had been completed, most of which were supplied to the French Army.

The EBR is still in service with the French Army; from 1979 it started to be replaced by the AMX-10RC (6 × 6) vehicle, but it is not expected to be finally phased out of French Army service until 1986/87.

Description

The hull of the EBR is made of welded steel with the driver seated at the front, fighting compartment in the centre and the second driver, who also operates the radio, at the rear, with the engine under the fighting compartment.

The front and rear drivers are both provided with a two-piece hatch cover that opens either side of their position, the left cover with one periscope and the right with two. In addition there is a small flap that opens upwards. Both drivers are provided with a full set of driving controls and the vehicle can be driven at the same speed in each direction. Mounted between each driver's feet is a 7.5 mm machine gun firing forwards, but these are not normally fitted today.

The FL-11 oscillating turret, manufactured by Fives-Cail Babcock, is in the centre of the vehicle with the commander on the left and the gunner on the right. The commander is provided with periscopes for all-round observation while the gunner has a telescope linked to the main armament and three periscopes. In the 1950s some Panhard EBRs were fitted with the FL-10 turret as installed on most production AMX-13 light tanks, which had the advantage of being fitted with an automatic loading system which enabled a high rate of fire to be achieved for a short time. But it also had two disadvantages: it increased the vehicle's weight to 15 200 kg (almost the same as the AMX-13 light tank) and its overall height to 2.58 metres. In the 1960s all EBRs were fitted with the FL-11 turret armed with the new 90 mm gun.

The engine is under the fighting compartment and air is drawn into the vehicle by two fans through oval holes between the top of the hull and the bottom of the turret; the air then passes over the engine and leaves the vehicle by similar oval holes at the rear of the turret. The engine consists of two

Panhard EBR with FL-11 turret armed with 90 mm gun, this is current model in service with French Army

The EBR is armed with a 90 mm gun which fires fin-stabilised HEAT and HE projectiles. A 7.5 mm machine gun is mounted coaxially with the main armament and two electrically-operated smoke dischargers are mounted on either side of the turret.

Type	HEAT	HE	Smoke	Canister
WEIGHT OF COMPLETE ROUND	7.1 kg	8.9 kg	9.1 kg	8.9 kg
WEIGHT OF PROJECTILE	3.65 kg	5.27 kg	5.4 kg	5.28 kg
MUZZLE VELOCITY	640 m/s	635 m/s	750 m/s	640 m/s

The EBR has no NBC system, no night vision equipment and no amphibious capability.

Variants

EBR ETT Armoured Personnel Carrier

There have been a number of experimental models of the EBR but the only variant known to be in current service is the EBR ETT armoured personnel carrier which has the Panhard designation model 238. The first prototype was completed in 1957 but only 30 were built for service in North Africa. They are no longer used by the French Army but a few are known to be used by Portugal.

The ETT has a superstructure that extends to the rear of the hull and is provided with hatches to enable the crew to use their small arms from within the vehicle. Normal means of entry and exit for the crew is via two doors in the rear of the hull which are also provided with firing ports. This model was fitted with a turret-mounted 7.5 mm machine gun or two small turrets each fitted with a rifle. The EBR ETT has a crew of three and can carry 12 fully-equipped troops; loaded weight is 13 000 kg.

Panhard EBR of French Army with FL-11 turret armed with 90 mm gun and driver's hatch in open position

opposed groups of six cylinders. Power is transmitted from the engine through a four-disc dry clutch to the four-speed gearbox, which is connected to the second transversely mounted gearbox by bevel gears giving forward and reverse. This gives the vehicle 16 gears in both directions. The second gearbox incorporates a differential (which can be locked for off-road travel) and power is then taken to a free-wheel transmission on each side of the vehicle and then via shafts to the four wheel stations. When travelling on roads the centre or intermediate wheels are raised off the ground, but still turn. Before crossing rough country, the intermediate wheels are lowered to the ground by a hydro-pneumatic unit operated by the driver. The front and rear wheels are sprung with two concentric coil springs and a telescopic damper. The front and rear wheels have tyres with bullet-proof inner tubes.

SPECIFICATIONS (EBR fitted with FL-11 turret armed with 90 mm gun)					
CREW	4	TRENCH	2 m	AMMUNITION	
CONFIGURATION	8 × 8	TURNING RADIUS		(main)	43
COMBAT WEIGHT	13 500 kg	(on front wheels)	7.974 m	(machine gun)	2000
POWER-TO-WEIGHT		(on front and rear		FIRE-CONTROL SYSTEM	
RATIO	14.81 hp/tonne	wheels)	3.962 m	Turret power control	hydraulic/manual
LENGTH GUN		ENGINE	Panhard model 12 H	By commander	yes
FORWARDS	6.15 m		6000 12-cylinder	By gunner	yes
LENGTH HULL	5.56 m		air-cooled petrol	Max rate of power	
WIDTH	2.42 m		developing 200 hp	traverse	360° in 12 s
HEIGHT			at 3700 rpm	Max rate of power	
(to turret top on 8		TRANSMISSION	2 4-speed gear boxes	elevation	5° in 1 s
wheels)	2.32 m	STEERING	hydraulic assisted	Gun elevation/	
(to turret top on 4		CLUTCH	4-disc dry	depression	+15°/−10°
wheels)	2.24 m	SUSPENSION		ARMOUR	
GROUND CLEARANCE		(front and rear wheels)	concentric coil springs	Hull front	40 mm
(on 8 wheels)	0.41 m		and telescopic damper	Hull sides	16 mm
(on 4 wheels)	0.33 m	(intermediate)	hydro-pneumatic	Hull top	20 mm
TRACK	1.74 m	ARMAMENT		Hull floor	16 mm
MAX SPEED (road)	105 km/h	(main)	1 × 90 mm gun	Hull rear	40 mm
FUEL CAPACITY	380 litres	(coaxial)	1 × 7.5 mm MG	Turret front	40 mm
MAX RANGE (road)	650 km	(fixed at both driver's		Turret sides	30 mm
FORDING	1.2 m	positions)	1 × 7.5 mm MG	Turret rear	20 mm
GRADIENT	60%	SMOKE-LAYING		Turret top	10 mm
VERTICAL OBSTACLE	0.4 m	EQUIPMENT	2 × 2 smoke dis-chargers either side of turret		

Status: Production complete. In service with France (being replaced by AMX-10RC), Mauritania, Morocco (being replaced by AMX-10RC), Portugal (armoured car and ETT APC) and Tunisia.

Manufacturer: Société de Constructions Mécaniques Panhard et Levassor, 18 avenue d'Ivry, 75621 Paris, France.

Renault VBC 90 Armoured Car

Development

The VBC 90 (Véhicule Blindé de Combat) was designed by Renault Vehicules Industriels specifically for the export market and was shown for the first time at the 1979 Satory Exhibition of Military Equipment. First production VBC 90 armoured cars were completed in September 1981. It shares many automotive components with the VAB (6 × 6) APC which is in production for the export market and the VAB (4 × 4) which is already in service with the French Army. The first of 28 VBC 90 armoured cars ordered by the French Gendarmerie were delivered in 1983 and are fitted with a SOPTAC fire control system incorporating a laser rangefinder.

Description

Its all-welded steel hull protects the crew from small arms fire and shell splinters and is divided into three compartments: driver's at the front, fighting in the centre and engine at the rear. The driver is seated at the front of the vehicle on the left side and has a single-piece hatch cover that opens to the right with three integral periscopes. Vehicles for the French Gendarmerie have bullet-proof windows rather than periscopes for greater all round observation, with centre one fitted with wiper.

The GIAT TS 90 turret is all-welded with the commander on the left and the gunner on the right, both with a single-piece hatch cover that opens to the rear and an adjustable seat. An extractor fan is mounted in the forward part of the

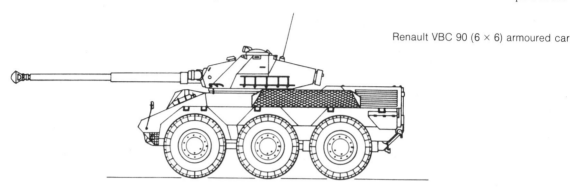

Renault VBC 90 (6 × 6) armoured car

Renault VBC 90 (6 × 6) armoured car as delivered to the French Gendarmerie with all hatches closed

GIAT 90 mm CS 90 gun as installed in TS 90 turret fitted on VBC 90 armoured car together with a selection of ammunition carried, that on the right being the APFSDS round

turret roof. Main armament consists of a long-barrelled 90 mm gun with a 35-degree oblique wedge breech-block, hydro-pneumatic recoil system, thermal sleeve and a muzzle brake. Twenty rounds of ready-use ammunition are carried, four in the turret basket and 16 in the turret bustle. The empty cartridge cases are ejected into a bag under the breech and the commander has an ammunition resupply hatch in the left side of the turret. A further 25 rounds of 90 mm ammunition are carried in the hull.

The 90 mm rifled gun fires the following fixed ammunition:

Type	Canister	HE	HEAT	Smoke
DESIGNATION	ODDR	OE 90 F1*	OCC 90-62†	OFUM PH‡
WEIGHT OF PROJECTILE	5.28 kg	5.28 kg	3.65 kg	5.4 kg
WEIGHT OF FILLING	4 kg	0.945 kg	0.67 kg	0.8 kg
LENGTH OF PROJECTILE	158 mm	480 mm	500 mm	480 mm
WEIGHT OF CARTRIDGE	10.4 kg	10.42 kg	8.95 kg	10.54 kg
MUZZLE VELOCITY	750 m/s	750 m/s	950 m/s	750 m/s

*practice projectile is OE 90 PLN
†will penetrate 320 mm of armour at 0° incidence
  will penetrate 120 mm of armour at 65° incidence
  practice version called SCC 90 F1
‡will lay 50-metre wide smokescreen which will last 20–30 seconds
Recently developed is an APFSDS projectile with a muzzle velocity of 1275 metres a second which will penetrate 120 mm of armour at an incidence of 60 degrees at a range of 2000 metres; projectile weight is 3.3 kg.

Mounted coaxially to the left of the main armament is a 7.62 mm machine gun and there are two electrically-operated smoke dischargers mounted either side of the turret towards the rear.

A PH 9A white light searchlight is mounted coaxially to the left of the main armament and a second white light searchlight is mounted in the forward part of the turret and operated by the commander. The commander has seven periscopes and the gunner five and the gunner also has an M563 telescopic sight with a magnification of ×5.9 for laying the main armament. The vehicle can also be fitted with the following SOPELEM sights:
SOPTAC 21 with a CILAS TCV 107 laser rangefinder
SOPTAC 6 with CILAS TCV 107 laser rangefinder which automatically displays target range in the gunner's sight
SOPTAC 13 with CILAS TCV 107 laser rangefinder which automatically displays target range in the gunner's sight, and also provides the crossing speed of the target

For engaging targets at night the SOPELEM TJN 20 gunner's sight is fitted, which has a day channel with a magnification of ×6 and an 8-degree field of view and a night

channel with a magnification of ×5.5 and an 8-degree field of view. This can be used in conjunction with the following control system:
SOPELEM SOPTAC 22 with a CILAS TCV 107 laser rangefinder
SOPELEM SOPTAC 10 with a CILAS TCV 107 laser rangefinder which automatically displays target range in the gunner's sight
SOPELEM SOPTAC 11 with a CILAS TCV 107 laser rangefinder which automatically displays target range in the gunner's sight and also provides crossing speed of target
Thomson-CSF Canasta passive night system which enables the gunner to detect and engage targets at a range of up to 2000 metres, aim the gun and fire in darkness.
GIAT M586 day and night firing system which uses components of the COTAC fire-control system and includes a TCV 107 laser rangefinder and a computer which integrates the various functions required for engaging stationary and moving targets, including wind speed, external temperature, speed and distance of target.

Optional equipment includes a 7.62 mm anti-aircraft machine gun. Future developments planned for the turret include independent elevation of the coaxial 7.62 mm machine gun, option of the 7.62 mm coaxial machine gun being replaced by a 12.7 mm machine gun, electric traverse (360 degrees in 14 seconds).

The engine, transmission and fuel tank are at the rear of the hull, with a large door, opening to the left, for access for maintenance.

Power is transmitted from the engine to the wheels by a torque converter and a gearbox with five forward and one reverse gears. Gears are shifted by a small pneumatically-operated lever which also operates the clutch. The axles have differential reduction gears with double reduction and differential locking. The wheels are independently suspended by torsion bars and hydraulic shock absorbers. Steering is hydraulically assisted on the front two axles and the tyre pressures can be adjusted to suit the type of ground being crossed. Unlike the VAB family of APCs the VBC 90 does not have any amphibious capability.

Optional equipment includes an NBC system and a front-mounted winch with a capacity of 7000 kg and supplied with 60 metres of cable.

Renault VBC 90 (6 × 6) armoured car with driver's hatch in closed position

One of the prototypes of VBC 90 fitted with Hispano-Suiza Lynx 90 turret armed with Cockerill 90 mm Mark III gun

VBC fitted with GIAT turret armed with 81 mm smooth-bore gun/mortar (Christopher F Foss)

Variants

The VBC 90 can be fitted with a number of other turrets including the following:

Hispano-Suiza Lynx 90 (already tested)
GIAT turret armed with 81 mm smooth-bore gun/mortar
ESD TA-20 anti-aircraft turret with twin 20 mm cannon
SAMM TTB 190 turret with 90 mm gun
Hispano-Suiza MARS 90 mm

Note: Automotive components of the VBC/VAB family are also used in a family of vehicles that the company has designed to meet the requirements of Argentina in competition with designs carried out by Panhard. Available details of this programme are given in this section under Argentina.

SPECIFICATIONS

CREW	3
CONFIGURATION	6 × 6
POWER-TO-WEIGHT RATIO	18.36 hp/tonne
WEIGHT	12 800 kg
LENGTH GUN FORWARD	8.152 m
LENGTH HULL	5.495 m
WIDTH	2.49 m
HEIGHT	
(to turret top)	2.55 m
(to hull top)	1.697 m
TRACK	2.035 m
WHEELBASE	1.5 m + 1.5 m
ANGLE OF APPROACH/ DEPARTURE	45°/45°
MAX ROAD SPEED	
(5th gear)	92 km/h
(4th gear)	58 km/h
(3rd gear)	34 km/h
(2nd gear)	20 km/h
(1st gear)	12 km/h
(reverse)	13 km/h
MAX RANGE (road)	1000 km
FORDING	1.2 m

GRADIENT	60%
SIDE SLOPE	30%
VERTICAL OBSTACLE	0.6 m
TRENCH	1 m
ENGINE	MAN D.2356 HM 72 in-line water-cooled 6-cylinder diesel developing 235 hp at 2200 rpm
TRANSMISSION	Renault Transfluid with 5 forward and 1 reverse gears
STEERING	recirculating ball, hydraulic assisted
TYRES	14.00 × 20
BRAKES	disc
SUSPENSION	independent (torsion bar and telescopic shock absorbers)
ELECTRICAL SYSTEM	24 V
BATTERIES	4 × 12 V 6TN
ARMAMENT	
(main)	1 × 90 mm
(coaxial)	1 × 7.62 mm MG
(anti-aircraft)	1 × 7.62 mm MG (optional)

SMOKE-LAYING EQUIPMENT	2 smoke dischargers either side of turret
AMMUNITION	
(main)	45
(coaxial)	4000
FIRE-CONTROL SYSTEM	
Turret power control	electrically assisted manual (traverse only)
Max rate of power traverse	360°/20 s
Max rate of manual elevation	23°/15 s
Gun elevation/ depression	+15°/−8°

Note: From 1983 the MAN engine was replaced in production vehicles by the Renault 6-2045, six-cylinder, in-line water-cooled turbo-charged diesel developing 230 bhp at 2200 rpm.

Status: In production. In service with France (Gendarmerie, 28 delivered in 1983), Oman (4) and the United Arab Emirates.

Manufacturer: Production of the VBC 90 is undertaken by Renault Véhicules Industriels.

Marketing: Société des Matériels Spéciaux Renault VI – Creusot-Loire, 316 Bureaux de la Colline, 92213 Saint-Cloud Cedex, France.

LOHR RPX 90 Armoured Car

Development

The RPX 90 (4 × 4) armoured car has been developed by the LOHR company as a private venture specifically for the export market and was shown for the first time at the 1983 Satory Exhibition of Military Equipment.

Description

The hull of the RPX 90 is of all-welded steel construction which provides the crew with protection from small arms fire and shell splinters.

The driver is seated at the front of the hull and has a single-piece hatch cover over his position. Bullet-proof windscreens at the front and sides provide excellent visibility, but when in a combat area these are covered by armoured shutters with integral vision slits that are hinged at the bottom.

LOHR RPX 90 armoured car fitted with turret armed with six MATRA SATCP surface-to-air missiles

Mounted on the roof in the centre of the vehicle is the Hispano-Suiza CNMP 90 mm MARS turret which is armed with the GIAT 90 mm Super 90 gun which has an elevation of +20 degrees and a depression of −8 degrees, instead of the 90 mm CN-90-F3. A 7.62 mm machine gun is mounted co-axially with the main armament.

The engine and transmission are at the rear of the hull. According to the manufacturer the excellent off-road mobility of the LOHR RPX 90 is made possible by its good power-to-weight ratio and its oversize and low pressure tyres.

In the either side of the hull is a two-part hatch, the upper part opening to the rear and the lower folding down to form an entry step.

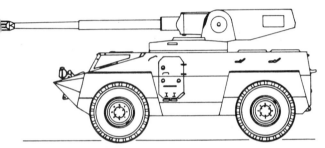

Provisional drawing of LOHR RPX 90 (4 × 4) armoured car

LOHR RPX 90 armoured car fitted with Hispano-Suiza CNMP 90 mm MARS turret which features an externally-mounted gun

Variants

Although the prototype was shown with the experimental Hispano-Suiza MARS 90 two-man turret, the RPX 90 armoured car can be fitted with a wide range of other turrets and has already been fitted with a Hispano-Suiza CNMP Serval turret armed with a 60 mm breech-loaded mortar, 20 mm cannon and 7.62 mm machine gun. This turret is fully decribed in the following entry. It has also been fitted with the turret armed with six MATRA SATCP surface-to-air missiles, although this system has yet to enter production.

LOHR RPX 90 armoured car fitted with Hispano-Suiza CNMP Serval turret armed with 60 mm breech-loaded mortar, 20 mm cannon and 7.62 mm machine gun

SPECIFICATIONS

CREW	3	TRACK	2.13 m	TRANSMISSION	automatic, 6 forward and 1 reverse gears
CONFIGURATION	4 × 4	WHEELBASE	2.95 m	STEERING	hydraulic assisted
COMBAT WEIGHT	10 000 kg	ANGLE OF APPROACH/ DEPARTURE	45°/45°	TYRES	20.5 R 20.5 S with run flat capability
WEIGHT UNLOADED AND WITHOUT TURRET	7000 kg	MAX ROAD SPEED	105 km/h	BRAKES	discs on all wheels
POWER-TO-WEIGHT RATIO	25 hp/tonne	MAX CROSS-COUNTRY SPEED	53 km/h	ARMAMENT (main)	1 × 90 mm
LENGTH (without armament)	5.20 m	MAX RANGE (road)	1000 km	(coaxial)	1 × 7.62 mm MG
WIDTH	2.65 m	FORDING	1.4 m	ARMAMENT (main)	1 × 90 mm
HEIGHT (hull top)	1.725 m	GRADIENT	60%	(coaxial)	1 × 7.62 mm
(turret)	2.52 m	SIDE SLOPE	40%	AMMUNITION (main)	60
GROUND CLEARANCE	0.5 m	VERTICAL OBSTACLE	0.6 m	(coaxial)	2000
		TURNING RADIUS	7.5 m		
		ENGINE	6-cylinder water-cooled turbo-charged diesel developing 250 hp		

Status: Prototype.

Manufacturer: LOHR, 67980 Hangenbieten, France.

Panhard ERC Armoured Car

Development

The ERC (Engin de Reconnaissance Cannon) range of armoured cars was developed by Panhard as a private venture from 1975 and is aimed specifically at the export market. The range was first shown in 1977 at the Satory Exhibition of Military Equipment and entered production the following year at Panhard's new factory at Marolles. First production vehicles were completed in 1979. The ERC range of armoured cars shares many automotive components with the Panhard VCR range of armoured personnel carriers which were also shown for the first time in 1977.

The French Army requires at least 53 Panhard ERC 90 F4 Sagaie armoured cars and the first of these were delivered in 1982. They are being issued to the two units assigned to rapid deployment overseas, the Regiment d'Infanterie de Chars de Marines which is based at Vannes in Brittany and the Regiment de Hussards Parachutistes based at Tarbes in the Pyrenees.

Panhard ERC 90 F4 Sagaie fitted with TS 90 turret with 90 mm gun depressed

Description

The all-welded steel hull provides the crew with protection from small arms fire and shell splinters. The floor of the hull consists of two plates welded together to form a flat V which helps the vehicle to slide off obstacles and stiffens the floor against damage from mines.

The driver is seated at the front of the hull, slightly to the left of the vehicle's centre line. His hatch is in two parts: one part, which contains the forward-facing periscope, folds forward onto the glacis plate and the second part folds upwards. The forward periscope can be replaced by an infra-red or image-intensification periscope for night driving, and there is an additional periscope either side of the driver's hatch cover.

The turret is mounted in the centre of the vehicle and as each version has a different turret they are described in detail under variants. All vehicles in the range are powered by a militarised version of a Peugeot V-6 petrol engine which develops 155 hp at 5500 rpm. Power is taken from the engine through a single-plate clutch to a transversely-mounted

Panhard ERC 90 F4 Sagaie fitted with TS 90 turret with 90 mm gun

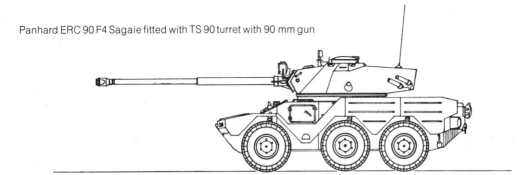

Panhard gearbox with six forward and one reverse gears and incorporating a Panhard cam-type limited slip differential from which the drive is taken to either side of the vehicle. Drive is then taken by half-shafts to bevel gears at the centre wheel stations and then shafts take power to the bevel gears at the front wheel stations. The rear wheel bevel gears are driven by shafts directly from the gearbox. The drive from the centre to the front wheel on each side incorporates another cam-type limited slip differential. Power is transmitted from the bevel boxes to the wheels by a train of gears housed within trailing arms which independently locate the wheels. The front and rear wheels are sprung by single coil springs with concentric telescopic hydraulic dampers. The centre wheels, which are raised off the ground when on roads, are sprung by hydro-pneumatic units. The centre wheels are powered even when raised clear of the road surface.

Only the front wheels are steered, and steering is hydraulically assisted. The low-pressure tyres are fitted with Hutchinson cellular inner tubes, which enable the vehicle to travel for at least 100 km at 30 km/h when the tyres have been punctured by bullets.

The basic vehicle can ford to a depth of 1.2 metres without preparation but two different amphibious models of the ERC have already been developed. Both models have a trim vane mounted at the front of the hull which is folded back onto the glacis plate when not in use and has a transparent panel in its centre to enable the driver to have a clear view ahead, and sheet metal floats over the wheel stations which are filled with closed-cell foam. A rear opening door is provided in the left side of the hull. Before entering the water the trim vane is erected and the two tubular ducts at the sides of the engine compartment are hydraulically swivelled into the vertical position to prevent water entering the engine compartment. The radiator compartment is allowed to flood, as when the vehicle is afloat cooling is by water-to-water heat transfer. The first amphibious model is propelled in the water by its wheels and the second by two Dowty-Messier hydrojets.

All models have a turret-mounted ventilator and internal lights as standard. Optional equipment includes an NBC system, ground navigation compass, air-conditioning equipment and a front mounted winch with 60 metres of cable and a capacity of 3500 kg.

Variants

ERC 90 F4 Sagaie

This was the first model to enter production and is fitted with a GIAT TS 90 turret armed with a 90 mm gun which can fire the following ammunition:

Panhard ERC 90 F4 Sagaie fitted with TS 90 turret firing its 90 mm gun. Note water jets at rear of hull

Type	Canister	HE	HEAT	Smoke
DESIGNATION	ODDR	OE 90 F1*	OCC 90-62†	OFUM PH‡
WEIGHT OF PROJECTILE	5.28 kg	5.28 kg	3.65 kg	5.4 kg
WEIGHT OF FILLING	4 kg	0.945 kg	0.67 kg	0.8 kg
LENGTH OF PROJECTILE	158 mm	480 mm	500 mm	480 mm
WEIGHT OF CARTRIDGE	10.4 kg	10.42 kg	8.95 kg	10.54 kg
MUZZLE VELOCITY	750 m/s	750 m/s	950 m/s	750 m/s

*practice projectile is OE 90 PLN
†will penetrate 320 mm of armour at 0° incidence
will penetrate 120 mm of armour at 65° incidence
practice version called SCC 90 F1
‡will lay a 50-metre wide smokescreen which will last 20–30 seconds
Recently developed is an APFSDS projectile with a muzzle velocity of 1275 metres a
second which will penetrate 120 mm of armour at an incidence of 60 degrees at a range
of 2000 metres; projectile weight is 3.3 kg

Panhard ERC 90 F1 Lynx with turret traversed left and
commander manning external machine gun

A 7.62 mm machine gun is mounted coaxially to the left of
the main armament and two smoke dischargers are mounted
either side of the turret at the rear. The commander is seated
on the left side of the turret and the gunner on the right, both
with a single-piece hatch cover that opens to the rear. The
commander is provided with seven periscopes and the gunner five and the gunner also has an M 563 telescopic sight
with a magnification of ×5.9. Of 20 rounds of 90 mm
ammunition carried in the turret, 12 are HEAT and 8 HE.
Optional turret equipment includes an anti-aircraft machine
gun, day/night telescope and a laser rangefinder, and
developments planned include independent elevation of the
coaxial machine gun, option of having the 7.62 mm machine
gun replaced by a 12.7 mm machine gun and a fire-control
system for engaging moving targets. The turret is mounted
with a new gun mantlet which allows super-elevation of the
main armament to +35 degrees enabling it to be used against
high and concealed targets.

Panhard offers six options for the vehicle, each with a
weight index of 1 or 2, and the user can select options up to an
index of four. The options are amphibious kit propelled in the
water by its wheels (1), amphibious kit propelled in the water
by hydrojets (2), NBC system (1), air-conditioning system/
heater (1), an additional 10 rounds of 90 mm and 1000
rounds of 7·62 mm ammunition (1) and a ground navigation
system (1).

ERC 90 F4 Sagaie TTB 190

This was shown for the first time at the 1983 Satory Exhibition of Military Equipment and is the basic chassis fitted with
the new SAMM TTB 190 two-man turret which is armed

Panhard ERC 90 F4 Sagaie fitted with SAMM TTB 190 turret

with the same GIAT 90 mm F4 gun as the original ERC 90
F4 Sagaie which has the GIAT TS 90 turret.

The commander is on the left and gunner on right, and
both have a combined day/night plus periscopes for observation The 90 mm gun has an elevation of +15 degrees and a
depression of −8 degrees with turret traverse a full 360
degrees. Turret traverse can be electric, hydraulic or
electro-hydraulic.

A 7.62 mm or 12.7 mm machine gun can be mounted
coaxial to the left and a 7.62 mm machine gun can be
mounted externally on commander's cupola for anti-aircraft
defence. A total of 23 rounds of 90 mm and 2000 rounds of
7.62 mm machine gun ammunition are carried. A wide range
of options is available for this turret including a stabilisation
system and various types of fire control system including a
laser rangefinder.

Loaded weight is 8300 kg, empty weight 7700 kg, length
hull 4.91 m, width 2.495 m, height overall 2.382 m and
height to hull top 1.502 m. Other data is identical to the
Panhard ERC 90 F4 Sagaie.

ERC 90 F1 Lynx

This is fitted with a Lynx 90 turret designed and manufactured by Hispano-Suiza and armed with a 90 mm F1 gun,
7.62 mm coaxial machine gun and two smoke dischargers on
either side of the turret at the rear. The gun fires the following
ammunition:

Type	HEAT	HE	Smoke	Canister
WEIGHT OF COMPLETE ROUND	7.1 kg	8.9 kg	9.1 kg	8.9 kg
WEIGHT OF PROJECTILE	3.65 kg	5.28 kg	5.4 kg	5.28 kg
MUZZLE VELOCITY	750 m/s	650 m/s	640 m/s	640 m/s

The commander is seated on the left of the turret with the
gunner on the right. The commander is provided with a
cupola with a single-piece hatch cover that opens to the rear
and eight periscopes for all-round observation. The gunner is
provided with a single-piece hatch cover that opens to the
rear. Vision equipment consists of a combined day and night
passive periscope model TJN 2.90 (SOPELEM), TCV 107
laser rangefinder (CILAS/SOPELEM) and 12 periscopes
(nine type L 794 B and three type L 794 D). A total of 21
rounds of 90 mm ammunition are carried in the turret and if

required a 7.62 mm machine gun can be fitted for anti-aircraft defence.

Panhard offers six options for the vehicle, identical to those offered for the ERC 90 F4 Sagaie except that it can carry an additional 20 rounds of 90 mm ammunition rather than the 10 in the ERC 90 F4 Sagaie.

ERC TG 120 Guepard
This model is no longer offered.

ERC 60-20 Serval
This is fitted with a 60-20 Serval turret designed and manufactured by Hispano-Suiza and is armed with a 60 mm breech-loaded mortar which can be elevated from −8 to +80 degrees and a 20 mm cannon mounted at the right rear of the turret which can be elevated from −8 to +50 degrees. The 60 mm mortar can be either a Hotchkiss Brandt HB 60 with a maximum range of 2600 metres or a Hotchkiss Brandt HB 60 LP with a maximum range of 5000 metres. The 20 mm cannon can either be a French M693 dual-feed cannon with 300 rounds of HE and 37 rounds of AP ammunition for ready use or an HS 820 (Oerlikon KAD-B16) single-feed cannon with 300 rounds of ready-use ammunition. If required, a

Panhard ERC 60-20 Serval armoured car

Panhard ERC 60/12 Mangouste armoured car, first shown in June 1983 (Christopher F Foss)

Panhard EMC 81 mm mortar gun carrier

7.62 mm machine gun can be mounted coaxially to the right of the 20 mm cannon.

Vision equipment includes one sighting periscope, nine observation periscopes and an optional night periscope.

Panhard offers seven options for this vehicle, identical to the ERC 90 F4 Sagaie except that an additional 100 rounds of 20 mm and 1000 rounds of 7.62 mm ammunition are carried (1) and/or 20 60 mm mortar projectiles (1).

ERC 60/12 Mangouste
This was shown for the first time at the 1983 Satory Exhibition of Military Equipment and is the basic chassis fitted with the new Hispano-Suiza 60/12 Mangouste turret armed with a 60 mm Brandt HB LP mortar, 12.7 mm M2 HB machine gun and a 7.62 mm anti-aircraft machine gun. The 60 mm mortar has an elevation of +85 degrees and the 12.7 mm machine gun an elevation of +55 degrees; both weapons have a depression of +12 degrees. Turret traverse and weapon elevation is manual. A total of 65 rounds (of which 30 are for emergency use) of 60 mm, 1200 rounds of 12.7 mm and 800 rounds of 7.62 mm ammunition are carried.

EMC 81 mm Mortar Gun Carrier
The EMC (Engin Blindé Mortier-Cannon) is fitted with an open-topped turret armed with an 81 mm breech-loaded mortar with a 7.62 mm machine gun mounted on the top of the turret for anti-aircraft use. The 81 mm mortar fires standard 6 kg HE mortar bombs to a range of more than 7000 metres and can also fire a 1.4 kg APFSDS projectile with a muzzle velocity of 100 metres a second. The 78 mortar bombs are carried in the rear of the turret but the six APFSDS projectiles are carried in the front of the turret basket ready for immediate use. Turret traverse and weapon elevation are manual.

Panhard offers five options for this vehicle, each with a weight index of 1 or 2 and the user can select options up to an index of four. The options are amphibious kit propelled in the water by its wheels (1), amphibious kit propelled in the water by hydrojets (2), air-conditioning/heating system (1), NBC system carried in the hull (1) and a ground navigation system (1).

ERC with SAMM TTB 125 turret
For trials purposes the ERC has been fitted with the SAMM TTB 125 two-man turret armed with a 25 mm Hughes Chain

Panhard ERC 25 Lanza fitted with SAMM TTB 125 two-man turret

Panhard ERC with SAMM twin 20 mm S 530 A anti-aircraft turret

gun and a coaxial 7.62 mm machine gun. Turret traverse is electric through a full 360 degrees with weapon elevation also electric from −8 to +50 degrees. A total of 140 rounds of ready use 25 mm and 200 rounds of ready use 7.62 mm ammunition are carried. This model is known as the ERC 25 Lanza and has a loaded weight of 7300 kg and an empty weight of 6800 kg. It has not yet been placed in production.

ERC with SAMM S 530 A 20 mm turret

Shown for the first time at the 1981 Satory Exhibition of Military Equipment was the Panhard ERC (6 × 6) chassis fitted with the SAMM twin 20 mm S 530 A anti-aircraft turret as fitted to the Panhard AML (4 × 4) armoured car. Details of this system are given in the entry for the Panhard AML armoured car.

ERC with ESD TA-20 turret

Shown for the first time at the 1981 Paris Air Show was the Panhard ERC (6 × 6) chassis fitted with the ESD TA-20 twin 20 mm turret. Turret traverse is a full 360 degrees and elevation from −5 to +50 degrees, both powered. Each of the 20 mm cannon is provided with 325 rounds of ready use ammunition. Mounted at the rear of the turret is a surveillance radar. This model has not entered production on this chassis, but the turret is being produced for the VAB (6 × 6) and Panhard M3 (4 × 4) armoured personnel carriers.

ERC with SAMM TAB 220 20 mm turret

This model, known as the ERC 20 Kriss was first shown in public during the 1983 Satory Exhibition of Military Equipment. The SAMM TAB 220 two-man turret is armed with twin 20 mm cannon with each being provided with 280 rounds of ready use ammunition. Turret traverse is powered through a full 360 degrees and the weapons can be elevated from −10 degrees to +70 degrees.

ERC with SATCP SAMS

MATRA has proposed using the ERC chassis for an anti-aircraft vehicle using the MATRA SATCP missiles, with six missiles in the ready to launch position, eg three either side of the turret.

Argentinian vehicles

Automotive components of the ERC/VCR family are also used in a family of vehicles that the company has developed to meet the requirements of Argentina in competition with designs carried out by Renault with their VBC/VAB. Available details are given in this section under Argentina.

Panhard ERC 20 Kriss fitted with SAMM TAB 220 two-man turret

Panhard ERC (6 × 6) vehicle with ESD TA-20 turret with twin 20 mm cannon

Panhard ERC 90 F1 Lynx showing amphibious capabilities with snorkels raised at rear of hull. This version has a 90 mm gun that can be elevated to +35 degrees

SPECIFICATIONS

Model	Sagaie	Lynx	Serval	EMC 81
CREW	3	3	3	3
CONFIGURATION	6 × 6	6 × 6	6 × 6	6 × 6
COMBAT WEIGHT	8100 kg	7700 kg	7000 kg	8000 kg
POWER-TO-WEIGHT				
RATIO	19.13 hp/tonne	20.12 hp/tonne	22.14 hp/tonne	19.37 hp/tonne
LENGTH GUN FORWARDS	7.693 m	6.115 m	5.26 m	5.26 m
LENGTH HULL	5.098 m	5.30 m	5.26 m	5.26 m
WIDTH	2.495 m	2.495 m	2.495 m	2.495 m
HEIGHT				
(overall)	2.254 m	2.147 m	2.333 m	2.348 m
(to hull top)	1.502 m	1.502 m	1.502 m	1.502 m
GROUND CLEARANCE				
(road)	0.294 m	0.294 m	0.294 m	0.294 m
(cross country)	0.344 m	0.344 m	0.344 m	0.344 m
TRACK	2.135 m	2.135 m	2.135 m	2.135 m
WHEELBASE	1.63 m + 1.22 m	1.63 m + 1.22 m	1.63 m + 1.22 m	1.63 m + 1.22 m
ANGLE OF APPROACH/				
DEPARTURE	48°/45°	48°/45°	45°/45°	45°/45°
MAX SPEED				
(road)	100 km/h	100 km/h	100 km/h	100 km/h
(water, wheels)	4.5 km/h	4.5 km/h	4.5 km/h	4.5 km/h
(water, hydro jets)	9.5 km/h	9.5 km/h	9.5 km/h	9.5 km/h
MAX RANGE (road)	800 km	800 km	800 km	800 km
FUEL CAPACITY	242 litres	242 litres	242 litres	242 litres
FORDING	1.2 m	1.2 m	1.2 m	1.2 m
GRADIENT	60%	60%	60%	60%
SIDE SLOPE	30%	30%	30%	30%
VERTICAL OBSTACLE	0.8 m	0.8 m	0.8 m	0.8 m
TRENCH	1.1 m	1.1 m	1.1 m	1.1 m
ENGINE	Peugeot V-6 petrol developing 155 hp at 5500 rpm			
TRANSMISSION	Panhard with 6 forward and 1 reverse gears			
STEERING	power-assisted			
CLUTCH	hydraulic controlled disc			
TYRES	11.00 × 16	11.00 × 16	11.00 × 16	11.00 × 16
ELECTRICAL SYSTEM	24 V	24 V	24 V	24 V
ARMAMENT				
(main)	1 × 90 mm	1 × 90 mm	1 × 60 mm	1 × 81 mm
(coaxial)	1 × 7.62 mm MG	1 × 7.62 mm MG	1 × 20 mm (independent elevation)	none
(anti-aircraft)	1 × 7.62 mm MG optional	1 × 7.62 mm MG optional	1 × 7.62 mm MG optional	1 × 7.62 mm MG
AMMUNITION				
(main)	20	21	50	84
(coaxial)	2000	2000	250	none
(anti-aircraft)	included in above	included in above	1000	2000
TURRET POWER				
TRAVERSE	manual	manual	manual	manual
GUN ELEVATION/				
DEPRESSION	+15°/−8°	+35°/−8°	+80° mortar + 50° cannon/−8°	+68°/−8°

The ERC armoured car is now being offered with the Mercedes-Benz OM 617 A super-charged diesel engine developing 115 hp at 4200 rpm. This gives a road range of 1000 km compared to the 800 km of the current production version.

Status: In production. In service with Argentina (36 Lynx ordered for Marines), Chad (four ERC 90 Lynx delivered in 1983 of which one has been lost in combat), France (53 ERC 90 F4 required of which 20 have been ordered), Iraq (unconfirmed), Ivory Coast (ERC 90 F4 Sagaie, seven ordered in 1979 and now delivered), Mexico (42 Lynx ordered and delivered) and Niger (ERC 60-20 Serval).

Manufacturer: Société de Constructions Mécaniques Panhard et Levassor, 18 avenue d'Ivry, 75621 Paris, France.

Panhard AML Light Armoured Car

Development

In 1956, following the successful use of the British Ferret scout car by the French Army in North Africa, the French Army issued a requirement for a similar vehicle but with a more powerful armament as the Ferret was armed only with a single 7.62 mm machine gun which, in the case of the Mk 1, was pintle mounted. At one time it was thought that the Ferret was to be manufactured under licence in France but the French armoured manufacturers resisted this suggestion.

Panhard, which was building the EBR (8 × 8) heavy armoured car at the time, was awarded a contract to build the prototype which was completed in 1959 under the Panhard designation Model 245. Saviem and DEFA-AMX also built prototype vehicles, but after trials the Panhard model was accepted for service with the French Army as the AML (Automitrailleuse Légère) and first production vehicles were delivered to the French Army in 1961.

Since then the AML has been built in very large numbers, although now it remains in production for export only. To date over 4000 AMLs have been built and the range has been continuously expanded to enable the vehicle to undertake additional roles. The AML has also been manufactured under licence in South Africa by Sandock-Austral Limited as the Eland. There is a separate entry for this vehicle under South Africa. The Panhard M3 armoured personnel carrier, uses 95 per cent of the automotive components of the AML, and many armies have bought complete fleets of AML armoured cars and M3 armoured personnel carriers.

Description (AML 90)

The all-welded steel hull of the AML is divided into three compartments: driver's at the front, fighting in the centre and the engine at the rear.

The driver is seated at the front of the hull and is provided with a single-piece hatch cover that opens to the right with three integral periscopes, the centre one of which can be replaced by an infra-red or image-intensification periscope for night driving.

The all-welded turret is manufactured by Hispano-Suiza. The commander is seated on the left of the turret and the gunner on the right, both with a single-piece hatch cover that opens to the rear. The commander and gunner each have four L794B periscopes and the gunner also has a type M262 or M37 sighting periscope. The M37 has a magnification of ×6. A searchlight is mounted forward of the commander's hatch. Either side of the hull below the turret ring is an entry door, the left door, on which the spare wheel and tyre is mounted, opens to the rear, the right door opens to the front.

The engine is at the rear of the hull and two access panels are provided over the engine compartment. The gearbox is crosswise and consists of two gearboxes in one (high and low), coupled on both sides of the bevel pinion. The low-range box is for cross-country use and comprises two low gears, a top gear and one reverse gear. When the low-range box is in normal drive the four ratios of the high-range box command the four upper gears of the range: sixth, fifth, fourth and third. The high-range box is for normal road use and has three low gears and one overdrive. There are Panhard type ball differentials in the gearbox and in each rear transfer box which automatically prevent gear slip.

Panhard AML with H 90 turret armed with 90 mm gun

French Army Panhard AML with H 90 turret

Panhard AML with H 90 turret of 1st Armoured Car Squadron, Irish Army (Denis McCarthy)

Drive is transmitted from the gearbox to two lateral transfer boxes via pinions to the rear wheels and via drive shafts that run along the inside of the hull to the front wheels.

The independent suspension at each wheel station consists of coil springs and hydro-pneumatic shock absorbers acting on the trailing arms of the wheel mechanism. The tyres are fitted with unpuncturable Hutchinson inner tubes.

The basic vehicle has no NBC system or night fighting aids, but they can be fitted as optional extras as can an air-conditioning system and an amphibious kit. The kit consists of a metal box structure which is permanently attached to the hull and filled with expanded polyurethane which forms a screen against hollow-charge projectiles and even if hit by an incendiary bullet will not catch fire. When in the

Panhard AML with H 90 turret armed with 90 mm gun

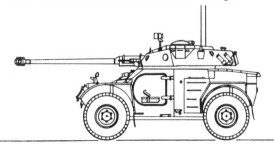

water it is propelled at a speed of 6 to 7 km/h by a single propeller at the rear of the hull, steering by using the front wheels as normal.

Variants

AML with H 90 Turret
This model is fitted with an H 90 turret manufactured by Hispano-Suiza and is armed with a 90 mm D 921 F1 gun which fires:

Type	HEAT	HE	Smoke	Canister
WEIGHT OF COMPLETE ROUND	7.1 kg	8.9 kg	9.1 kg	8.9 kg
WEIGHT OF PROJECTILE	3.65 kg	5.28 kg	5.4 kg	5.28 kg
MUZZLE VELOCITY	750 m/s	640 m/s	640 m/s	640 m/s

All of the above are fin-stabilised and the HEAT projectile will penetrate 320 mm of armour at an incidence of 0° or 120 mm at 65°.

A 7.62 mm machine gun is mounted to the left of the main armament and a similar weapon, or a 12.7 mm (0.50) machine gun, can be mounted on the roof for anti-aircraft defence. Two smoke dischargers mounted on either side of the turret are electrically fired from within the vehicle. This model was originally offered with two SS-11 or ENTAC ATGWs mounted either side of the main armament. This model is no longer in production.

AML with Lynx 90 Turret
This has now replaced the AML with H 90 turret in production and has the same armament as the H 90 turret but can be fitted with passive night vision equipment, laser rangefinder and powered traverse.

AML with HE 60-7 Turret
This model is fitted with an H 60 turret armed with twin 7.62 mm machine guns on the left and a single 60 mm mortar on the right. The machine guns can be elevated from −15 to +60 degrees and the mortar from −15 to +80 degrees. The Hotchkiss Brandt Model HB 60 can be used in the direct role up to a range of 300 metres or in the indirect role up to a range

Panhard AML with Lynx 90 turret and Thomson-CSF passive night vision equipment over main armament

51

of 2600 metres. In the basic model 53 mortar bombs and 3800 rounds of 7.62 mm machine gun ammunition are carried; if additional radios are installed for the command role ammunition is reduced to 32 mortar bombs and 3200 rounds of machine gun ammunition. Types of mortar bomb include HE, canister, smoke and illuminating.

The turret is provided with a large two-piece hatch cover that opens to the front and rear of the vehicle, seven periscopes (model L794B) and an M112/M113 periscope with a magnification of ×5 for aiming. This model was originally offered with four ENTAC ATGWs mounted at the rear of the turret, which slid out on rails, two either side of the turret, before being launched.

AML with HE 60-12 Turret
This is almost identical to the HE 60-7 turret but is armed with a 12.7 mm (0.50) machine gun and a 60 mm HB 60 Brandt mortar. The machine gun can be elevated from −15 to +60 degrees and the mortar from −15 to +80 degrees. Forty-three mortar bombs and 1300 rounds of 12.7 mm machine gun ammunition are carried. If additional radios are carried ammunition load is reduced to 31 rounds of 60 mm and 900 rounds of 12.7 mm machine gun ammunition.

AML with HE 60-20 Turret
This is almost identical to the HE 60-7 turret but is armed with a 20 mm cannon and a 60 mm DTAT Model CS or an HB 60 Brandt mortar. The cannon can be elevated from −8 to +50 degrees and the mortar from −15 to +80 degrees.

Panhard AML with HE 60-7 turret armed with 60 mm mortar and two 7.62 mm machine guns

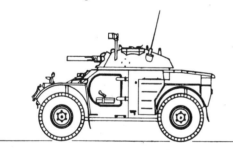

Panhard AML with Lynx 90 turret

Panhard AML with HE 60-7 turret armed with 60 mm mortar and two 7.62 mm MGs (ECP Armées)

Panhard AML with HE 60-12 turret armed with 60 mm mortar and 12.7 mm MG (ECP Armées)

When fitted with the DTAT mortar 53 mortar bombs and 500 rounds of 20 mm ammunition are carried, and if the Brandt mortar is installed 43 mortar bombs are carried and 20 mm ammunition supply remains the same. If additional radios are installed for command vehicle use the DTAT mortar is provided with 32 mortar bombs and the Brandt with 31, and in both cases 500 rounds of 20 mm ammunition are carried. If required a 7.62 mm machine gun can be mounted on the roof of the turret for anti-aircraft defence (This applies to all HE 60 turrets). This turret is no longer in production. Loaded weight of an AML with the HE 60-20 turret is 4800 kg.

AML with HE 60-20 Serval Turret
This is one of the latest versions of the AML and is fitted with an HE 60-20 Serval turret designed and manufactured by Hispano-Suiza and is armed with a 60 mm breech-loaded mortar which can be elevated from −8 to +80 degrees, and a 20 mm cannon mounted on the right side of the turret which can be elevated from −8 to +50 degrees. The 60 mm mortar can be either a 60 mm HB 60 Hotchkiss Brandt (maximum

range 2600 metres with M72 bomb) or a 60 mm HB 60 LP Hotchkiss Brandt long mortar (maximum range with LP bomb being 5000 metres). The 20 mm cannon can be either a French M693 dual-feed cannon with 300 rounds of HE and 37 rounds of AP ammunition for ready use or an HS-820 Oerlikon KAD-B16 single-feed cannon with 300 rounds of ready-to-use ammunition. If required a 7.62 mm machine gun can be mounted coaxially to the right of the 20 mm cannon. Vision equipment includes a sighting periscope, nine observation periscopes with the option of fitting a night periscope.

AML with S 530 Turret

This was developed specifically for export and is a basic AML fitted with a turret manufactured by SAMM (Société d'Applications des Machines Motrices), armed with twin M621 cannon with an elevation of +75 degrees, depression of −10 degrees, and turret traverse of 360 degrees. Elevation and traverse are both powered, maximum elevation speed being 40 degrees a second and maximum traverse speed

AMI with SAMM S 530 turret armed with twin 20 mm cannon

being 80 degrees a second. The all-welded steel turret's front is 15 mm thick and the sides and rear are 7 mm thick.

A total of 600 rounds of 20 mm ammunition are carried and the gunner can select either single shots, bursts or full automatic. Cyclic rate of fire is 740 rounds per minute per barrel. The following types of 20 mm ammunition can be fired: HE-T with a muzzle velocity of 900 metres a second, HE with a muzzle velocity of 1026 metres a second, HE-I with a muzzle velocity of 1026 metres a second and AP with a muzzle velocity of 1000 metres a second. The AP projectile will penetrate 23 mm of armour at a range of 1000 metres. Automotive characteristics are similar to the basic AML 90 but the overall length of the vehicle with turret traversed forward is 3.95 metres, length of hull is 3.79 metres and height to top of turret is 2.24 metres. The only known user of this version is Venezuela.

AML with TG 120 Turret

This is fitted with the TG 120 turret designed and manufactured by SAMM and is armed with a 20 mm cannon with a 7.62 mm machine gun mounted coaxially to the left of the main armament. Of 240 rounds of ready-use ammunition carried 140 are HE and 80 are AP rounds. Four smoke dischargers are mounted at the rear of the turret. Both the commander and the gunner are provided with a single-piece hatch cover that opens to the rear. This model of the AML has yet to enter production. In 1983 the TG 120 turret was renamed the TTB 120.

EPR Scout Car

The EPR (4 × 4) scout car is the standard AML with the turret removed and replaced by a ring-mounted 12.7 mm M2 HB machine gun and two lateral 7.62 mm machine guns. This vehicle is also available with the standard Panhard petrol engine replaced by the Peugeot XD 3T diesel engine. It has a three-man crew and weighs between 3700 and 4200 kg depending on the armament installation. The following versions of the EPR are being offered:
ERA armed raid vehicle: armed with one 12.7 mm and two 7.62 mm machine guns or one 20 mm cannon and two lateral 7.62 mm machine guns, or one Euromissile MILAN firing post (and six missiles) and two lateral machine guns.
EPF border protection vehicle: armed with one 12.7 mm machine gun and a searchlight or two 7.62 mm machine guns equipped with a searchlight and 50 hand grenades.
EPA airfield protection vehicle: armed with three 7.62 mm machine guns with a searchlight and 50 hand grenades.

Panhard AML with HE 60-20 turret armed with 60 mm mortar and 20 mm cannon

Panhard AML with HE 60-20 Serval turret

Prototype of Panhard EPR (4 × 4) scout car armed with 12.7 mm M2 HB machine gun

Command model AML 20 (4 × 4) scout car with TL 20 SO turret, 7.62 mm MG fixed on left mudguard and two radio antennas

AML 20 Scout Car

This is the AML chassis fitted with a TL 20 SO (Tourellaeau Léger 20 mm Semi Ouvert) turret which is armed with a 20 mm M693 F2 cannon with an elevation of +50 degrees and a depression of −8 degrees. A total of 1000 rounds of 20 mm ammunition are carried of which 100 are armour-piercing.

Two versions of the AML 20 are available; command and rank which both have the same turret. They each have a 7.62 mm machine gun mounted on the forward left wing, fixed, and fired electrically by the driver. The command model has a similar weapon mounted on the upper part of the turret roof which has an elevation of +45 degrees and a depression of −15 degrees.

The command version has two radios while the rank version has one. Optical equipment fitted includes three L794 periscopes for the driver (plus spare), one day telescope Zeiss Hensold with a magnification of ×4, one night telescope Zeiss Orian 110 with a magnification of ×4, one pair of night driving binoculars OB41 with a magnification of ×1 and one pair of night observation binoculars model OB42 with a magnification of ×4.

Automotive characteristics are similar to the basic AML but this model has a weight of 5100 kg and an overall height of 2 metres.

AML Jungle

This model was announced in June 1983 and is also called the AML scout car type BTM and is fitted with a SAMM one-man manual turret armed with one 12.7 mm and one 7.62 mm machine gun which have an elevation of +45 degrees and a depression of −8 degrees, with turret traverse being a full 360 degrees. A total of 1000 rounds of 12.7 mm and 2300 rounds of 7.62 mm ammunition are carried in the vehicle. Mounted on the right side of the turret is a white light searchlight that moves in elevation with the main armament. On the forward part of the turret are smoke dischargers/ fragmentation grenade launchers firing forwards. The AML Jungle is powered by the Peugeot XD 3T diesel developing 95 hp at 2500 rpm coupled to the standard Panhard transmission. Loaded weight is 4400 kg and empty weight is 4100 kg. This model has yet to enter production.

Panhard AML Jungle scout car showing forward-firing smoke/fragmentation launchers (Christopher F Foss)

Panhard AML 20 scout car with turret traversed to right and fitted with high-powered binoculars

AML scout car

This model was announced in June 1983 and is also known as the AML 20 scout car or Eclairge and is fitted with a new Panhard-designed two-man turret with an open roof. Armament consists of a 20 mm GIAT M693 cannon with a 7.62 mm machine gun mounted coaxially to the left with both weapons having an elevation of +45 degrees and depression of −8 degrees; turret traverse is a full 360 degrees. A total of 1050 rounds of 20 mm and 2000 rounds of 7.62 mm ammunition are carried. Mounted either side of the forward part of the turret is a bank of two electrically operated smoke dischargers. Optional equipment includes high power binoculars on a pintle mounting and Euromissile MILAN ATGW system. This model is also powered by the Peugeot XD 3T diesel engine and has a loaded weight of 5400 kg and an empty weight of 4600 kg. It has yet to enter production.

Panhard AML 20 scout car fitted with high-powered binoculars and MILAN ATGW installation (Christopher F Foss)

SPECIFICATIONS (AML with H 90 turret)

CREW	3	FORDING	1.1 m	ELECTRICAL SYSTEM	24 V
CONFIGURATION	4 × 4	(with kit)	amphibious	BATTERIES	2 × 12 V
COMBAT WEIGHT	5500 kg	GRADIENT	60%	ARMAMENT	
POWER-TO-WEIGHT		SIDE SLOPE	30%	(main)	1 × 90 mm
RATIO	16.36 hp/tonne	VERTICAL OBSTACLE	0.3 m	(coaxial)	1 × 7.62 mm MG
LENGTH GUN		TRENCH		SMOKE-LAYING	
FORWARDS	5.11 m	(with 1 channel)	0.8 m	EQUIPMENT	2 × 2 smoke dis-
LENGTH HULL	3.79 m	(with 4 channels)	3.1 m		chargers
WIDTH	1.97 m	TURNING RADIUS	6 m	AMMUNITION	
HEIGHT		ENGINE	Panhard Model 4 HD*	(main)	20
(overall)	2.07 m		4-cylinder air-cooled petrol	(coaxial)	2000
(to hull top)	1.385 m		developing 90 hp at 4700	(smoke grenades)	12
GROUND CLEARANCE	0.33 m		rpm	FIRE-CONTROL SYSTEM	
TRACK	1.62 m	TRANSMISSION	manual with 6 forward	Turret power control	manual
WHEELBASE	2.5 m		and 1 reverse gears	Max rate of traverse	360° in 20 s
MAX ROAD SPEED		CLUTCH	centrifugal with	Gun elevation/	
(6th gear, high range)	90 km/h		electro-magnetic	depression	+15°/−8°
(5th gear, high range)	61 km/h		automatic control	Gun stabiliser	
(4th gear, high range)	35 km/h	SUSPENSION	independent, coil	(vertical)	no
(3rd gear, high range)	18.8 km/h		spring and hydro-	(horizontal)	no
(3rd gear, low range)	18.8 km/h		pneumatic shock	ARMOUR	8 –12 mm
(2nd gear, low range)	9.3 km/h		absorbers acting on sus-		
(1st gear, low range)	4.5 km/h		pension trailing arms		
(reverse)	5.5 km/h		of wheel mechanism	*The AML 90 with the Hispano-Suiza Lynx turret and other	
FUEL CAPACITY	156 litres	TYRES	11.00 × 16	members of the AML family are now being offered with	
MAX RANGE (road)	600 km	BRAKES		the Peugeot XD 3T 95 hp diesel in place of the standard	
		(main)	hydraulic, dual circuit	Panhard petrol engine which gives an operational range	
		(parking)	handbrake operating	of 1000 km compared to 600 km of the original version.	
			on gearbox output		
			shaft		

Status: In production. In service with Algeria (AML 60/7), Angola (AML 90), Argentina (AML 90), Bahrain (AML 90), Burundi (AML 90 Lynx, AML 60), Chad (AML 90 and AML 60), Ecuador (AML 90, AML 60/7), El Salvador (AML 90), France (Army and Gendarmerie, AML 90 and AML 60/7), Gabon (AML 90, AML 60/7), Iraq (AML 90 and AML 60/7), Ireland (AML 90 and AML 60/7), Ivory Coast (AML 90 and AML 60/7), Jibuti (AML 60/7 and AML 90), Kenya (AML 90, AML 60/7), Malaysia (AML 60, AML 90), (Mauritania (AML 90 and AML 60/7), Morocco (AML 90 and AML 60/7), Niger (AML 60/7, AML 90, Serval 60/20), Nigeria (AML 90, AML 60/7), Polisairo guerillas, Portugal (AML 60/7), Rwanda (AML 60/7), Saudi Arabia (AML 90 and AML 60), Senegal (AML 60/7, AML 90), Somalia (AML 60/7, AML 90), South Africa (see entry under South Africa), Spain (Army AML 60/7 and AML 90, Marines AML 60/7), Togo (AML 60/7, AML 90), Tunisia (AML 90), United Arab Emirates (AML 90), Upper Volta (AML 90), Venezuela (twin 20 mm self-propelled anti-aircraft gun, AML 60, AML 90), Zaïre (AML 90, AML 60/7) and Zimbabwe (from South Africa). As far as it is known it is no longer used by Cambodia, Ethiopia, Israel, Lebanon or Pakistan.

Manufacturer: Société de Constructions Mécaniques Panhard et Levassor, 18 avenue d'Ivry, 75621 Paris, France.

Véhicule Blindé Léger (VBL)

The French Army has a requirement for a scout car in the three-tonne class which has been called the Véhicule Blindé Léger. To meet this requirement Renault and Panhard have each built prototypes which were delivered to the French Army in 1983. The Renault vehicle has its engine at the rear while the Panhard model has its at the front. The total requirement is for 600 vehicles with a final selection expected some time in 1984.

The Panhard model is called the M11, has a three-man crew and weighs 3300 kg. It is powered by a Peugeot diesel engine coupled to an automatic transmission which gives a power-to-weight ratio of 28 hp/tonne. The hull is of all welded steel construction that provides protection for 7.62 mm rounds at all ranges and against 12.7 mm rounds at 400 metres. Standard equipment includes ZF powered steering and an NBC system. It is fully amphibious, being propelled in the water by its wheels.

A range of armament installations can be fitted including 7.62 mm or 12.7 mm machine guns, 20 mm cannon or a Euromissile MILAN ATGW system. In addition to building three prototypes for the French Army Panhard has built an additional three vehicles for export designated the XM11 and is developing an armoured personnel carrier based on the same automotive components.

Status: French Army trials. Production decision due in 1984 with an in service date on 1986.

LOHR RPX 6000 Scout Car

Development
The RPX 6000 (4 × 4) Véhicule Blindé Léger a Roues has been developed as a private venture by the LOHR company and was shown for the first time at the 1981 Satory Exhibition of Military Equipment.

Description
The vehicle has an all-welded steel hull with the three-man crew compartment at the front and the engine compartment at the rear. The driver is seated at the front of the hull and has a bullet-proof windscreen to his front and sides which in action are covered by hinged flaps raised by the driver from inside the vehicle. There is a single-piece hatch cover over the driver's position.

In either side of the hull is a two-part entry hatch, the upper part folding to the rear and the lower part folding downwards to form a step. There is a circular roof hatch in the centre of the hull roof on which a variety of armament installations are mounted including a Euromissile MILAN MCT turret with two MILAN ATGWs ready to launch, Euromissile HOT HCT turret with two or four HOT ATGW in ready to launch position with 7.62 mm machine gun mounted over centre of turret, SAMM BTM 208 one-man turret (former designation S 365-1) armed with a 12.7 mm and a 7.62 mm machine gun, Helio turret with 12.7 mm machine gun and external grenade launchers, turret mounted 20 mm cannon, 60 mm breech loaded mortar and other light turrets not exceeding a diameter of 1.28 m.

LOHR RPX 6000 scout car fitted with Euromissile HOT HCT turret with four HOT ATGWs in ready to launch position and 7.62 mm MG above turret centre

LOHR RPX 6000 scout car fitted with British Helio turret armed with 12.7 mm MG and grenade launchers

Variants

Variants of the RPX 6000 suggested by the manufacturer include a command vehicle, personnel carrier, radar vehicle, command/radio vehicle and a recovery vehicle.

LOHR RPX 6000 scout car with SAMM turret armed with 12.7 mm machine gun and 60 mm grenade launcher which have an elevation of +70° and depression of −7°

SPECIFICATIONS		MAX ROAD SPEED	110 km/h	FRONT SUSPENSION	transveral parallelogram,
		RANGE	600 km or 10 hours		coil spring, hydraulic shock
CREW	3 (or 2 to 4)	FORDING	0.95 m		absorber and stabilisation
CONFIGURATION	4 × 4	GRADIENT	60%		bar
COMBAT WEIGHT	5200 kg to 6300 kg	SIDE SLOPE	30%	REAR SUSPENSION	trailing arm type, coil spring,
LENGTH	4.585 m	VERTICAL OBSTACLE	0.4 m		hydraulic shock absorber
WIDTH	2.164 m	ENGINE	BMW 6-cylinder		and stabilisation device
HEIGHT			petrol developing	TYRES	12.5 × 20 XS
(without armament)	1.65 m		180 hp	BRAKES	hydraulic drums on all
GROUND CLEARANCE	0.4 m	TRANSMISSION	automatic		wheels
TRACK	1.828 m	TRANSFER CASE	2-speed manual with		
WHEELBASE	2.7 m		differential locks		

Status: Prototype.

Manufacturer: LOHR, 67980 Hangenbieten, France.

LOHR VPX 5000 Light Armoured Tracked Vehicle

Development

Shown for the first time at the 1981 Satory Exhibition of Military Equipment was the LOHR VPX 5000 light armoured tracked vehicle, which can undertake a wide range of roles including anti-tank and reconnaissance. This series was preceded by the VPX 110 family of light tracked vehicles which is no longer offered by the company.

Description

The VPX 5000's hull is made of all-welded steel with the engine at the right front, driver to the left of the engine and the crew compartment at the rear. There are two openings in the roof on which various armament systems can be mounted and a door in the rear of the hull on the left side.

The suspension consists of six road wheels with the idler at the front, drive sprocket at the rear and two track return rollers. The track consists of an endless rubber band internally reinforced.

Variants

The LOHR VPX 5000 can be fitted with a wide range of armament installations including the following:

Euromissile MILAN MCT compact turret with two MILAN ATGWs in ready to launch position, one either side of turret. Euromissile HOT HCT turret with two or four HOT ATGWs in ready to launch position with 7.62 mm machine gun mounted over the centre of the turret.

GIAT Mascot 7.62 mm remote controlled machine gun mount with infantry MILAN over second hatch at rear of hull.

LOHR VPX 5000 light tracked armoured vehicle with GIAT Mascot 7.62 mm remote mount forwards and MILAN ATGW mount at rear

LOHR VPX 5000 light tracked armoured vehicle fitted with SAM BTM 208 turret with 7.62 mm and 12.7 mm MGs

SAMM BTM 208 turret (former designation S 365-1) armed with 12.7 mm and 7.62 mm machine guns.

Other turrets armed with 20 mm cannon and various combinations of 7.62 mm and 12.7 mm machine guns with a turret diameter of no more than 1.18 m.

In addition to being fitted with the various armament installations described previously the manufacturer has suggested the following roles that the vehicle could also undertake: ambulance, logistic support, radio/command and recovery. At the 1983 Satory Exhibition of Military Equipment one prototype was shown fitted with the RASIT battlefield surveillance radar on a hydraulic arm that could be raised above the chassis.

SPECIFICATIONS

CREW	2 to 4	GROUND CLEARANCE	0.35 m	FORDING	0.95 m
WEIGHT	4600–5800 kg	MAX ROAD SPEED	80 km/h	ENGINE	BMW 6-cylinder petrol
LENGTH	4.2 m	RANGE	350 km		developing 180 hp at
WIDTH	2 m	GRADIENT	60%		5500 rpm
HEIGHT		SIDE SLOPE	30%	TRANSMISSION	automatic
(without armament)	1.6 m	VERTICAL OBSTACLE	0.5 m	TRANSFER CASE	2-speed

Status: Prototype.

Manufacturer: LOHR, 67980 Hangenbieten, France.

LOHR VPX 5000 light tracked armoured vehicle fitted with Euromissile HOT HCT turret with four HOT ATGWs in ready to launch position and 7.62 mm machine gun mounted over centre of turret

LOHR VPX 5000 light tracked vehicle with Euromissile MILAN MCT turret

APE Amphibious Engineer Reconnaissance Vehicle

Development

In the early 1960s EWK (Eisenwerke Kaiserslautern Göppner GmbH) developed a cross-country trials vehicle known as the P3 Erprobungswagen. This vehicle featured large Michelin low-pressure tyres (2100 × 25XL) with a diameter of 1.744 metres and a tread of 0.569 metre and a central tyre pressure system that allowed the driver to adjust the ground pressure to suit the type of ground being crossed. The P3 had a wheelbase of 3.3 metres and a low centre of gravity owing to its overall height of only 2.05 metres, and was fully amphibious being propelled in the water at a speed of 12 km/h by one propeller. Extensive trials showed that the P3 had excellent cross-country and amphibious capabilities and could climb and descend steep river banks with ease.

In the early 1970s EWK, with Daimler-Benz as the major sub-contractor, started development work on the APE (Amphibisches Pionier-Erkundungsfahrzeug), or Amphibious Engineer Reconnaissance Vehicle, to meet the requirements of the Federal German Army. EWK also call the vehicle the AMF (Amphibische Mehrzweck-Fahrzeuge) or Amphibious Reconnaissance Vehicle.

The first prototype of the APE was completed in 1977. The vehicle is basically a slightly larger version of the Transportpanzer 2 (4 × 4) vehicle incorporating many of the concepts already proved in the earlier P3 prototype. The Transportpanzer 1 (6 × 6) vehicle is currently in production for the Federal German Army by Thyssen Henschel and the first of 996 vehicles were handed over late in 1979. About 90 per cent of the automotive components of the APE are identical to those of the Transportpanzer 1 but its suspension is quite different and for this reason it has superior amphibious and cross-country capabilities to the Transportpanzer 1. EWK

built four prototypes of the APE for the West German Army and one of these was subsequently bought back by the company for further development work. This was subsequently renamed the Alligator.

The main features of the APE are low-pressure balloon tyres, tyre pressure regulation system, good angles of approach and departure, hydraulic retraction of the axles when the vehicle is swimming, reducing drag to an absolute minimum, ability of the two propellers to swivel through 360 degrees for increased manoeuvrability, capability of the wheels and propellers to be driven simultaneously to assist in climbing out of the water, and excellent forward visibility.

Description

The all-welded steel hull of the APE provides the crew with protection from small arms fire and shell splinters. The hull has a rhomboid cross section and incorporates spaced armour in certain areas.

The driver is seated at the front of the hull on the left with the vehicle commander to his right. A bullet-proof windscreen in front of them can be covered by an armoured shutter. The driver is provided with a circular roof hatch that opens forwards and the commander has a similar rear-opening hatch. Periscopes are fitted in the roof of the vehicle, in front of the driver's and commander's hatches, for use when the windscreen is covered by the armoured shutter. Both the driver and commander are provided with an entrance door in the side of the vehicle with an integral bullet-proof window which is also covered by an armoured shutter in combat areas.

The complete powerpack is behind the driver and commander and access is by a hatch in the roof. There is a small passage between the front of the vehicle and the passenger/cargo area at the rear on the right side of the hull. The vehicle is powered by the same engine as the Transportpanzer 1

APE amphibious engineer reconnaissance vehicle armed with 20 mm cannon

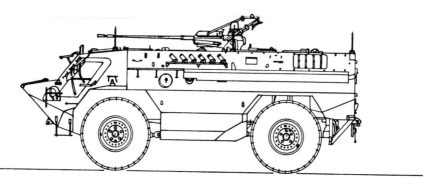

APE amphibious engineer reconnaissance vehicle armed with 20 mm cannon

which can be replaced by a Daimler-Benz diesel which develops 265 hp giving the vehicle a power-to-weight ratio of 18.27 hp/tonne, a maximum road speed of 70 km/h and a water-speed of 11 km/h.

The load area is at the rear of the hull and is 3.15 metres long and 1.25 metres high with a small vision port protected by an armoured shutter in each side. There are three roof hatches over the load area. The first circular hatch is normally used to mount the main armament installation and the second and much smaller circular hatch is to the right and rear of the first one. The third hatch is square and is at the left rear and opens forward. Normal means of entry is by two large doors at the rear of the hull. The right door has a vision port covered by an armoured shutter when not required.

The APE has a central tyre pressure regulation system which allows the driver to adjust the tyre pressure to suit the type of ground being crossed, which is of particular use when climbing steep banks and crossing deep mud.

The vehicle is fully amphibious, being propelled in the water by two Schottel four-bladed propellers beneath the floor level of the vehicle at the rear of the hull which remain in the water as long as possible when the vehicle is leaving the

water. When afloat the axles and wheels are retracted to reduce drag. Before entering the water a trim vane is erected at the front of the vehicle and standard equipment includes three bilge pumps with a capacity of 180 litres a minute each. The APE is fitted with an NBC system.

The basic vehicle is armed with a Rheinmetall 20 mm cannon mounted on a Keller and Knappich E-6 mount, and six smoke dischargers mounted on the left side of the hull.

Variants

EWK has suggested that the vehicle could be used for a variety of other roles including armoured personnel carrier, anti-tank (with turret-mounted gun or ATGWs), artillery fire-control vehicle, ambulance, command vehicle, communications vehicle, internal security vehicle, mortar carrier, NBC reconnaissance vehicle, reconnaissance vehicle, repair vehicle or a supply carrier.

The company is also developing, as a private venture, an armoured car in the 5000 to 7000 kg range which will incorporate features of the APE and will be armed with a turret-mounted 35 mm cannon and a coaxial 7.62 mm machine gun.

SPECIFICATIONS

CREW	12 (10 in troop compartment)	GRADIENT	75%
CONFIGURATION	4 × 4	SIDE SLOPE	30%
COMBAT WEIGHT	14 500 kg	TURNING RADIUS	8.5 m
POWER-TO-WEIGHT		ENGINE	Mercedes-Benz OM
RATIO	22 hp/tonne (approx)		402A V-8 liquid-cooled
LENGTH	6.93 m		diesel developing 320
WIDTH	3.08 m		hp at 2500 rpm
HEIGHT (to hull top)	2.4 m	TRANSMISSION	ZF 4 HP 500-1 6-speed
GROUND CLEARANCE			automatic with in-line
(axles)	0.485 m		torque converter
(hull)	0.555 m	STEERING	hydraulic, recirculating
TRACK		TYRES	20.50 × 25 XL
(front/rear)	2.54 m/2.56 m	BRAKES	
WHEELBASE	3.5 m	(main)	hydraulic, air-assisted
ANGLE APPROACH/			(dual circuit)
DEPARTURE	45°/45°	(parking)	mechanical
MAX SPEED		ELECTRICAL SYSTEM	28 V dc
(road forwards)	83 km/h	BATTERIES	4 × 12 V, 200 Ah
(water)	12 km/h	ARMAMENT (main)	1 × 20 mm
MAX RANGE		SMOKE-LAYING	
(cross-country)	800 km	EQUIPMENT	6 smoke dischargers

Status: Development complete. Ready for production.

Manufacturer: Eisenwerke Kaiserslautern Göppner GmbH, Barbarossa 30, D-6750 Kaiserslautern, Federal Republic of Germany.

Spähpanzer Luchs Armoured Amphibious Reconnaissance Vehicle

Development

In 1964 the West Germany Ministry of Defence examined its requirements for a new generation of military vehicles for the 1970s. This generation was to have included an 8 × 8 armoured amphibious reconnaissance vehicle, 4 × 4 and 6 × 6 armoured amphibious load carriers and a complete range of 4 × 4, 6 × 6 and 8 × 8 tactical cargo trucks, some of which were to be amphibious. All were to share many common components which would, where possible, be from commercial sources.

In 1965 a Joint Project Office was formed to undertake development of the complete range of vehicles. Companies in the Joint Project Office were Büssing, Klöckner-Humbolt-Deutz, Friedrich Krupp, MAN and Rheinstahl-Henschel. Daimler-Benz did not join the Joint Project Office but went ahead on its own to develop a similar range of vehicles.

The JPO and Daimler-Benz each built nine prototypes of the 8 × 8 armoured amphibious reconnaissance vehicle. The JPO delivered its prototypes to the Trier testing ground in April 1968 and Daimler-Benz delivered its in December the same year. Each differed in some detail as both manufacturers tested various engines and transmissions to find the right combination for the vehicle.

Extensive trials were carried out over the following two years and in January 1971 it was decided that work on the JPO vehicle would stop and that the Daimler-Benz model would enter production. In December 1973 Rheinstahl Wehrtechnik was awarded a contract worth DM300 million for 408 vehicles.

First production vehicles were completed in May 1975 and the first vehicle was officially handed over to the Federal German Army in September 1975 and production continued until early 1978.

The West German Army calls the vehicle the Spähpanzer Luchs and it replaced the American-supplied M41 light tanks and the Hotchkiss SPz 11-2 reconnaissance vehicles.

The Luchs has established a reputation for its excellent cross-country mobility and quietness, both of which are essential to a reconnaissance vehicle.

The 4 × 4 armoured amphibious load carrier became the Transportpanzer 2 and the 6 × 6 armoured amphibious load carrier became the Transportpanzer 1. The Transportpanzer 2 was not placed in production but further development was undertaken by EWK and the eventual result was the APE Amphibious Engineer Reconnaissance Vehicle for which there is a separate entry. The 6 × 6 armoured amphibious load carrier was placed in production as the Transportpanzer 1 with Rheinstahl Wehrtechnik, now Thyssen Henschel.

Description

The all-welded steel hull of the Luchs provides the crew with protection from small arms fire and shell splinters. The hull and turret are immune over their frontal area to penetration from 20 mm projectiles.

The driver is seated at the front of the hull on the left side and is provided with a single-piece hatch cover that opens to his right. There are three periscopes in front of the driver's

Spähpanzer Luchs armoured reconnaissance vehicle crossing bridge laid by M48 AVLB. This particular vehicle is not fitted with 7.62 mm MG3 MG at commander's station (C R Zwart)

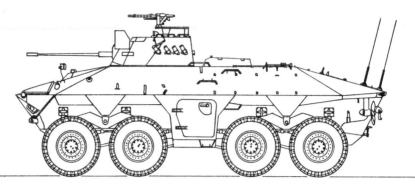

Spähpanzer Luchs armoured amphibious reconnaissance vehicle

hatch cover, the centre one of which can be replaced by a passive periscope for night operations.

The Rheinmetall TS-7 turret is located in the centre of the hull and has spaced armour for improved protection. The commander is seated on the left and the gunner on the right, both with a single-piece hatch cover that opens to the rear. Both the commander and gunner are provided with a PERI Z-11 A-1 periscope for aiming the 20 mm cannon, and a total of 12 periscopes. Mounted to the left of the turret is a searchlight which moves in elevation with the main armament and can be used in both infra-red and passive modes. Turret traverse and weapon elevation/depression is electro-

hydraulic and can be operated by the commander or gunner. The fire-control system includes an azimuth indicator.

An entry door is provided in the left side of the hull. The fourth crew member, the radio operator/rear driver, is seated to the rear of the turret on the left side facing the rear and is provided with a single-piece hatch cover that opens to the right. There are three periscopes in front of the cover, the centre one of which can be replaced by a passive periscope for night operations.

The engine is behind the turret on the right side and access is by a large oblong hatch that opens to the right. The engine compartment, cooling and exhaust systems are separated from the fighting compartment by gastight welded bulkheads. The engine compartment is fitted with an automatic fire-extinguishing system. The complete powerpack, consist-

Spähpanzer Luchs armoured amphibious reconnaissance vehicle from rear showing smoke dischargers on right side of turret and propellers under hull rear

Rheinmetall TS-7 two-man turret armed with 20 mm cannon and 7.62 mm MG3 anti-aircraft machine gun as fitted to the Luchs (8 × 8) reconnaissance vehicle

Luchs with trim vane folded onto glacis plate (Federal German Army)

Luchs showing amphibious capabilities, with trim vane erected

ing of the engine, transmission, air filter, oil cooler and parking brake, can be removed as a complete unit and run outside the vehicle. The cooling system is at the back of the hull and the exhaust outlet is at the very rear of the hull.

Power is transmitted from the engine to a four-speed hydraulic torque converter and then via a distributor gear with differential locks to the wheels. The Luchs has the same speed in both directions.

The suspension consists of four Daimler-Benz rigid axles with differential locks which are supported by longitudinal bars, with bogies for the first and second and third and fourth axles. Each wheel station has a vertical coil spring and a hydraulic shock absorber. All eight wheels are steered but for road use the front four wheels only are normally used.

The Luchs is fully amphibious, being propelled in the water by two Schottel steerable propellers at the rear of the hull, one on each side. These are powered by a PTO on the main transmission via a bevel-type distributor gear. Before entering the water a trim vane is hydraulically erected at the front of the hull and the bilge pumps, two in the fighting compartment and one in the engine compartment, are switched on.

In 1982 it was announced that a total of 423 sets of thermal night vision equipment would be purchased for the Luchs, 63 sets in 1984 and 120 a year in 1985, 1986 and 1987. Standard equipment includes a pre-heater for the cooling liquid, engine oil and transmission oil and pre-heater for the batteries. The NBC system can also be used for ventilating the vehicle when all the hatches are closed.

The Luchs is armed with a 20 mm Rheinmetall Mk 20 Rh 202 cannon which is also installed in the Marder MICV. This cannon has dual feed and the empty cartridge cases and beltlinks are ejected externally to the right of the turret. A Rheinmetall 7.62 mm MG3 machine gun mounted on a skate mount over the commander's hatch can be used for both ground and anti-aircraft defence. Four smoke dischargers are mounted either side of the turret.

Variants

Luchs with Oerlikon 35 mm Turret Model GDD-BOE
Oerlikon has proposed that the Luchs could be fitted with its Model GDD-BOE turret which is armed with a 35 mm KDE cannon.

Luchs with Roland 2 SAMs
It has been proposed that the chassis of the Luchs with a redesigned hull to include the front of the Transportpanzer 1 could be used to mount the Euromissile Roland 2 SAM system. Two missiles would be carried ready to launch and a further supply of missiles would be carried inside the hull. To reduce the overall height of the vehicle the two radar scanners would fold down to the front and rear of the turret respectively. The West German Army already has the Roland 2 system in service mounted on the Marder chassis but this 8 × 8 system offers higher strategic mobility and could meet the requirements of the West German Air Force and Navy. But this latter requirement will not be met in the near future owing to budgetary considerations.

SPECIFICATIONS

CREW	4	GRADIENT	60%	BRAKES	
CONFIGURATION	8 × 8	SIDE SLOPE	30%	(main)	hydraulic, dual circuit
COMBAT WEIGHT	19 500 kg	VERTICAL OBSTACLE	0.6 m	(parking)	mechanical operating
POWER-TO-WEIGHT		TRENCH	1.9 m		on transmission
RATIO	20 hp/tonne	TURNING RADIUS		ELECTRICAL SYSTEM	24 V
LENGTH	7.743 m	(8 wheels)	11.5 m	BATTERIES	6 × 12 V, 100 Ah
WIDTH	2.98 m	(4 wheels)	19.4 m	ARMAMENT	
HEIGHT		ENGINE	Daimler-Benz OM 403 A	(main)	1 × 20 mm
(to top of machine			10-cylinder 90°	(anti-aircraft)	1 × 7.62 mm MG
gun rail)	2.905 m		V-4 stroke	SMOKE-LAYING	
(to top of hull top)	2.125 m		multi-fuel with 2	EQUIPMENT	2 × 4 smoke
FIRING HEIGHT	2.342 m		exhaust driven turbo-		dischargers
GROUND CLEARANCE			chargers developing	AMMUNITION (in turret)	
(hull)	0.44 m		390 hp at 2500 rpm	(main)	375
(axles)	0.58 m		(diesel fuel) or 320 hp	(anti-aircraft)	100 round box
TRACK	2.54 m		at 2500 rpm (petrol)	TURRET POWER	
WHEELBASE	1.4m + 2.365m +	TRANSMISSION	ZF 4 PW 95 H 1	CONTROL	electro-hydraulic/
	1.4m		4-speed		manual
ANGLE OF APPROACH/			with torque converter	GUN ELEVATION/	
DEPARTURE	66°/53°	SUSPENSION	coil springs and	DEPRESSION	+69°/−15°
MAX SPEED			hydraulic shock	GUN STABILISER	
(road forwards)	90 km/h		absorbers	(vertical)	no
(reverse)	90 km/h	STEERING	re-circulating ball	(horizontal)	no
(water)	9 km/h		power-assisted		
ACCELERATION	0 – 80 km/h: 65 s	TURNING RADIUS			
FUEL CAPACITY	500 litres	(all wheel steering)	5.75 m		
MAX RANGE	800 km	(front wheel steering)	9.7 m		
FORDING	amphibious	TYRES	14.00 × 20		

Status: Production complete. In service with the Federal German Army.

Manufacturer: Thyssen Henschel, Postfach 102969, D 3500 Kassel, Federal Republic of Germany.

Wiesel Airportable Vehicle

Development/Description

Porsche has developed to the prototype stage an airportable vehicle to meet the requirements of West German airborne units, called the Wiesel, or Waffenträger II-LL. Its development has been cancelled following a decision to buy the American AWACS aircraft, which meant that a number of West German defence projects had to be cancelled or post-poned. It is believed that the Federal German Army still has a requirement for between 400 and 500 vehicles of this type. Early in 1982 West Germany loaned the United States four Wiesel airportable vehicles for trials at the Yakima firing centre/proving ground between April and May 1982.

The Wiesel can be carried slung underneath helicopters such as the Puma and is airportable in the C-160 (four), C-130 (three) and CH-53 (two).

Under a recent agreement Krupp Mak will be responsible

Wiesel armed with Rheinmetall MK 20 Rh 202 cannon in KUKA gun mount E6-II

Wiesel armed with Hughes TOW ATGW system

for any series production of the Wiesel while Porsche are responsible for logistic support and the development of specialised versions.

Description

The hull of the Wiesel is of all-welded steel construction which provides the crew with protection from 7.62 mm small arms fire and shell splinters. The driver is seated at the front of the vehicle on the right and has three periscopes for observation to the front and sides; the centre one can be replaced by a passive periscope for driving at night.

The engine, which is a standard production model, is to the left of the driver with an access hatch being provided in the glacis plate. The five-speed Porsche transmission, a modified version of a standard production model, drives via a torque converter and clutch. The complete powerpack can be removed and replaced in 10 minutes. Starting and gear shifting do not require clutch pedal operation. The Wiesel is fitted with a Cletrac reverse transmission. The steering gear is operated by the driver via a steering wheel and allows an infinitely variable turning radius from infinite to 2.3 metres. Pivoting on one track is possible by the engagement of the parking brake on one side.

The engine exhaust system is located in the cooling air exhaust flow on the left side of the vehicle. The exhaust gases are passed to the rear, being cooled in the process. The open-topped crew compartment is at the rear of the hull and entry to this is by climbing over the sides of the vehicle. The flexible self-sealing rubber fuel tank has an explosion polyurethane liner and is mounted externally on the rear of the hull.

Suspension either side consists of three dual road wheels, drive sprocket at the front, idler at the rear on one track return roller. A Belleville spring assembly automatically provides track tension when the vehicle is travelling. The track consists of an endless rubber band with wire reinforcements. An amphibious kit is available for the Wiesel.

Variants

Wiesel with 20 mm cannon
This was built to meet the requirements of the West German Army and is fitted with a one-man Keller and Knappich Type E6-II mount armed with a 20 mm Rheinmetall dual feed cannon with 250 rounds of ready use ammunition (125 rounds either side). The weapon can be elevated from −10 degrees to +60 degrees and traversed 50 degrees left and right. Elevation and traverse is manual and the gunner aims the weapon via a Zeiss PERI Z-11 periscopic sight, passive night sight is also available.

Wiesel with TOW
This was built to meet the requirements of the West German Army and is fitted with a Hughes TOW ATGW launcher on an elevating pedestal with a traverse of 45 degrees left and right and an elevation and depression of 15 degrees. A total of eight missiles are carried of which two are for ready use. This model has a three-man crew, driver, gunner and loader.

Wiesel command and control vehicle
This proposed vehicle would have a fully enclosed hull, a three-man crew and be fitted with extensive communications equipment. A 7.62 mm MG3 machine gun with 100 rounds of ready use ammunition and another 400 in reserve would be fitted.

Wiesel battlefield surveillance vehicle
This proposed vehicle would have a two-man crew, radar operator and driver, and be fitted with a hydraulic mast on top of which is a RASIT battlefield surveillance radar. A 7.62 mm MG3 machine gune with 100 rounds of ready use ammunition and another 400 in reserve would be fitted.

Wiesel ammunition resupply vehicle
This would act as the resupply vehicle for the Wiesel fitted with the TOW ATGW system, would have a two-man crew, carry 14 missiles and be armed with a 7.62 mm MG3 machine gun with 100 rounds of ready use ammunition and a further 400 rounds in reserve.

Wiesel recovery vehicle
This proposed vehicle would have a two-man crew and be fitted with a slewing crane with a telescopic boom that can also be used as winch, stabilisers at the hull rear, electric screwdriver, electric welding set, tow cable, tow bars, block and tackle, hydraulic jack, bolt cutters, tool kit, and a radio.

Wiesel SAM vehicle
This propsed vehicle would have a longer hull with an additional road wheel either side and be fitted with the Bofors RBS-70 SAM system with a total of 10 missiles being carried. A 7.62 mm MG3 machine gun with 100 rounds of ready use ammunition and a further 400 rounds in reserve is fitted.

Wiesel reconnaissance vehicle
This proposed vehicle would have a longer hull with an additional road wheel either side and be fitted with the Rheinmetall turret TF 20.15 armed with a Rheinmetall 20 mm cannon with an elevation of +60 degrees, depression of −7 degrees, and a traverse of 360 degrees. A total of 420 rounds of ammunition would be carried of which 220 would be for ready use.

Wiesel ambulance
This proposed vehicle would have a longer hull with an additional road wheel either side and have a two-man crew and be capable of carrying two stretcher and one seated patients or four seated patients. When being used in the cargo role a maximum of 600 kg can be carried.

Wiesel armoured personnel carrier

This proposed vehicle would have a longer hull with an additional road wheel either side and carry a half-squad of infantry (6 men) in additional to its two-man crew. The roof would be fully enclosed and fitted with a commander's cupola with an externally-mounted 7.62 mm MG3 machine gun with 100 rounds of ready use ammunition and a further 400 rounds in reserve. The infantry would enter and leave via a door in the hull rear.

Status: Trials. Not yet in production. In 1982 the vehicle was evaluated in the USA.

Manufacturer: Dr.h.c. F. Porsche Aktiengesellschaft, 7000 Stuttgart 40, Federal Republic of Germany.

SPECIFICATIONS		
Model	**TOW**	**20 mm**
CREW	3	2
COMBAT WEIGHT	2600 kg	2635 kg
UNLOADED WEIGHT	2011 kg	2011 kg
POWER-TO-WEIGHT		
RATIO	37.9 hp/tonne	37.4 hp/tonne
GROUND PRESSURE	0.32 kg/cm²	0.32 kg/cm²
LENGTH GUN		
FORWARDS	n/app	3.51 m
LENGTH HULL	3.263 m	3.263 m
WIDTH	1.82 m	1.82 m
HEIGHT	1.84 to 2.15 m	1.97 m
HEIGHT HULL TOP	1.252 m	1.252 m
FIRING HEIGHT	1.462 m	1.585 m
GROUND CLEARANCE	0.302 m	0.302 m
TRACK	1.62 m	1.62 m
TRACK WIDTH	200 mm	200 mm
LENGTH OF TRACK		
ON GROUND	1.825 m	1.825 m
MAX ROAD SPEED	85 km/h	85 km/h
FUEL CAPACITY	80 litres	80 litres
MAX RANGE		
(road)	300 km	300 km
(cross country)	200 km	200 km
GRADIENT	60%	60%
SIDE SLOPE	30%	30%
VERTICAL OBSTACLE	0.4 m	0.4 m
TRENCH	1.5 m	1.5 m
TURNING RADIUS		
(Cletrac)	7.19 m	7.19 m
(pivot)	4.67 m	4.67 m
ENGINE	VW-Audi petrol developing 98 hp	
TRANSMISSION	5 speed	5 speed
ARMAMENT	1 × TOW launcher	1 × 20 mm cannon
AMMUNITION	8 missiles	400 rounds of 20 mm

HUNGARY

FUG (or OT-65) Amphibious Scout Car

Development

The FUG (Felderítő Úsó Gépkosci) fulfils a similar role in the Hungarian Army to the Soviet BRDM-1 amphibious scout car but has its engine at the rear rather than the front and two instead of one water jets for amphibious operations. The vehicle entered service with the Hungarian Army in 1964 and with the Polish and Czechoslovak armies in 1966. The Czechoslovaks call the vehicle the OT-65.

Description

The hull of the FUG is all-welded steel with the driver seated at the front on the left and the vehicle commander on the right. Both are provided with a hatch cover to their front that is hinged at the top and opens upwards, and a windscreen with a wiper. The hatch is equipped with an integral vision block for when the hatch is closed.

The crew compartment is behind the driver and the only means of entry is by the hatch in the roof that opens either side of the vehicle. The roof hatches can be locked vertical to give a measure of protection when the machine gun is being used. A ventilator is mounted in the roof of the vehicle over the commander's position. Six circular firing ports are provided, two in each side and two in the rear. A vision slit is provided to the left of the driver and the right of the commander.

The engine compartment is at the rear of the hull with the air-inlet immediately behind the crew compartment, the air-outlets in either side and the exhaust pipe on the right side.

On either side of the vehicle, between the front and rear wheels, are two belly wheels, which are lowered by the driver and driven from a PTO and give the FUG improved cross-country ability and allow it to cross trenches. When the belly wheels are lowered the vehicle is driven in first gear.

The FUG is fully amphibious, being propelled in the water by two water jets at the rear of the hull. Before entering the water a trim board is erected at the front of the vehicle which is stowed under the nose when not in use, and the bilge pumps are switched on. Standard equipment includes infra-red driving lights and some models are also fitted with an infra-red searchlight, and a central tyre-pressure system that allows the driver to adjust the tyre pressure to suit the type of ground being crossed. It has no NBC system.

Main armament comprises a pintle-mounted 7.62 mm SGMB machine gun with limited traverse, which is aimed

FUG amphibious scout car with roof hatches open

FUG amphibious scout car clearly showing belly wheels lowered with BRDM-1 with Snapper ATGWs in background

and fired by one of the crew members with the two hatches open.

Variants

Ambulance
The FUG is known to be used as an ambulance although it is clearly unsuited to this role.

Radiological-Chemical Reconnaissance Vehicle
This performs a similar role to the Soviet BRDM-1 rkh vehicle and is used to mark lanes through contaminated areas. Mounted on either side of the hull rear is a rack that carries lane marking poles. When required the racks are swung vertically through 90 degrees so that they are over the rear of the hull and lane marking poles can then be dispensed into the ground from inside the vehicle.

OT-65A
This is a Czechoslovak modification and is the basic vehicle with the turret of the OT-62B tracked armoured personnel carrier mounted on the roof. The turret is armed with a 7.62 mm M59T machine gun with an elevation of +20 degrees and a depression of −10 degrees. The turret can be traversed manually through 360 degrees. Mounted externally on the right side of the turret is an 82 mm T-21 Tarasnice recoilless gun which can be aimed and fired from inside the turret but can be reloaded only from the outside.

The T-21 fires a HEAT projectile weighing 2.13 kg with a muzzle velocity of 250 metres a second which will penetrate 230 mm of armour. Maximum range is 2500 metres, effective

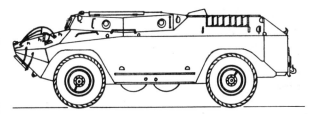

FUG (or OT-65) amphibious scout car without fitted armament

FUG radiological-chemical reconnaissance vehicle with lane marking equipment on top of hull at rear

range 450 metres and about 300 metres against moving targets. The crew of the OT-65A enters and leaves the vehicle by a small roof hatch that opens either side of the roof immediately behind the turret.

PSZH-IV APC

This was originally called the FUG-66 and later the FUG-70 until it was established that it was an armoured personnel carrier and not an amphibious scout car.

SPECIFICATIONS					
CREW	2 + 4	FUEL CAPACITY	200 litres	TYRES	12.00 × 18
CONFIGURATION	4 × 4	MAX CRUISING RANGE		SUSPENSION	
COMBAT WEIGHT	7000 kg	(road)	600 km	(front)	helical springs
POWER-TO-WEIGHT		FUEL CONSUMPTION	0.28 litre/km	(rear)	semi-elliptical
RATIO	15.87 hp/tonne	FORDING	amphibious		springs
LENGTH	5.79 m	GRADIENT	60%	ARMAMENT (main)	1 × 7.62 mm MG
WIDTH	2.5 m	SIDE SLOPE	30%	AMMUNITION (main)	1250
HEIGHT		VERTICAL OBSTACLE	0.4 m	ARMOUR (max)	13 mm
(to hull top)	1.91 m	TRENCH	1.2 m		
(with turret OT-65A)	2.25 m	ENGINE	Csepel D.414.44		
GROUND CLEARANCE	0.34 m		4-cylinder in-line		
TRACK	1.9 m		water-cooled		
WHEELBASE	3.3 m		diesel developing		
MAX SPEED			100 hp at		
(road)	87 km/h		2300 rpm		
(water)	9 km/h	TRANSMISSION	manual with 5 forward		
			and 1 reverse gears		

Status: Production complete. In service with Czechoslovakia, Hungary and Poland (limited use).

Manufacturer: Hungarian state arsenals.

ISRAEL

RAM Family of Light AFVs

Development

The RAM family of light armoured fighting vehicles has been developed by RAMTA Structures and Systems, a subsidiary of Israel Aircraft Industries, as a successor to the company's earlier RBY Mk 1 light armoured reconnaissance vehicle (fully described in the following entry) and was announced at the Paris Air Show in June 1979.

The RAM family has now been expanded into two basic groups, RAM V-1 and RAM V-2. The former are open topped and are produced in two wheelbases, V-1 short

RAM V-1 (short) light armoured reconnaissance vehicle with 40 mm grenade launcher and two 7.62 mm machine guns

RAM V-1 (short) fitted with TCM-20 twin 20 mm anti-aircraft gun system

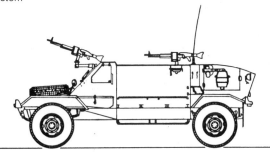

RAM V-1 (short) light armoured reconnaissance vehicle with 7.62 mm machine guns

(3.4-metre wheelbase) and V-1L (3.8-metre wheelbase). The V-2 series has an enclosed troop compartment and comprises the V-2 short (3.4-metre wheelbase) and V-2L long (3.8-metre wheelbase).

Description (RAM V-1)

The layout of the RAM V-1 is almost identical to the earlier RBY Mk 1 light armoured reconnaissance vehicle and the short model has the same wheelbase. The most significant improvements are the increased ground clearance achieved by the fitting of larger tyres, increased radius of action as the original petrol engine has been replaced by a diesel engine, and the replacement of the manual gearbox by an automatic one to reduce driver fatigue. Crew comfort has also been improved. Mounted at the front of the vehicle is a Koenig EC-100 winch with a capacity of 3629 kg.

Variants

Infantry fighting vehicle

This model is equipped with three 7.62 mm machine guns, 5000 rounds of ammunition, one anti-tank launcher, six rockets, fragmentation grenades, night vision equipment and a multi-channel transceiver.

Infantry combat vehicle

This model carries up to three 7.62 mm machine guns, 5000 rounds of ammunition, 52 mm mortar, 36 mortar bombs, two anti-tank rockets, fragmentation grenades, night vision equipment and a multi-channel transceiver.

TCM-20 AA

This is the basic vehicle fitted with the RAMTA Structures and Systems' TCM-20 twin 20 mm LAAG system. A total of 720 rounds of 20 mm ammunition are carried for the cannons, in addition one 7.62 mm machine gun, night vision equipment and a multi-channel transceiver are fitted. The model, which is only available based on the chassis of the RAM V-1L, has a four-man crew consisting of driver/loader, commander, gunner and loader. When in the firing position four hydraulic jacks are lowered to the ground to provide a more stable firing platform, although it is possible to fire against both ground targets and aerial targets while the vehicle is travelling. The current TCM-20 can be replaced by the new TCM Mk 3 system.

Close range anti-tank

This carries a 106 mm M40 series recoilless rifle built in Israel by IMI which can be traversed through a full 360 degrees. Eighteen rounds of ammunition are carried in the vehicle as well as night vision equipment and a multi-channel transceiver.

Long range anti-tank

This carries a Hughes TOW launcher on a telescopic pedestal, 16 TOW ATGWs, two 7.62 mm machine guns and 2500 rounds of ammunition, night vision equipment and a multi-channel transceiver.

RAM V-2 AFV

This has a fully enclosed troop compartment that carries a crew of eight to ten men and their personal equipment. It has a unique system of folding armour plate hatches which can be fully or partially opened so providing all round observation while affording protection against AP small arms fire and shell fragments. The personnel, seated or standing, can fire in all directions.

Various types of armament can be fitted according to mission requirements including: one 12.7 mm machine gun or 40 mm grenade launcher, 1500 rounds of 12.7 mm ammunition or six ammunition boxes for grenade launcher, three 7.62 mm machine guns plus 5000 rounds of ammunition, one rocket launcher plus six rounds, 24 fragmentation grenades, nine smoke grenades and two smoke flares. In addition the vehicle carries night vision equipment and a multi-channel transceiver.

RAM V-2L (long) AFV with 12.7 mm and 7.62 mm machine guns

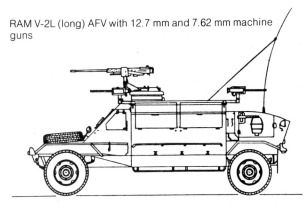

RAM V-2L (long) APC with 12.7 mm and 7.62 mm MGs

SPECIFICATIONS

Model	RAM V-1 (short)	RAM V-1 (long)	RAM V-2 (short)	RAM V-2 (long)
CREW (max)	2 + 6	2 + 8	2 + 6	2 + 8
CONFIGURATION	4 × 4	4 × 4	4 × 4	4 × 4
COMBAT WEIGHT	5400 kg	5600 kg	5700 kg	6000 kg
UNLOADED WEIGHT	3900 kg	4300 kg	4200 kg	4700 kg
PAYLOAD	1300 kg	1300 kg	1300 kg	1300 kg
LENGTH	5.02 m	5.42 m	5.02 m	5.42 m
WIDTH	2.03 m	2.03 m	2.03 m	2.03 m
HEIGHT (overall)	1.72 m	1.72 m	2.2 m	2.2 m
GROUND CLEARANCE				
(hull)	0.575 m	0.575 m	0.575 m	0.575 m
(axles)	0.31 m	0.31 m	0.31 m	0.31 m
TRACK	1.726 m	1.726 m	1.726 m	1.726 m
WHEELBASE	3.4 m	3.8 m	3.4 m	3.8 m
ANGLE OF APPROACH/				
DEPARTURE	60°/43°	60°/43°	60°/43°	60°/43°
MAX SPEED (road)	96 km/h	96 km/h	96 km/h	96 km/h
FUEL CAPACITY	120 litres	160 litres	120 litres	160 litres
RANGE (road)	800 km	1000 km	750 km	950 km
FORDING	1 m	1 m	1 m	1 m
GRADIENT	70%	60%	65%	60%
SIDE SLOPE	35%	35%	35%	35%
VERTICAL OBSTACLE	0.8 m	0.8 m	0.8 m	0.8 m
ENGINE	Deutz air-cooled, 6-cylinder diesel developing 132 bhp			
TRANSMISSION	Allison AT-540 automatic with 4 forward and 1 reverse gears			
TRANSFER CASE	Harwaythorn 2-speed			
STEERING	power-assisted ZF			
TURNING RADIUS	7.2 m	7.5 m	7.2 m	7.5 m
SUSPENSION	semi-elliptical springs and hydraulic shock absorbers			
TYRES	9.00 × 20	9.00 × 20	9.00 × 20	9.00 × 20
BRAKES				
(main)	hydraulic	hydraulic	hydraulic	hydraulic
(parking)	mechanical	mechanical	mechanical	mechanical
ELECTRICAL SYSTEM	24 V	24 V	24 V	24 V
BATTERIES	2 × 12 V	2 × 12 V	2 × 12 V	2 × 12 V
ARMOUR	8 mm	8 mm	8 mm	8 mm

Status: Development complete. Ready for production. It is reported that Morocco has taken delivery of a quantity of these vehicles.

Manufacturer: RAMTA Structures and Systems, Israel Aircraft Industries POB 323, Beer Sheba, 84102 Israel.

RBY Mk 1 Light Armoured Reconnaissance Vehicle

Development

The RBY Mk 1 light armoured reconnaissance vehicle was developed by RAMTA Structures and Systems, a subsidiary of Israel Aircraft Industries, and was first announced at the Paris Air Show in May 1975.

The design of the vehicle is based on an analysis by RAMTA of experience obtained during two decades of field operations in the Middle East. This showed that a reconnaissance vehicle required a very low profile, good all-round visibility for all crew members, to be airportable, be able to carry different armament installations and provide the crew with the maximum protection against mines.

The RBY Mk 1 is suitable for a wide range of roles including reconnaissance, long-range patrols and commando type operations, internal security operations and the evacuation of wounded in forward battlefield areas. Its low weight enables it to be carried by light aircraft and helicopters such as the CH-53s used by the Israeli Air Force.

Description

The all-welded hull of the RBY Mk 1 has 8 mm armoured steel (MIL-A-46100) sides inclined at an angle, and a floor of 10 mm thick plain carbon steel (SAE-1020). The shape of the hull has been designed to give the crew maximum possible protection from mine explosions. The axles and wheels are at the extreme ends of the vehicle and the effect of a mine explosion when touched off by one of the wheels is that the respective axle is damaged or cut, the fibreglass bumpers disintegrate, but the hull stays intact. The survivability of the vehicle to mine explosions was proved in a test programme using different types of mine.

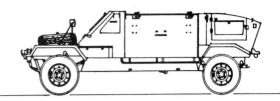

Basic RBY Mk 1 light armoured reconnaissance vehicle without armament installed

The driver is seated at the front of the vehicle on the left with the commander to his right. The front part of the crew compartment can be folded down into the horizontal for increased visibility and is provided with two integral observation hatches that are hinged at the top and open outwards. To the left of the driver and the right of the commander is another observation hatch, also hinged at the top and opening outwards.

The six passengers are seated three each side, facing outwards, back-to-back for all-round observation. There are no doors in the hull as this would weaken the structure and the crew enter and leave the vehicle by climbing over the sides.

The engine is at the rear of the hull and has a fibreglass cover and side doors for ease of access. The automotive components of the RBY Mk 1 are of a standard commercial design that meet current military requirements. Two spare wheels are carried, one at the front of the vehicle and one at the rear. Infra-red driving lights and a front-mounted winch with a capacity of 2722 kg can be fitted if required. Up to five 7.62 mm or 12.7 mm machine guns can be pintle-mounted around the top of the hull to provide suppressive fire.

RBY Mk 1 light armoured reconnaissance vehicle fitted with 7.62 mm MGs and front-mounted winch

RBY Mk 1 fitted with Hughes TOW ATGW system and front-mounted winch

RBY Mk 1 fitted with 106 mm M40 series recoilless rifle manufactured in Israel by IMI

Variants

Anti-tank armed with 106 mm M40 rifle
This model has the 106 mm M40 recoilless rifle manufactured by Israel Military Industries, with 16 anti-tank rounds. Secondary armament consists of two 7.62 mm machine guns with 5000 rounds and anti-tank missiles. A long range anti-tank model is also offered.

Communications
The RBY Mk 1 can be fitted with a variety of communications equipment.

SPECIFICATIONS

CREW	2 + 6	MAX SPEED		STEERING	worm and sector, power assisted
CONFIGURATION	4 × 4	(road)	100 km/h		
UNLOADED WEIGHT	3600 kg	(cross-country)	50 km/h	CLUTCH	single dry plate
LENGTH	5.023 m	FUEL CAPACITY	140 litres	SUSPENSION	semi-elliptical springs and hydraulic shock absorbers
WIDTH	2.03 m	MAX RANGE			
HEIGHT		(road)	550 km		
(empty without armament)	1.66 m	(cross-country)	400 km	BRAKES	
(loaded without armament)	1.54 m	FORDING	0.75 m	(main)	hydraulic
GROUND CLEARANCE		GRADIENT	60%	(parking)	mechanical mounted on drive shaft
(hull)	0.48 m	SIDE SLOPE	30%		
(axle)	0.27 m	ENGINE	Chrysler 225-2	ELECTRICAL SYSTEM	24 V
(transfer case)	0.375 m		6-cylinder water-cooled petrol developing 120 hp	BATTERIES	2 × 12 V
TRACK	1.665 m			ARMOUR	8 mm
WHEELBASE	3.4 m	TRANSMISSION	Model 435 manual with 4 forward and 1 reverse gears		
ANGLE OF APPROACH/ DEPARTURE	60°/50°	TRANSFER CASE	2-speed		

Status: Production as required. In service with Israel and Guatemala and two other countries.

Manufacturer: RAMTA Structures and Systems, Israel Aircraft Industries POB 323, Beer Sheba, 84102 Israel.

ITALY

FIAT-OTO Melara Type 6616 Armoured Car

Development
The Type 6616 armoured car is a joint development between FIAT and OTO Melara, with the former responsible for the hull and automotive components and the latter for the turret and armament installation. Final assembly and testing is carried out by FIAT at its Bolzano factory. The vehicle shares many common components with the Type 6614 armoured personnel carrier which is currently being built under licence in South Korea for the Korean Army.

The first prototype of the Type 6616 was completed in 1972 and after trials a production order was placed by the Italian Government for 50 vehicles for the Carabinieri. Production vehicles differ from the prototypes in that the turret front has been redesigned. The smoke discharger on the commander's hatch has been removed and the engine compartment grilles are now on either side of the hull, towards the rear, rather than on the top of the hull. The Type 6616 armoured car has recently been evaluated by the Italian Air Force in the airfield security role as the replacement for the old Staghound armoured cars dating back to the Second World War.

Description
The all-welded steel armour hull has a hull escape hatch in either side.

The driver is seated at the front of the vehicle on the right side and is provided with a single-piece hatch cover that opens to the right with an opening in the roof for a passive night driving periscope. To the front and side of the driver are five vision blocks which cover an arc of 200 degrees, the centre three with a wiper blade.

The all-welded turret is in the centre of the hull with the commander on the left and the gunner on the right. Their seats, which can be adjusted for height, are mounted on the turret basket. The commander has nine periscopes for all-round observation and a single-piece hatch cover that opens to the rear. The gunner has a single-piece hatch cover that opens to the rear and a periscope sight mounted in the turret roof forward of the hatch cover. The Aeritalia P204 gunner's periscope has a magnification of ×1 for general observation and ×8 for aiming purposes in daylight (with a nine degree field of view). It can be replaced by a P194 image intensifier with a magnification of ×8 and a 7.9 degree field of view for engaging targets at night. The periscopic head has an elevation of +60 degrees and a depression of −10 degrees. The radio is mounted in the turret bustle.

The engine compartment at the rear of the hull is separated from the fighting compartment by a fireproof bulkhead. The engine is at the very rear of the hull and is coupled to a manual five-speed transmission from which power is transmitted to the two-speed transfer case and then to the front and rear axles by propeller shafts. Both front and rear differentials are mechanically lockable. The planetary final drives, front and rear, consist of epicyclic gear trains in the wheel hubs.

The suspension, front and rear, is of the independent strut and link type with a helical spring and coaxial rubber bump stop. Each wheel station is provided with hydraulic shock absorbers and anti-roll bars are fitted as standard. The tyres are of the run-flat type, and the steering is power-assisted.

Optional equipment includes an NBC system, air-conditioning system, fire-extinguishing system and a front-mounted winch powered by a PTO with a maximum

FIAT-OTO Melara Type 6616 armoured car showing coaxial 7.62 mm machine gun over 20 mm cannon

capacity of 4500 kg and provided with 40 metres of 12 mm diameter cable.

The Type 6616 armoured car is fully amphibious, being propelled in the water by its wheels. Four bilge pumps, each with a capacity of 180 litres a minute are fitted and it is possible to pressurise the submerged mechanical components.

The main armament consists of a Rheinmetall 20 mm MM 20 Rh 202 cannon. The empty cartridge cases are automatically ejected outside the vehicle. A total of 250 rounds of ready use 20 mm ammunition are carried with a further 150 rounds in reserve. Mounted coaxially over the main armament is a 7.62 mm machine gun with 300 rounds of ready-use ammunition, and further 700 rounds carried in reserve. Mounted on either side of the turret are three smoke dischargers which are electrically fired from within the vehicle. If required a 106 mm M40 type recoilless rifle can be mounted forward of the commander's position on the turret roof.

FIAT-OTO Melara Type 6616 armoured car

FIAT-OTO Melara Type 6616 armoured car

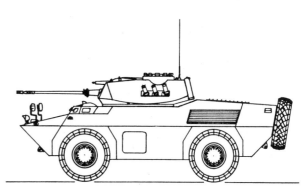

FIAT-OTO Melara Type 6616 armoured car fitted with two-man turret armed with 90 mm Cockerill Mk III gun

Left to right: FIAT 6614 APC, Type 6616 armoured car with 20 mm cannon and Type 6616 armoured car with 90 mm Cockerill Mk III gun

FIAT-OTO Melara Type 6616 armoured car from rear

Variants

For trials purposes the Type 6616 armoured car has been fitted with the OTO Melara OTO T 90 CKL turret which is armed with a 90 mm Cockerill Mk III gun. The vehicle can be fitted with various other turrets and cupolas as required by the user.

Status: In production. In service with Italian Carabinieri, Peru, Somalia (30 ordered in 1977 and delivered in 1978/79) and other undisclosed countries.

Manufacturer: Invecto Defence Vehicle Division, Corso Lombardia, 20 1099 S. Mauro Torinese, (20) Italy.

SPECIFICATIONS

(those in square brackets relate to the 90 mm version where this differs from the standard 20 mm version)

CREW	3
CONFIGURATION	4 × 4
COMBAT WEIGHT	8000 kg (8200 kg)
POWER-TO-WEIGHT RATIO	20.20 hp/tonne (19.51 hp/tonne)
LENGTH GUN FORWARDS	n/app (6.64 m)
LENGTH HULL	5.37 m
WIDTH	2.5 m
HEIGHT (to turret roof)	2.035 m (2.06 m)
FIRING HEIGHT	1.76 m (1.785 m)
GROUND CLEARANCE	
(hull front)	0.485 m
(hull centre)	0.44 m
(hull rear)	0.506 m
(axle)	0.37 m
TRACK	1.96 m
WHEELBASE	2.75 m
ANGLE OF APPROACH/ DEPARTURE	45°/45°
MAX SPEED	
(road)	100 km/h
(water)	5 km/h
FUEL CAPACITY	150 litres
MAX RANGE	
(road at 70 km/h)	700 km
(water at 5 km/h)	20 km
FORDING	amphibious

GRADIENT	60%
SIDE SLOPE	30%
VERTICAL OBSTACLE	0.45 m
TURNING RADIUS	
(land)	7 m
(water)	7.5 m
ENGINE	Model 8062.24 super-charged liquid-cooled in-line diesel developing 160 hp at 3200 rpm
TRANSMISSION	manual with 5 forward and 1 reverse gears
TRANSFER CASE	2-speed
STEERING	assisted
CLUTCH	single dry plate, hydraulic operated
SUSPENSION	independent
TYRES	14.50 × 20
BRAKES	
(main)	drum, air over hydraulic (dual circuit)
(parking)	drum, hand-operated, on transfer front output shaft
ELECTRICAL SYSTEM	24 V
BATTERIES	4 × 12 V, 100 Ah
ARMAMENT	
(main)	1 × 20 mm cannon (1 × 90 mm)
(coaxial)	1 × 7.62 mm MG

SMOKE-LAYING EQUIPMENT	3 smoke dischargers either side of turret
AMMUNITION	
(main)	400 (16 + 20)
(coaxial)	1000 (1000 + 1250)
(smoke grenades)	39 (6 + 10)
FIRE-CONTROL SYSTEM	
Turret power control	electric/manual
Maximum elevation speed	10°/s
Maximum elevation acceleration speed	46°/s²
Maximum turret traverse speed	10°/s (30°/s)
Maximum turret traverse acceleration speed	46°/s² (45°/s²)
Traverse speed (commander controlled)	30°/s
Gun elevation/ depression	+35°/−5° (+27°/−9°)
Gun stabiliser	
(vertical)	no
(horizontal)	no
ARMOUR	
Hull and turret	6 mm–8 mm

OTO Melara OTO R3 Capraia Reconnaissance Vehicle

Development

The OTO R3 reconnaissance vehicle has been developed as a private venture by OTO Melara and the prototype was shown for the first time at the 1982 Italian Naval Exhibition held in Genoa.

The lower part of the body, engine and mechanical groups are the same as on the special task vehicle Gorgona. Two versions have so far been developed; a scout/reconnaissance vehicle which has a four-man crew and an armoured personnel carrier which has a five-man crew including the commander and driver.

Description

The hull of the OTO R3 is of all-welded aluminium armour construction with a maximum thickness of 32 mm which provides the crew with complete protection from small arms fire (7.62 mm NATO) and shell splinters.

The driver is seated at the front of the vehicle with a single-piece hatch cover above his position that opens to the left. To his immediate front are five vision blocks each with a wiper which give excellent observation to his front and sides.

The commander is seated to the rear of the driver, offset to the right and has a single-piece hatch cover that opens to the rear and six periscopes for all-round observation.

The armament is mounted to the rear of the commander's position and the following installations are currently being offered by OTO Melara:

T 12.7 FA

This consists of an externally-mounted 12.7 mm M2 HB machine gun provided with 100 rounds of ready use ammu-

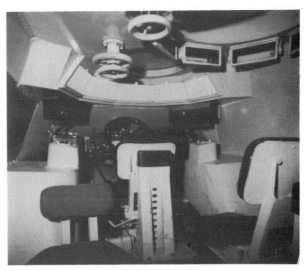

Driver's position in OTO R3 reconnaissance vehicle looking forward

OTO R3 reconnaissance vehicle with T 20 FA–HS turret

Prototype of OTO R3 reconnaissance vehicle being tested. Prototype has different vision blocks to that anticipated in production vehicles

nition. The turret, which consists of the carriage, machine gun, sighting system, power drives and ammunition weighs 120 kg. Turret traverse is a full 360 degrees at a speed of 60 degrees a second, with elevation being from −10 degrees to +50 degrees at a speed of 40 degrees a second. The gunner has a sight with a magnification of ×1.5 and ×5.

T 7.62 FA

This consists of an externally-mounted 7.62 mm machine gun provided with 80 rounds of ready use ammunition. The turret, which consists of the carriage, machine gun, sighting system, power drives and ready use ammunition weighs 180 kg. Turret traverse is a full 360 degrees at a speed of 60 degrees a second, with elevation being from −10 degrees to +25 degrees at a speed of 40 degrees a second. The gunner has a sight with a magnification of ×1.

T 20 FA – HS

This turret is fitted with an externally-mounted Oerlikon KAD-B17 20 mm cannon which is provided with 120 rounds of ready use ammunition. The turret, which consists of the carriage, armament, sighting system, power drives and ready use ammunition, weighs about 450 kg. Turret traverse is a full 360 degrees at a speed of 45 degrees a second, with elevation being from −10 to +60 degrees at a speed of 30 degrees a second. The gunner has a sight with a magnification of ×1.5 and ×5.

Folgore ×2 FA

This turret is armed with two Breda Folgore anti-tank launchers with a 7.62 mm machine gun being mounted slightly above and between the weapons. Each launcher has one missile in the ready-to-launch position with the machine gun having 80 rounds of ready use ammunition. The turret, which consists of the weapons, ready use ammunition, carriage, sighting system and power drives, weighs 150 kg. The turret can be traversed through a full 360 degrees at a speed of 30 degrees a second and the weapons can be elevated from −7 to +10 degrees at a speed of 5 degrees a second. The gunner has a sight with a magnification of ×1.5 and ×5.

OTO R3 reconnaissance vehicle from rear fitted with T 20 FA–HS turret armed with 20 mm cannon

T 106 ×2 FA

This turret is armed with two externally-mounted 106 mm M40 type recoilless rifles and consists of the carriage, armament, sighting system, power drives and two rounds of ready use ammunition, weighing a total of 550 kg. The turret can be traversed through a full 360 degrees at a speed of 30 degrees a second and elevated from −7 to +10 degrees at a speed of 5 degrees a second. The gunner has a sight with a magnification of ×1.5 and ×5.

TOW turret

This has an externally-mounted launcher for a Hughes TOW ATGW system which can be traversed through a full 360 degrees and elevated from −7 to +10 degrees. The turret, which consists of the carriage, launcher, sighting system and ammunition, weighs 150 kg.

In the roof of the R3, to the rear and either side of the armament installation are two periscopes that give observation to the front of the vehicle; a further two periscopes are mounted in the very rear to give rearward observation.

There is an entry door in each side of the hull with two vision blocks being provided in the left and one in the right side of the hull. Under the forward vision block, which is to the left of the vehicle commander, is a circular firing port.

The power plant is installed in the rear of the vehicle and includes the engine, automatic transmission and transfer case. The automatic transmission is coupled to the two-speed transfer case which permanently drives the front and rear wheels through a controlled differential. The cooling system consists of two radiators installed in the rear of the vehicle cooled by two fan-air conveyor units driven by the engine through V-belts and thermostatic devices. Engine oil is cooled by a heat exchanger. The electric system is powered at 24 V by a 1200 W generator through two 90 Ah batteries.

The vehicle is fully amphibious being propelled in the water by two water jets mounted at the hull rear.

Standard equipment includes run-flat tyres, air conditioning, servo-assisted steering with the steering wheel being adjustable in height, heating and ventilation system and a front-mounted electrically operated winch with a capacity of 2000 kg.

OTO R3 reconnaissance vehicle fitted with T 20 FA–HS turret armed with 20 mm cannon

Optional equipment includes air pressurisation with filtering system and infra-red or passive night vision equipment.

Variants

There are no variants apart from the different armament installations mentioned previously.

SPECIFICATIONS

CREW	4 or 5 (depending on role)	MAX ROAD SPEED (forwards)	120 km/h	SUSPENSION TYPE	independent, McPhearson type with longitudinal torsion bars
CONFIGURATION	4 × 4	MAX WATER SPEED	6 km/h		
COMBAT WEIGHT	3200 kg	RANGE	500 km	TYRES	7.50 × 16
MAXIMUM PERMITTED WEIGHT	3500 kg	FORDING	amphibious	BRAKES	servo-assisted dual hydraulic circuit, acting on front disc brakes and on rear drum brakes. Parking brake acts on rear brakes
		GRADIENT	75%		
POWER-TO-WEIGHT RATIO	29.68 bhp/tonne (at weight of 3200 kg)	SIDE SLOPE	40%		
		TURNING RADIUS	5.5 m		
LENGTH	4.86 m	ENGINE	FIAT model 8144.81.200 4-cylinder water-cooled supercharged diesel developing 95 hp at 4200 rpm	ELECTRICAL SYSTEM	24 V
WIDTH	1.78 m			BATTERIES	2 × 12 V, 90 Ah
HEIGHT (to hull top)	1.55 m				
GROUND CLEARANCE	0.35 m				
TRACK		TRANSMISSION	OTR 6 automatic, 4 forward and 1 reverse gears (or S5/18 manual with 5 forward and 1 reverse gears)		
(front)	1.418 m				
(rear)	1.45 m				
WHEELBASE	2.5 m				
ANGLE OF APPROACH/ DEPARTURE	40°/40°	TRANSFER CASE	2-speed		
		STEERING	servo-assisted		

Status: Prototype.

Manufacturer: OTO Melara, via Valdilocchi 15, 19100 La Spezia, Italy.

OTO Melara OTO R 2.5 Gorgona Reconnaissance Vehicle

Development

The OTO R 2.5 Gorgona vehicle has been developed as a private venture by OTO Melara and was announced in 1982. Two versions are currently being offered; an unarmed police model and a combat model which can be fitted with various types of armament. Many of the automotive components are also used in the OTO R3 reconnaissance vehicle which is fully described in the preceding entry.

Description

The body of the Gorgona is of welded aluminium armour 15 mm thick with the bullet-proof glass being 32 mm thick which gives the same degree of protection to the crew as the aluminium armour. This provides complete protection from 7.62 mm (NATO) small arms fire.

There is a stowage area at the front, commander, driver and two men in the centre, and the engine and transmission at the rear. Each crew member enters and leaves the vehicle via an individual side door which has an electrically-operated window in its upper part. Mounted in the forward part of the vehicle is an electrically-operated winch with a capacity of 2000 kg.

The power plant is installed in the rear of the vehicle and includes the engine, automatic transmission and the transfer case. The engine oil is cooled by a heat exchanger that transfers heat to the water of the main circuit. The automatic transmission is coupled to the two-speed transfer case which permanently drives the front and rear wheels through a controlled differential. The cooling system consists of two radiators installed in the rear of the vehicle cooled by two fan-air conveyor units driven through V-belts and thermostatic devices. Electric power is supplied at 24 V by a 1200 W generator to two 90 Ah batteries. The vehicle is fully amphibious, being propelled in the water by its wheels with steering being accomplished in a similar manner to that of land operations.

Standard equipment includes run-flat tyres, air conditioning, heating and ventilation system, power-assisted steering and an adjustable steering wheel.

Optional equipment includes air pressurisation and filtering system, infra-red night driving equipment and a water-jet propulsion system.

The following armament installations can be fitted on the roof of the vehicle:
TPT shield for gunner on right side of roof
T 12.7 FA turret with 12.7 mm MG, elevation +50°, depression −10°, traverse 360°
T 7.62 FA turret with 7.62 mm MG, elevation +25°, depression −10°, traverse 360°

Variants

None apart for those mentioned in the text.

Side-view of OTO Melara OTO R 2.5 Gorgona (4 × 4) reconnaissance vehicle showing side doors and engine compartment at rear

77

OTO Melara OTO R 2.5 Gorgona (4 × 4) reconnaissance vehicle without armament installed

OTO Melara OTO R 2.5 Gorgona (4 × 4) reconnaissance vehicle fitted with remote-controlled 7.62 mm machine gun

SPECIFICATIONS

CREW	4	RANGE	500 km	TYRES	7.50 × 16
CONFIGURATION	4 × 4	FORDING	amphibious	BRAKES	service brakes are assisted
COMBAT WEIGHT	2850 kg	GRADIENT	75%		by a vacuum pump through a
MAXIMUM PERMISSIBLE		SIDE SLOPE	40%		dual hydraulic circuit, acting
WEIGHT	3150 kg	TURNING RADIUS	5.5 m		on front discs and rear brake
POWER-TO-WEIGHT		STEERING	servo assisted		drums. Parking brake acts on
RATIO	33.33 bhp/tonne	ENGINE	FIAT model 8144.81.200		rear brakes
LENGTH	4.5 m		4-cylinder water-cooled	ELECTRICAL SYSTEM	24 V
WIDTH	1.7 m		supercharged diesel	BATTERIES	2 × 12 V, 90 Ah
HEIGHT	1.62 m		developing 95 bhp at		
GROUND CLEARANCE	0.35 m		4200 rpm		
TRACK		TRANSMISSION	OTR 6, automatic, 4 forward		
(front)	1.418 m		and 1 reverse gears,		
(rear)	1.45 m		hydraulic torque converter		
WHEELBASE	2.5 m		with lock up clutch (or S5/18		
ANGLE OF APPROACH/			manual with 5 forward and 1		
DEPARTURE	40°/40°		reverse gears)		
MAX SPEED		TRANSFER CASE	2-speed		
(road)	120 km/h	SUSPENSION	independent, McPhearson		
(water)	5 km/h		type with longitudinal torsion		
			bars		

Status: Development complete. Ready for production.

Manufacturer: OTO Melara, via Valdilocchi 15, 19100 La Spezia, Italy.

Lizard F333E Light Armoured Vehicle

Development

The Lizard F333E light armoured vehicle has been developed as a private venture by Ferrari Engineering SRL. The first of three prototypes was completed in 1980 and early in 1983 a batch of 15 pre-production vehicles was being built.

Description

The hull of the Lizard is of all-welded steel that provides the crew with protection from small arms fire and shell splinters. The floor is of double-skinned construction for increased protection against mines. Provision is made to prevent magnetic mines being attached to the hull. Its small size and low profile also increase its survivability.

The driver is seated at the front of the hull with bullet-proof windows to his front and sides. A 5.56 mm machine gun can be mounted to the right of the driver firing to the front of the vehicle. The commander and gunner are seated in the centre

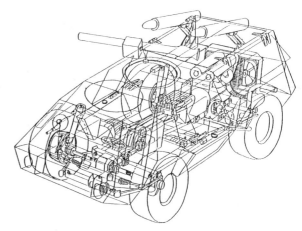

Cutaway drawing of Lizard fitted with two anti-tank missiles in ready to launch position and Folgore anti-tank launcher on commander's hatch

Lizard F333E light armoured vehicle with all roof hatches open

Close-up of commander's hatch fitted with Folgore anti-tank launcher

of the vehicle with a forward opening door being provided in each side of the hull. In the forward part of the roof is a single-piece circular hatch that opens forward where the light armament, for example, the 5.56 mm or 7.62 mm machine gun, is mounted. In the roof to the rear of the circular hatch is a two-part roof hatch that opens either side; a retractable missile launcher system can be installed at this position.

The engine compartment is in the lower part of the hull rear with the radiator at the very rear. The Lizard has permanent 4 × 4 drive and front, central and rear self locking differentials are fitted as standard.

Variants

The manufacturer has suggested the following basic variants of the F333E:

Scout

This would have a two-man crew and be armed with a bow-mounted 5.56 mm machine gun and a roof-mounted 12.7 mm machine gun. The former would have an elevation of +25 degrees, depression of −10 degrees and a total traverse of 50 degrees. A total of 2000 rounds of ammunition are carried for this weapon in boxes of 200 rounds. The roof-mounted 12.7 mm M2 HB machine gun has an elevation of +50 degrees, depression of −15 degrees and a total traverse of 360 degrees, with 500 rounds of ammunition being carried in boxes of 100 rounds.

Anti-tank

This would have a two-man crew and have the same bow-mounted 5.56 mm machine gun as the scout model. Anti-

Lizard F333E showing low profile compared to M47 tank in background

Lizard F333E light armoured vehicle with rear roof hatches open

Close-up of bow machine gun installation in Lizard F333E light armoured vehicle

tank armament consists of a Folgore weapon with an elevation of +20 degrees, depression of −6 degrees and a total traverse of 360 degrees; 8 projectiles are carried. As an alternative to the Folgore a Euromissile MILAN ATGW launcher and four missiles can be carried.

Anti-riot/Basic fighter

This would have a two- or three-man crew and have the same bow-mounted 5.56 mm machine gun as the anti-tank and scout models. In addition, mounted on the roof is a 7.62 mm machine gun with an elevation of +45 degrees, depression of

−15 degrees and a total traverse of 360 degrees, with 2000 rounds of ammunition being carried. In either side door is a firing port through which a weapon can be safely used with an elevation of +45 degrees, depression of +20 degrees and a total traverse of 90 degrees. As an alternative a flame thrower can be fitted in place of the bow-mounted 5.56 mm machine gun.

Commando

Three-man crew and fitted only with the bow-mounted 5.56 mm machine gun with a maximum payload of 200 kg being carried, including explosives, small arms and supplies.

SPECIFICATIONS					
		TRACK		TRANSFER CASE	1, 5, 3, reduction
		(front)	1.385 m	STEERING	power assisted, rack and
		(rear)	1.424 m		pinion
CREW	2 or 3	WHEELBASE	1.8 m	SUSPENSION	independent, telescopic
CONFIGURATION	4 × 4	ANGLE OF APPROACH/			struts with double acting
COMBAT WEIGHT	2600 kg	DEPARTURE	45°/47°		hydraulic shock absorbers
UNLOADED WEIGHT	2100 kg	MAX ROAD SPEED	120 km/h		(twin on rear wheels), four
POWER-TO-WEIGHT		FUEL CAPACITY	2 × 50 litres		longitudinal torsion bars
RATIO	44.23 hp/tonne	RANGE AT 60 km/h	800 km	TYRES	11.00 × 15 bullet-proof
GROUND PRESSURE	1 kg/cm²	FORDING	0.6 m	BRAKES	power-assisted, dual-circuit,
TOWED LOAD	1000 kg	GRADIENT	60%		mechanical parking brake
LENGTH	3.3 m	ENGINE	FIAT 4-cylinder petrol		operates on rear wheels
WIDTH	1.7 m		developing 115 hp at	ELECTRICAL SYSTEM	12 V
HEIGHT (hull top)	1.42 m		5600 rpm	BATTERY	1 × 12 V, 63 Ah
GROUND CLEARANCE	0.3 m	TRANSMISSION	manual, 5 forward and 1 reverse gears		

Status: Prototypes.

Manufacturer: Ferrari Engineering SRL, 10 via San Quintino, 10121 Turin, Italy.

JAPAN

New Japanese Wheeled Reconnaissance Vehicles

Development

In 1974 two-wheeled reconnaissance vehicles were designed to meet the requirements of the Japanese Ground Self-Defence Forces. The 4 × 4 vehicle was designed and built by Komatsu Seisaku-Jyo while the 6 × 6 vehicle was designed and built by Mitsubishi Heavy Industries. After trials it was decided to concentrate on the 6 × 6 model.

Two models of the 6 × 6 vehicle are now being developed, a reconnaissance patrol vehicle and a command and communications vehicle. The reconnaissance patrol vehicle is being built by Mitsubishi Heavy Industries and 342 million yen was allocated in the 1978 budget for the construction of two prototype vehicles. If the trials are satisfactory 50 will be procured from 1985 at a unit cost of 110 million yen. The vehicle will be armed with a Swiss Oerlikon-Bührle 25 mm KBA cannon which will be manufactured under licence by

Prototype of Type 82 6 × 6 command and communications vehicle showing mount for 12.7 mm machine gun (Kensuke Ebata)

Nippon Seiko Jyo (Japan Steel Works) and six 60 mm smoke grenade launchers.

The command and communications vehicle is being developed by Komatsu Seisaku-Jyo with the assistance of Mitsubishi. A total of 456 million yen was allocated in the 1978 budget for the construction of four prototypes. The first prototypes were completed in 1980. A total of 250 vehicles will be produced at a unit cost of 58 million yen. Eighty per cent of its components will be identical to those used in the 6 × 6 reconnaissance patrol vehicle. First funding was for 13 vehicles in the fiscal year 1982 defence budget.

This was subsequently standardised as the Type 82 command and communications vehicle with 18 being requested in the 1982 defence budget, but only ten being approved. A further 10 were ordered in the 1983 defence budget and another 19 in the 1984 defence budget. A total of 127 vehicles are expected to be procured under the FY 1981 mid-term defence plan which started in FY83. By the end of 1988 137 vehicles are expected to be in service.

Type 82 command and communications vehicle fitted with one 7.62 mm and one 12.7 mm machine gun

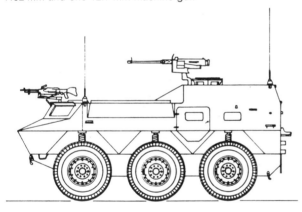

Description (Type 82)

The hull of the Type 82 command and communications vehicle is of all-welded construction with the driver being seated at the front of the hull on the right side. Above his position is a single-piece hatch cover with an integral periscope that can be traversed left and right. A second crew member is seated to the left of the driver and over his position is a single-piece hatch cover with a rotatable periscope, forward of this is a pintle-mounted 7.62 mm machine gun. The windscreens to the front and either side of this position are covered in combat areas by armoured shutters hinged at the top, the forward shutter being provided with two vision slits.

The engine compartment is in the forward part of the hull on the left side, to the rear of the front two crew members, with the air inlet and air outlet louvres in the roof. There is a gangway in the right side of the hull which connects the front and rear crew compartments.

The rear crew compartment, which also houses most of the communications equipment, is raised above the roof of the vehicle and has two circular hatch covers, the left one being provided with six observation periscopes and on the right

One of the first production Type 82 command and communications vehicle fitted with 7.62 mm and 12.7 mm roof-mounted machine guns (K Nogi)

Close up of the 12.7 mm (0.50) M2 HB machine gun with shield as installed on the Type 82 command and communications vehicle (K Nogi)

with an externally pintle-mounted 12.7 mm machine gun with a shield.

In the hull rear is a large door opening to the right in which is a single firing/observation port that opens upwards. In the left side of the hull, between the second and third axle, is a single forward opening door again with a single firing/observation hatch opening upwards. To the rear of this door is another single firing/observation port opening upwards. In the right side of the hull, between the first and second axle, is a forward opening door with an integral firing/observation port that opens upwards and to the rear of this are a further two firing/observation ports.

SPECIFICATIONS (provisional)

CREW	8
CONFIGURATION	6 × 6
COMBAT WEIGHT	13 600 kg
LENGTH	5.72 m
WIDTH	2.48 m
HEIGHT	2.38 m
GROUND CLEARANCE	0.45 m
WHEELBASE	1.5 m + 1.5 m
MAX ROAD SPEED	100 km/h
FORDING	1 m
GRADIENT	60%
VERTICAL OBSTACLE	0.6 m
ENGINE	Isuzu 10PB1 water-cooled diesel developing 305 hp at 2600 rpm
TRANSMISSION	6 forward and 1 reverse gears
TURNING RADIUS	8.4 m (with 1st and 3rd axles)
TRENCH	1.5 m
TYRES	14.00 × 20

Description (Type 87 reconnaissance and patrol vehicle)

This vehicle uses the same automotive components as the Type 82 command and communications vehicle but has a redesigned all steel hull. The five-man crew consists of the driver, assistant driver/radio operator, commander, gunner and observer.

The driver is seated at the left front of the vehicle on the right and has a single piece hatch cover with an integral periscope and three fixed forward-facing periscopes. The

radio operator is to the left of the driver and has a single piece hatch cover which opens upwards and a single forward facing periscope.

The two-man power operated turret is in the centre of the hull slightly forward of the second axle. The gunner is seated on the left with a single piece hatch cover and two periscopes while the commander is seated on the right with a single piece hatch cover and six periscopes.

The prototypes were fitted with a West German Rheinmetall 20 mm cannon but production vehicles will be armed with the Swiss Oerlikon-Bührle 25 mm KBA cannon with a 7.62 mm Type 74 machine gun coaxially to the right. Mounted either side of the turret are three Type 74 60 mm electrically operated smoke dischargers.

The engine compartment is at the rear of the hull of the right side with an aisle for the observer on the left side. In the hull roof to the rear of the turret is a single rearward-facing periscope for the observer.

The either side of the hull between the first and second axles is an observation block and in the left side of the hull between the second and third axles is a crew entry door with an integral window and observation flap that opens towards the front.

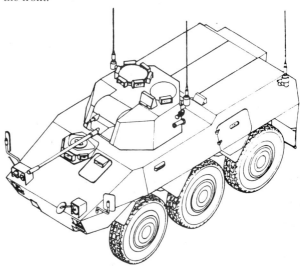

Type 87 reconnaissance and patrol vehicle which shares many common components with the Type 82 command and communications vehicle (Kensuke Ebata)

The Type 87 reconnaissance and patrol vehicle is not fitted with a NBC system and has no amphibious capability. Specifications are similar to the Type 82 command and communications vehicle with the exception of the following:

CREW	5
COMBAT WEIGHT	13 500 kg
LENGTH	5.37 m

Status: Type 82 is in production for the Japanese Self-Defence Forces.

Manufacturers: Komatsu Seisaku-Jyo, 2-3-6, Akasaka, Minato-ku, Japan. Mitsubishi Heavy Industries, 5-1, Marunouchi 2-chome, Chiyoda-ku, Tokyo, Japan.

MEXICO

Mexico has recently completed 17 ND-3 Caballo 4 × 4 reconnaissance vehicles. Some of these were fitted with a French SAMM S 365 series of one-man turret (recently redesignated the BTM series) while others has a cupola armed with a 7.62 mm machine gun similar to that fitted to the MOWAG Roland (4 × 4) armoured personnel carrier

NORWAY

Modernised M24 Light Tank

Development
To meet the requirements of the Norwegian Army the Oslo-based company of Thune-Eureka A/S developed a modernised version of the M24 Chaffee light tank. The first prototype was completed in January 1973 and after extensive trials the Norwegian Army decided to refit its fleet of M24s to this new standard for anti-tank use. Fifty-four of these tanks, designated the NM-116, were delivered to the Norwegian Army between January 1975 and October 1976. According to Thune-Eureka the modification cost can be kept down to one-third of the cost of a comparable new tank. NAPCO Industries Incorporated of the USA has obtained a licence to market this vehicle world-wide.

Description
The modernisation of the tank has been extensive and includes the installation of a new powerpack, new transmission, new gun and numerous other improvements.

The original twin Cadillac petrol engines have been replaced by a single super-charged Detroit Diesel model 6V-53T which develops 250 hp at 2800 rpm. This is coupled to an Allison pre-selector gearbox model MT 650 with a torque converter giving five forward speeds and one in reverse. In addition to the main transmission another gearbox provides the correct speed to the differential at the front of the tank.

There are two radiators with hydraulically-driven and thermostatically-governed fans and four heat exchangers for cooling the oil. The two heat exchangers for the transmission

M24 light tank with new French 90 mm gun, laser rangefinder over main armament and bow machine gun removed as used by Norwegian Army (Norwegian Army)

Engine compartment of modernised M24 from rear with new engine

and differential are on the engine, one exchanger for the additional gearbox is in the air flow of one of the radiators and one for the oil of the hydraulic system is built into pipes for the water cooling of the engine. The air from the radiators blows through the engine compartment and is ejected with the exhaust.

The fighting compartment is equipped with a manual fire extinguisher and the engine compartment is fitted with a Freon fire-extinguishing system, consisting of two bottles of Freon 1301 with a tripping device hand-operated from the driver's seat and a single bottle of Freon 1301 which is automatically released when the temperature in the engine compartment reaches a predetermined level. Each bottle has sufficient capacity to extinguish any possible fire in the engine compartment.

To increase the comfort of the crew and improve the gunner's and loader's ability to operate the 90 mm gun the modified turret is fitted with a basket which both eliminates the need for the loader to work kneeling and enables a number of ready rounds to be carried in the basket.

The bow machine gunner's position in the front right side of the hull has been eliminated and the associated ball mounting has been welded shut. The space saved is used to stow 20 rounds of 90 mm ammunition. To suit the Norwegian environment a new heating system has been installed and the batteries have been moved to the floor of the fighting compartment and have hot air piped to them to increase their capacity in winter.

The original 75 mm gun has been replaced by a French D/925 90 mm low pressure gun. The modifications include the replacement of the barrel, removal of the gyrostabiliser, modifying the breech assembly (breech ring, breech block and extractor), replacement of the telescope reticle and the adjustment of the ammunition racks. The recoil mechanism has not been modified. The gun fires the following types of ammunition:

Type	Canister	HE-FS	HEAT-FS*	Smoke FS
WEIGHT OF COMPLETE ROUND	8.9 kg	8.9 kg	7.1 kg	9.1 kg
WEIGHT OF PROJECTILE	5.28 kg	5.27 kg	3.65 kg	5.4 kg
MUZZLE VELOCITY	640 m/s	635 m/s	640 m/s	750 m/s

*has tracer will penetrate 340 mm of armour at an incidence of 0° or 120 mm of armour at an incidence of 65°.

Modernised M24 light tank with West German smoke dischargers on turret side

The 7.62 mm (0.30) coaxial machine gun has been replaced by a 12.7 mm (0.50) Browning M2 HB machine gun and a similar anti-aircraft weapon is mounted on the roof of the turret. Four German type smoke dischargers are mounted on either side of the turret. Forty-one rounds of 90 mm and 500 rounds of 12.7 mm ammunition are carried.

Vehicles used by the Norwegian Army have a Simrad LV3 laser rangefinder mounted over the main armament and other optional equipment includes two different types of tracks (West German Diehl or Swedish Hägglund), new shock absorbers, new communications equipment and either infra-red or passive night vision equipment for the driver, commander and gunner.

Dimensions of the modernised M24 are almost identical to those of the standard M24 Chaffee but the modernised version has the following performance figures:

SPECIFICATIONS

MAX ROAD SPEED	57 km/h
AVERAGE ROAD SPEED	45 km/h
AVERAGE CROSS-COUNTRY SPEED	26 – 30 km/h
ROAD RANGE	400 km

Variants

BK 710 recovery vehicle

This has been designed to meet the requirements of the Norwegian Army by A/S Moelven Brug and is essentially an M24 Chaffee light tank with its turret removed and replaced by a hydraulic crane with a maximum winching capacity of 19 tonnes, maximum lifting capacity of 11 tonnes at 1.8 metres reach and a maximum outreach of 5 metres with 5 tonnes. When travelling the crane is normally traversed to the rear.

Status: In service with Norway. The modernisation programme is still available from NAPCO Incorporated and has been sold to an Asian country, probably Taiwan.

Manufacturer: Original manufacturer for the modernised M24 was Thune-Eureka A/S, Drammensveien 130, Oslo 2, Norway. Licence is now held by NAPCO Industries Incorporated, 1600 Second Street South, Hopkins, Minnesota 55343, USA.

SOUTH AFRICA

Eland Light Armoured Car

In the early 1960s South Africa obtained a licence from Panhard of France to undertake production of the Panhard AML armoured car in its 60 mm and 90 mm versions. Following the supply of a batch of vehicles from France production commenced in the mid-1960s. The first models were armed with a 60 mm mortar and twin 7.62 mm machine guns, and were designated the Eland Mk 1.

The Mk 1 was followed by the Mk 2 which entered production in 1967 and had a number of improvements includ-

Eland light armoured car family, left to right, 60 mm mortar, 90 mm gun and 20 mm cannon

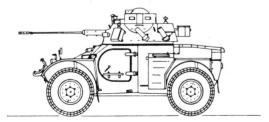

Eland light armoured car with 20 mm turret

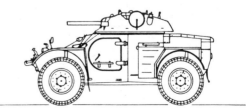

Eland light armoured car with 60 mm mortar turret

Sandock-Austral built Eland light armoured car armed with 90 mm gun and 7.62 mm coaxial machine gun plus 7.62 mm machine gun on commander's cupola

Eland light armoured car armed with 90 mm gun and 7.62 mm coaxial machine gun. The 7.62 mm anti-aircraft machine gun is not fitted to the mount on the commander's cupola (Christopher F Foss)

Eland light armoured car fitted with breech-loaded 60 mm mortar and coaxial 7.62 mm machine gun (Christopher F Foss)

ing a new engine. The Mk 3 and Mk 4 were not produced in large numbers. The Mk 5 and Mk 6 were earlier versions rebuilt to the latest production standard.

By early 1983 some 1300 vehicles had been completed with the current production model being the Mk 7. This has many improvements as a result of combat experience including a new petrol engine that can be changed in 40 minutes, new transmission, improved suspension, new turret and improved armour protection.

Current production models are armed with a 90 mm gun/ 7.62 mm coaxial and 7.62 mm anti-aircraft MGs or a 60 mm mortar/twin 7.62 mm machine guns. A model with a two-man turret armed with a 20 mm cannon and a coaxial

7.62 mm MG has been built but this has not yet entered production.

Sandock-Austral can make up to 35 vehicles a month if required, while still producing the Ratel (6 × 6) infantry fighting vehicles. Ninety-five per cent of the Eland are now produced in South Africa.

Status: In production. In service with South Africa and Zimbabwe.

Manufacturer: Sandock-Austral Beperk Limited, West Street Industrial Sites, Boksburg, Transvaal, South Africa.

VEC Cavalry Scout Vehicle

Development

The VEC (Vehículo de Exploración de Caballeria), or cavalry scout vehicle, has been developed by ENSA to meet the requirements of the Spanish Army and shares many common components with the BMR-600 infantry fighting vehicle. The VEC is also known as the Pegaso VEC 3562. The first of five prototypes was completed in 1977–78 with the total Spanish Army requirement being for 235 vehicles.

Description

The hull of the VEC is of all-welded aluminium construction providing protection over its frontal arc against 7.62 mm × 51 armour-piercing ammunition, and standard 7.62 mm × 51 rounds over the remainder of the vehicle. Some areas of the VEC have spaced armour protection.

The driver is seated at the front of the vehicle on the left side and has a single-piece hatch cover that opens to the right, in front of which are three periscopes for forward observation.

VEC Cavalry Scout Vehicle fitted with FIAT-OTO Melara turret

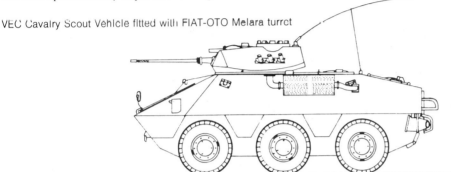

VEC Cavalry Scout Vehicle with all hatches open. This vehicle is fitted with FIAT-OTO Melara turret armed with 20 mm cannon, 7.62 mm coaxial machine gun and electrically-operated smoke dischargers.

VEC Cavalry Scout Vehicle fitted with Oerlikon-Bührle one-man
turret armed with 25 mm cannon and 7.62 mm MG

The centre periscope can be replaced by an infra-red or
image intensification periscope for night driving.

The turret is in the centre of the vehicle, between the first
and second axles. A variety of turret installations can be fitted
including the same turret as fitted to the Italian FIAT-OTO
Melara type 6616 (4 × 4) armoured car which is fully
described previously, or an Oerlikon-Bührle model GBD-
COA (25 mm) or GAD-BOA (20 mm).

The GBD-COA is a one-man manually operated turret
armed with a 25 mm Oerlikon cannon type KBA-B with 120
rounds of HE and 80 rounds of APDS-T ammunition and a
7.62 mm machine gun. The weapons have an elevation of
+52 degrees and a depression of −12 degrees with turret
traverse a full 360 degrees.

The GAD-BOA is of a similar design to the GBD-COA but
is armed with a 20 mm KAA cannon with 250 rounds of
ready use ammunition and a coaxial 7.62 mm machine gun
with 300 rounds of ready use ammunition.

The engine compartment is to the rear of the vehicle on the
left side with air inlet and outlet louvres in the roof, silencer
on the left side of the hull and a door in the rear of the hull on
the left side.

In the hull to the rear of the turret on the right side is a seat
for the fourth crew member and above this is a single-piece
hatch cover opening to the right with a periscope in the hull
roof. The fifth crew member is seated at the very rear on the
right side and has a single-piece hatch cover that opens to the
rear and three periscopes for observation. There is also a door
in the hull rear on the right side.

SPECIFICATIONS

CREW	5	MAX ROAD SPEED		TORQUE CONVERTER	
CONFIGURATION	6 × 6	(1st gear position,		AND HYDRAULIC	
COMBAT WEIGHT	13 750 kg	1 gear)	17 km/h	RETARDER	ZF
WEIGHT ON FRONT		(2nd gear position,		TYRES	13.00 × 20
AXLE (loaded)	5000 kg	1, 2, 3, 4 gear)	56 km/h	STEERING	hydraulic, power assisted on
WEIGHT ON CENTRE		(3rd gear position,			first and third axles
AXLE (loaded)	4450 kg	1, 2, 3, 4, 5 gear)	69 km/h	SUSPENSION	independent each wheel,
WEIGHT ON REAR		(4th gear position,			MacPhearson type,
AXLE (loaded)	4300 kg	2, 3, 4, 5, 6 gear)	100 km/h		hydro-pneumatic
POWER-TO-WEIGHT		(reverse)	12 km/h		
RATIO	22.25 hp/tonne	FUEL CAPACITY	300 litres	BRAKES	
LENGTH	6.25 m	MAX RANGE ROAD	800 km	(main)	disc, hydraulic, dual circuit,
WIDTH	2.5 m	GRADIENT	60%		air assisted on all wheels
HEIGHT (hull top)	2 m	SIDE SLOPE	30%	(parking)	disc, operating on propeller
GROUND CLEARANCE	0.4 m	TURNING RADIUS	7.5 m		transmission
TRACK	2.08 m	ENGINE	Pegaso model 9157/8	(emergency)	hydraulic, air operated MGM
WHEELBASE	1.65 m + 1.65 m		6-cylinder in-line		chambers
ANGLE OF APPROACH/			turbo-charged diesel	ELECTRICAL SYSTEM	24 V
DEPARTURE	50°/45°		developing 306 hp at	BATTERIES	2 × 12 V, 150 Ah
			2200 rpm		
		TRANSMISSION	ZF 6 HP 500, fully automatic,		
			6 forward and 1 reverse gears		

Status: Production. In service with the Spanish Army.

Manufacturer: ENSA, Military Division, Av Aragón, 402
Madrid 22, Spain

All three axles are of Pegaso design and manufacture and are of the double reduction type with self-locking differentials. Suspension is of the hydro-pneumatic type that allows the driver to alter the ground clearance to suit the type of ground being crossed. It has four positions: cross country, high, road and minimum. The suspension can be adjusted longitudinally and transversely and individual road wheels can be raised off the ground if required. Steering is power assisted on the front and rear axles.

Standard equipment includes tool set, 4500 kg winch, semi-automatic fire-extinguishing system protecting the engine and transmission and two 5 kg portable fire extinguishers.

Optional equipment includes an NBC system, water-jet propulsion system (one unit either side of the hull at the rear and a trim vane that folds back onto the glacis plate), 14.00 × 20 tyres, run-flat tyres and an air-conditioning system.

Variants

The VEC can also be used in the anti-aircraft role (guns or missiles) and the anti-tank role with ATGWs.

SWITZERLAND

MOWAG Shark Weapons Carrier

Development

The Shark has been developed by the MOWAG company as a private venture specifically for the export market. It was first shown in public at the 1981 Paris Air Show fitted with the Oerlikon-Bührle Type GDD-BOE two-man turret armed with a 35 mm cannon and a coaxial 7.62 mm machine gun. A further two prototypes were completed in mid-1983.

In 1982 the Shark was successfully tested in Switzerland fitted with a French Fives-Cail Babcock FL-12 turret armed with a 105 mm gun and fitted with a SOPTAC fire-control system. In West Germany it was successfully tested with an experimental Rheinmetall turret armed with the Rheinmetall 105 mm Rh 105-11 super low recoil gun which fires all standard NATO tank ammunition, including the APFSDS-T.

The chassis has been designed to be easily adapted for a wide range of roles including anti-aircraft (eg fitted with the same turret as the Wildcat twin 30 mm SPAAG or the new

MOWAG (8 × 8) Shark weapons carrier fitted with Fives-Cail Babcock FL-12 turret armed with 105 mm gun, with turret traversed to rear

MOWAG (8 × 8) Shark weapons carrier fitted with Fives-Cail Babcock FL-12 turret armed with 105 mm gun, with empty cartridge case being ejected out of trap door in turret bustle

Swiss ADATS missile system), anti-tank (including missile), fire support, reconnaissance and rocket launcher. Late in 1983 one of the three Shark prototypes was fitted with the one-man turret of the Wildcat twin 30 mm SPAAG system and this was tested in Canada early in 1984.

Wherever possible proven assemblies, such as engine and transmission, have been used in the design of the vehicle to simplify both training and logistics.

Description

The hull of the MOWAG Shark is of all-welded steel construction which provides complete protection up to and including the Soviet 14.5 mm KPV armour piercing round. A 155 mm HE projectile landing ten metres away from the vehicle will cause no damage according to the manufacturer.

The driver is seated at the front of the hull on the left side and has a single-piece hatch cover that opens to the left. Forward of this are three periscopes, the centre one of which can be replaced by an image intensification periscope for driving at night. A second crew member can be seated to the right of the driver or this space can be used for special equipment such as an NBC pack or for additional ammunition stowage.

The fighting compartment is in the centre of the vehicle and a wide range of armament installations can be fitted up to and including an FL-12 turret with a 105 mm gun. Full details of the FL-12 turret are given in the entry for the

MOWAG (8 × 8) Shark weapons carrier fitted with Fives-Cail Babcock FL-12 turret armed with 105 mm gun, coaxial 7.62 mm MG and electrically operated smoke dischargers

MOWAG (8 × 8) Shark weapons carrier fitted with trials turret armed with Rheinmetall Rh 105-11 super low recoil gun fitted with muzzle brake

Austrian Steyr-Daimler-Puch Jagdpanzer SK 105 light tank/tank detroyer.

The engine, transmission and fuel tanks are at the rear of the hull and engine access panels are provided in the top of the engine compartment. The air inlet louvres are in the top of the hull, one either side, while the air outlets at the hull rear.

Steering is power assisted on the front and rear axles and vertical suspension travel is 420 mm.

A wide range of optional equipment can be fitted to the Shark including various types of NBC system, passive night vision equipment and fire-extinguishing systems.

SPECIFICATIONS

CREW	3 or 4	MAX ROAD SPEED	100 km/h	SUSPENSION	
CONFIGURATION	8 × 8	FUEL CAPACITY	400 litres	(1st and 4th axles)	coil springs with
WEIGHT		RANGE (road)	500 km		wishbone
(loaded)	21 000 kg*	FORDING	1.3 m	(2nd and 3rd axles)	torsion bars
(empty)	16 000 kg*	GRADIENT	60%	(all wheels have hydraulic shock absorbers)
POWER-TO-WEIGHT		SIDE SLOPE	35%	BRAKES	
RATIO	25.2 hp/tonne	VERTICAL OBSTACLE	0.46 m	(main)	dual circuit, hydraulic,
LENGTH	7.52 m	TRENCH	2.3 m		air assisted
WIDTH	3 m	TURNING CIRCLE	12.5 m	(parking)	spring loaded
HEIGHT (hull)	1.9 m	ENGINE	Detroit Diesel 8V-71T		brake cylinder
AXIS OF FIRE			turbo-charged diesel	(engine)	Jacobs brake
(105 mm gun)	2.16 m		developing 530 hp at		system
GROUND CLEARANCE	0.46 m		2500 rpm	ELECTRICAL SYSTEM	24 V
TRACK	2.62 m	TRANSMISSION	Allison HT 750 DRD		
WHEELBASE	1.51 m + 1.4 m +		automatic with 5	* depends on armament installation
	1.49 m		forward and 1 reverse		
ANGLE OF APPROACH/			gears		
DEPARTURE	40°/45°	TYRES	13.00 × 20 run-flat		
			(insert)		

Status: Trials.

Manufacturer: MOWAG Motorwagenfabrik AG, 8280 Kreuzlingen, Switzerland.

MOWAG SPY Reconnaissance Vehicle

Development

The SPY reconnaissance vehicle was developed as a private venture by the MOWAG company specifically for the export market; the first prototypes were completed in 1980. Drive train components, pressure, hydraulic and electrical components of the SPY are also used in the MOWAG Piranha range of 4 × 4, 6 × 6 and 8 × 8 armoured vehicles.

In 1982 it was announced that an undisclosed Far Eastern country had placed an order for between 20 and 50 SPYs fitted with a MOWAG designed one-man turret armed with a 12.7 mm and a 7.62 mm machine gun.

Description

The hull of the SPY is made of all-welded steel and gives complete protection against small arms fire up to 7.62 mm AP calibre over the front, sides and rear, against anti-personnel mines exploding under the hull and against shell splinters above the hull.

The driver is seated at the front of the hull on the left with the commander immediately behind him. The driver has a single-piece hatch cover and three periscopes for forward observation, the centre one of which can be replaced by an infra-red or image intensification periscope for night driving. The commander has a cupola mounted on a plinth above the roof to give observation over the driver. The cupola has a single-piece hatch cover and a periscope. In the side of the hull behind the commander is a small door that opens forwards.

The engine compartment is to the right of the driver with the air-inlet and air-outlets in the roof and the exhaust pipe alongside the right side of the hull.

A variety of armament installations can be mounted at the rear of the hull including the MOWAG Type V 041 and Type V 042 turrets. The former is armed with a remote-controlled 12.7 mm M2 HB machine gun with an elevation of +45 degrees, depression of −8 degrees and turret traverse of 360 degrees. Turret traverse and weapon elevation is manual, with 100 rounds of ready use ammunition being provided. The gunner aims the machine gun with a roof-mounted PERI Z12 sight with a magnification of ×1 and either side of this is a periscope for lateral observation.

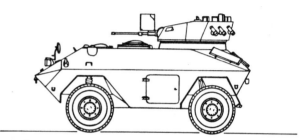

MOWAG SPY reconnaissance vehicle fitted with Type V 041 one-man turret armed with 12·7 mm and 7·62 mm MGs

MOWAG SPY reconnaissance vehicle fitted with MOWAG designed Type V 042 turret with remote controlled 12.7 mm machine gun and three smoke dischargers either side

The Type V 042 turret is armed with a 12.7 mm and a 7.62 mm machine gun with an elevation of +50 degrees, depression of −10 degrees and turret traverse of 360 degrees. Turret traverse and weapon elevation is manual with 200 rounds of 12.7 mm and 500 rounds of 7.62 mm ammunition being carried for ready use. The gunner aims the weapons via a PERI Z11 sight with a magnification of ×2 and ×6 and also has seven periscopes for all-round visibility.

All four wheels have independent suspension and the front axle can be disengaged for road driving. Automatic locking differentials and run-flat core tyres are fitted as standard.

Optional equipment includes various radio installations and an air-conditioning system.

SPECIFICATIONS

CREW	3	RANGE (road)	700 km	TYRES	11.00 × 16
CONFIGURATION	4 × 4	FORDING	1.3 m	BRAKES	dual circuit, hydraulic, air assisted
COMBAT WEIGHT	7500 kg	GRADIENT	60%		
UNLOADED WEIGHT	5900 kg	SIDE SLOPE	35%	ELECTRICAL SYSTEM	24 V
POWER-TO-WEIGHT		VERTICAL OBSTACLE	0.5 m	ARMAMENT	
RATIO	27 hp/tonne	TURNING RADIUS	6.3 m	(main)	1 × 12.7 mm MG
LENGTH	4.52 m	ENGINE	Detroit Diesel V-8	(coaxial)	1 × 7.62 mm MG
WIDTH	2.5 m		developing 205 hp	(smoke dischargers)	2 × 3
HEIGHT (hull)	1.66 m		at 3000 rpm	AMMUNITION	
GROUND CLEARANCE		TRANSMISSION	Allison AT-540 auto-	(12.7 mm)	3000
(hull)	0.5 m		matic, 4 forward and	(7.62 mm)	2000
(axles)	0.39 m		1 reverse gears	(smoke grenades)	20
TRACK		TRANSFER CASE	2-speed	FIRE-CONTROL SYSTEM	
(front)	2.18 m	SUSPENSION		Turret traverse	360°/manual
(rear)	2.205 m	(front)	coil spring and	Gun elevation/	
WHEELBASE	2.5 m		wishbone	depression	+50°/−10°
ANGLE OF APPROACH/		(rear)	torsion bars	GUN STABILISER	
DEPARTURE	50°/70°		all wheels have	(vertical)	no
MAX ROAD SPEED	110 km/h		hydraulic shock	(horizontal)	no
FUEL CAPACITY	200 litres		absorbers		

Status: Production. In service with an undisclosed country.

Manufacturer: MOWAG Motorwagenfabrik AG, 8280 Kreuzlingen, Switzerland.

TAIWAN

Type 64 Light Tank

Development/Description

In the early 1970s Taiwan began design work on a vehicle based on the American M41 light tank. The first prototype was a copy of the M41 but with further modifications it was standardised in 1975 as the Type 64 Light Tank. Recent information has indicated that it was not produced on a large scale and that many Type 64s were in fact conversions of the original American M41.

The Type 64 is similar to the M41A2/M41A3 in automotive and mechanical details and has the same dimensions, chassis, engine and transmission but an improved electrical system. The hull is of all-welded construction as in the M41 but incorporates advanced welding techniques in its manufacture and uses a new high-hardness alloy steel. The all-cast turret has the same layout as the original M41 although slight alterations have been made to suit the medium stature of the Chinese tank crews. An additional layer of laminated high-hardness alloy steel armour plate is bolted/welded onto the hull and turret sides to provide greater protection against HEAT and APDS projectiles.

The Type 64 is armed with a 76 mm gun as in the M41 but made in Taiwan and claimed to have a performance superior to the M32 gun. A 7.62 mm machine gun is mounted coaxially wih the main armament and a 12.7 mm MG is mounted at the commander's station for use in the anti-aircraft role. Both of these weapons are made in Taiwan and the coaxial weapon probably resembles a modified version of the American M60.

Chinese sources state that the Type 64 has an improved fire-control system. Ammunition stowage is probably identical to that of the M41A2/M41A3.

Later Type 64 tanks may incorporate laser rangefinders, ballistic computers and passive night vision equipment. All of these have been developed by the Sun Yat-sen Scientific Research Institute of Taiwan. It is reported that some consideration is being given to replacing the 76 mm gun.

The Type 64 has the same mobility, agility and range characteristics as the M41 but in view of its additional armour is probably heavier. Like the M41 it can be fitted for deep fording, but it is not amphibious and has no NBC system. It is fitted with IR driving lights and improved Taiwan-built communications equipment.

Status: In service with Taiwan. Possibly still in production. Improvement and modernisation programmes may be continuing.

Manufacturer: Fighting Vehicles Command, ROC Army, Taichung, Taiwan. Development by Fighting Vehicles Development Center, ROC Army, Taichung, Taiwan 400.

PT-76 Light Amphibious Tank

Development

The PT-76 light amphibious tank, designed by the Zh Ya Kotin design team of heavy tank fame was introduced into service in 1952. In many Soviet units it has been replaced by MBTs such as the T-54, T-55, T-62 or T-72, or BMPs.

The tank has been used in combat in Africa, the Middle East, during the Indo-Pakistan conflict and widely used in Viet-Nam by both the North Vietnamese Army and the Viet Cong. The main drawbacks of the PT-76 are its large size necessitated by the requirement to be amphibious, lack of NBC or night fighting equipment and very thin armour that can be penetrated even by heavy machine gun fire. It does

have an excellent amphibious capability and is also used by the Soviet Marines.

The chassis of the PT-76 has been used as the basis for a complete family of armoured and unarmoured vehicles including the ASU-85 self-propelled anti-tank gun, BTR-50 and OT-62 (Czechoslovak) armoured personnel carriers, FROG-2, FROG-3, FROG-4 and FROG-5 surface-to-surface missile systems, GT-T and MT-L tracked over-snow vehicles, GSP heavy amphibious ferry, Pinguin (on BTR-50 chassis) over-snow vehicle, PVA amphibious crawler tractor, SAM-6 surface-to-air missile launcher and its associated radar vehicle, ZSU-23-4 self-propelled anti-aircraft gun system and the 122 mm self-propelled M1974 howitzer.

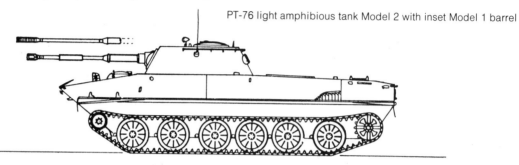

PT-76 light amphibious tank Model 2 with inset Model 1 barrel

PT-76 light amphibious tank Model 2 at Fort Irwin, California, showing modified turret rear and waterjet outlets with covers closed (Donald C Spaulding)

Egyptian PT-76 Model 2 captured by Israel in the 1973 Middle East campaign (Israeli Ministry of Defence)

Description

The hull of the PT-76 is welded steel and is divided into three compartments with the driver at the front, fighting compartment in the centre and the engine at the rear. The driver is seated in the centre of the hull and is provided with a single-piece hatch cover that swings to the right. Three periscopes are mounted forward of his hatch cover; the centre one can be raised to enable the driver to see over the front of the vehicle when the trim vane is erected.

The turret is all-welded steel, with the commander, who also acts as the gunner, being seated on the left and the loader on the right. The turret has an oval-shaped hatch cover that hinges forwards and can be locked vertical. Mounted in the left side of the hatch cover is a circular cupola for the commander which houses three integral periscopes and can be traversed through 360 degrees by hand. The commander is provided with an optical TSh-66 sight mounted to the left of the main armament and the loader has a periscope mounted in the turret roof, forward of the hatch cover.

The engine compartment is at the rear and the Model V-6 engine used in the PT-76 is one bank of that fitted to the T-54 MBT. As the tank operates in a very cold climate an engine pre-heater is fitted as standard.

The manual gearbox has five forward and one reverse gears and steering is of the clutch and brake type.

The torsion bar suspension consists of six road wheels with the idler at the front and the drive sprocket at the rear. The first and sixth road wheel stations have hydraulic shock absorbers and the steel tracks each have 96 links when new. Tracks are steel with single dry pin.

The PT-76 is fully amphibious, being propelled in the water by two water jets mounted at the rear of the hull. The only preparation required before entering the water is to erect the trim vane at the front of the hull and switch on the two electric bilge pumps. A manual bilge pump is provided for emergency use. Steering is accomplished by opening and closing the two hatches over the rear water jets: to go left the left water jet is covered up and to turn left through 180 degrees the left water jet sucks in water while the right water jet pushes it out.

The PT-76 is not fitted with an NBC system although there is a ventilator mounted in the turret rear and many vehicles

PT-76 Model 2 fitted with snorkel to rear of turret coming ashore

PT-76 Model 2 without trim vane erected swimming across a river during training (TASS)

PT-76 Model 2s show their amphibious capabilities. Note snorkel attached to turret rear (TASS)

used by marines have been fitted with a snorkel extension piece to this ventilator which often sucked exhaust gases into the fighting compartment. To increase the PT-76's operational range additional fuel tanks can be fitted; these can be of the drum type or flat type as fitted to one side of the T-54/T-55 MBT. A white light searchlight is mounted on the right side of the turret (some models have an infra-red searchlight on the turret) and one of the driving lights may be infra-red. When being used by the Soviet Marines the vehicle is often fitted with a complete set of navigation lights.

The main armament of the PT-76 is the D-56T gun which is a development of the gun used in the T-34/76 and KV-1 tanks during the Second World War. The gun has a semi-automatic vertical sliding wedge breech-block, hydraulic buffer and a hydro-pneumatic recuperator. The gun is 42 calibres long and has an overall length of 3.455 metres and weighs 1150 kg. The gun has a maximum rate of fire of between six and eight rounds per minute, maximum range in the indirect fire role of between 12 000 and 13 290 metres, and can fire the following types of fixed ammunition:

Other types of projectiles are also available, some with cartridges with reduced propellant charges, for HE-FRAG and AP-T projectiles.

A 7.62 mm SGMT machine gun is mounted coaxially to the right of the main armament. Many PT-76s have been fitted with 12.7 mm DShKM anti-aircraft machine guns.

Variants

Model 1 with the D-56T gun with a multi-slotted muzzle brake and no bore evacuator. This model has not been observed for some years.

Model 2 with D-56T gun with double-baffle muzzle brake and a bore evacuator towards the muzzle.

Model 3 is similar to Model 2 but has no bore evacuator. It was probably the Model 2 with the bore evacuator removed. Model 4 with the fully-stabilised gun designated the D-56TM is known as the PT-76B.

It is believed that all current PT-76 Model 2s used by the Warsaw Pact have been fitted with a stabilisation system.

AMMUNITION TYPE	AP-T	API-T	HE-FRAG	HEAT‡	HVAP-T
PROJECTILE DESIGNATION	BR-350*	BZR-350B	OF-350†	BP-350M	BR-354P
FUZE MODEL	MD-5	MD-5	KTM-1	BM	n/app
WEIGHT OF PROJECTILE	6.5 kg	6.48 kg	6.2 kg	3.94 kg	2.98 kg
WEIGHT OF BURSTING CHARGE	0.15 kg	0.11 kg	0.712 kg	0.51 kg	n/app
TYPE OF BURSTING CHARGE	TNT	TNT	TNT	RDX/TNT	n/app
MUZZLE VELOCITY	655 m/s	655 m/s	680 m/s	325 m/s	950 m/s
ARMOUR PENETRATION AT 0°	61 mm/1000 m 69 mm/500 m	61 mm/1000 m	n/app	120 mm/at any range	58 mm/1000 m 92 mm/500 m

* later types are BR-350A and BR-350B
† later type is OF-350A
‡ Second World War. Possibly replaced by improved model

CREW	3	
COMBAT WEIGHT	14 000 kg	
POWER-TO-WEIGHT		
RATIO	17.1 hp/tonne	
GROUND PRESSURE	0.479 kg/cm²	
LENGTH GUN		
FORWARDS	7.625 m	
LENGTH HULL	6.91 m	
WIDTH	3.14 m	
HEIGHT OVERALL		
(late model)	2.255 m	
(early model)	2.195 m	
FIRING HEIGHT	1.82 m	
GROUND CLEARANCE	0.37 m	
TRACK	2.74 m	
TRACK WIDTH	360 mm	
LENGTH OF TRACK		
ON GROUND	4.08 m	
MAX SPEED		
(road)	44 km/h	
(water)	10 km/h	
FUEL CAPACITY	250 litres	
MAX RANGE		
(road)	260 km	
(water)	65 km	

FUEL CONSUMPTION	0.96 litre/km	
FORDING	amphibious	
GRADIENT	70%	
VERTICAL OBSTACLE	1.1 m	
TRENCH	2.8 m	
TURNING RADIUS	skid turns	
ENGINE	Model V-6 6-cylinder	
	in-line water-cooled	
	diesel developing	
	240 hp at 1800 rpm	
AUXILIARY ENGINE	none	
TRANSMISSION	manual with 4 forward	
	and 1 reverse gears	
STEERING	clutch and brake	
SUSPENSION	torsion bar	
ELECTRICAL SYSTEM	24 V	
BATTERIES	2 × 12 V, 100 Ah	
	each	
ARMAMENT		
(main)	1 × 76.2 mm gun	
(coaxial)	1 × 7.62 mm MG	
SMOKE-LAYING		
EQUIPMENT	diesel fuel injected	
	into exhaust system	
AMMUNITION		
(main)	40	
(MG)	1000	

FIRE-CONTROL SYSTEM		
Turret power control	manual or electric	
By commander	yes	
Max rate of power		
traverse	360°/21 s	
Gun elevation/		
depression	+30°/−4°	
Gun stabiliser		
(vertical)	only on PT-76B	
(horizontal)	only on PT-76B	
ARMOUR		
Hull front upper	11 mm at 80°	
Hull front lower	14 mm at 45°	
Hull side upper	14 mm at 0°	
Hull side lower	14 mm at 0°	
Hull rear upper	7 mm at 0°	
Hull rear lower	7 mm at 45°	
Hull top	7 mm	
Hull belly front	5 mm	
Hull belly rear	5 mm	
Turret front	17 mm at 35°	
Turret sides	16 mm at 35°	
Turret rear	11 mm at 35°	
Turret top	8 mm	

Status: Production complete. In service with Afghanistan, Angola, China, Congo, Cuba, Egypt, Equatorial Guinea, Finland, East Germany, Guinea, Guinea-Bissau, Hungary, India, Indonesia, Iraq, Israel, Madagascar, Mozambique, North Korea, Laos, Pakistan, Poland, USSR (Army and Marines), Viet-Nam and Yugoslavia. China manufactures a similar vehicle called the Type 63 light tank with a similar hull but fitted with a new turret armed with an 85 mm gun. There is a separate entry for this tank.

Manufacturer: Soviet state arsenals.

BRDM-2 Amphibious Scout Car

Development

The BRDM-2 was developed in the early 1960s as the successor to the earlier BRDM-1 and was first seen in public during 1966. Main improvements over the earlier vehicles are its fully-enclosed armament installation, more powerful rear-mounted engine which gives it a higher road and cross-country performance and better water performance.

Each Soviet motorised rifle division has a total of 28 BRDM-2s, 12 in the reconnaissance battalion and four each in the tank regiment, BMP-equipped motorised rifle regiment and in each of the two BTR-60/BTR-70-equipped motorised rifle regiments. Each tank division has a total of 28 BRDM-2s, 12 in the reconnaissance battalion, four in the motorised rifle regiment and four in each of the three tank regiments.

BRDM-2 in travelling configuration with driver's and commander's hatches locked in open position. Note the turret has no roof hatch

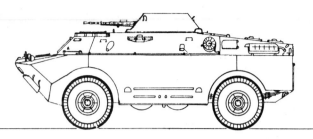

BRDM-2U command vehicle with roof mounted generator

Description

The all-welded steel armour hull of the BRDM-2 provides the crew with protection from small arms fire and shell splinters.

The driver is seated at the front of the hull on the left with the vehicle commander to his right. Both are provided with a bullet-proof windscreen to their front which is covered by an armoured shutter, hinged at the top, when the vehicle is in combat areas. When the shutters are in position the driver and commander observe the terrain through periscopes around the front and sides of their position, mounted level with the roof of the vehicle. The only means of entry to the BRDM-2 is by two circular roof hatches immediately behind the commander and driver, hinged towards the centre of the vehicle and opening only as far as the vertical.

The turret is mounted in the centre of the vehicle and is the same as that mounted on the Soviet BTR-60PB and Czechoslovak OT-64 Model 2A armoured personnel carriers.

There is a single firing port in each side of the hull and immediately behind it are three vision blocks which protrude from the outside of the hull to give a degree of vision to the front and rear of the vehicle.

BRDM-2 with Sagger ATGWs with missiles raised in ready to launch position

The engine compartment is at the rear of the hull and there are two air-inlet louvres in the forward part of the engine compartment roof and four smaller air-inlet louvres to the rear. The exhaust pipes are on either side of the hull.

On each side of the vehicle, between the front and rear wheels are two chain driven belly wheels, which are lowered by the driver and give the BRDM-2 improved cross-country performance and also allow it to cross ditches. A central tyre pressure regulation system allows the driver to adjust the tyre pressure to suit the type of ground being crossed.

The BRDM-2 is fully amphibious being propelled in the water by a single water jet at the rear of the hull. Before entering the water a trim vane which is stowed under the nose of the hull when travelling is erected at the front of the hull. When not in use the water jet outlet is covered by a triangular plate pivoted at the top.

The vehicle is fitted with an NBC system and its air inlet is on the top of the hull to the left rear of the turret. Standard equipment includes infra-red driving lights, an infra-red searchlight mounted over the commander's position which can be operated from within the vehicle, a winch mounted internally at the front of the hull, a radio and a land navigation system.

Armament consists of a 14.5 mm KPVT machine gun with a 7.62 mm PKT machine gun mounted coaxially to the right. A telescopic sight is mounted to the left of the main armament. The turret has manual traverse and is provided with an adjustable seat for the gunner. The KPVT machine gun fires an API projectile that weighs 64.4 grams which will penetrate 32 mm of armour at a range of 500 metres.

Variants

BRDM-2-RKh (Radiological-Chemical Reconnaissance Vehicle)

This is easily distinguishable from the basic vehicle by two rectangular racks which contain lane-marking poles with pennants on either side of the hull at the rear. The racks are

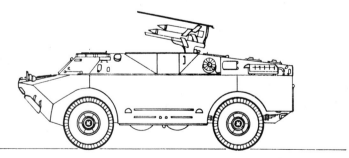

BRDM-2 with launching system for Sagger ATGWs raised and commander's and gunner's roof hatches open (Israeli Army)

BRDM-2 with Sagger ATGWs

This was first used in combat by the Egyptian and Syrian forces during the 1973 Middle East campaigns. It is a BRDM-2 with its turret removed and fitted with an arm on top of which are mounted six Sagger AT-3 ATGWs. When travelling they are within the hull but in action the arm is raised above the top of the hull complete with overhead armour protection. The missiles can be launched from within the vehicle or up to 80 metres away with the aid of a separa-

BRDM-2 with launcher for Sagger ATGWs raised but not fitted with missiles. Note belly wheels in lowered position and trim vane under nose of vehicle (US Army)

normally covered with a canvas cover and when required are swung through 90 degrees so that they are vertical over the rear of the vehicle. The poles are used to mark lanes through contaminated areas. Some of these versions lack the 14.5 mm KPV machine gun in the turret.

BRDM-2U Command Vehicle

This has its turret removed and replaced by a hatch that opens forwards. Mounted to the rear of this hatch is a generator used to power the additional communications equipment carried inside the vehicle. Two radio antennas are mounted one each side of the hull.

Hungarian Army BRDM-2 Saggers with launcher and missiles in ready to fire position

BRDM-2 on static display without armament but showing belly wheels lowered, commander's and driver's hatches open, armoured shutters over windscreens open and winch cover under nose open. This vehicle was captured by the South African Defence Force during Operation Protea in August 1981 (Terry J Gander)

tion sight. When launched from within the vehicle they are guided by the missile operator/vehicle commander who is seated at the front of the vehicle on the right side and is provided with a sight in the forward part of the hull. A total of eight missiles is carried in reserve and the radio antenna is at the rear on the right side rather than at the front. Full details of the missile are given in the following entry on the BRDM-1

vehicle. In 1977 it was reported that the Sagger was being converted from its normal wire command guidance system to a semi-automatic infra-red wire guidance system, which would increase the effectiveness of the missile at its maximum range of 3000 metres.

Each Soviet Motorised Rifle Division has 36 BRDM-2 vehicles armed with ATGWs, nine in the anti-tank battalion, nine in the BMP-equipped motorised rifle regiment and nine in each of the two motorised rifle regiments equipped with the BTR-60/BTR-70 series APCs. Each Soviet tank division has nine BRDM-2s armed with ATGWs in the BMP-equipped motorised rifle regiments.

BRDM-2 with Swatter-B ATGWs

This was first seen in 1973 and is similar in appearance to the BRDM-2 with the Sagger ATGW but has a quadruple launcher for the AT-2 ATGW converted from its original radio command-to-line-of-sight guidance to semi-active infra-red/command guidance. This missile weighs 29.48 kg and has a range of 3500 metres compared with the 3000 metres of the original Swatter. A total of eight Swatters is carried including the three in the ready to launch position. As far as is known the improved Swatter has not been fitted to the original BRDM-1 installation.

BRDM-2 with Spandrel ATGWs

Shown for the first time at the military parade held in Moscow in November 1977 was a BRDM-2 fitted with a turret on top of which were mounted five new ready to launch missiles

BRDM-2 with AT-5 Spandrel ATGWs in travelling configuration showing tracking sight forward and below launcher in roof of vehicle

SA-9 Gaskin SAM system based on BRDM-2 vehicle (TASS)

which have been given the NATO code name of Spandrel, or AT-5. This vehicle is sometimes referred to as the BRDM-3. To the rear of the turret in the top of the hull is a hatch which enables the launcher to be reloaded without the crew leaving the vehicle. It is estimated that in addition to the five visible missiles a further 10 are carried inside the hull. It is believed that it is the second-generation type (semi-automatic, command-to-line-of-sight) and that all the operator has to do is to keep the cross-hairs of his sight on the target to ensure a hit. The sight is in the roof of the vehicle on the right side and can be traversed through 180 degrees.

The HEAT warhead weighs about 7 kg and will penetrate between 500 mm and 600 mm of armour at an incidence of 0 degrees. The launch tube has a blow-out cap at the front and is flared at the rear. It is thought that a bowed hatch in the roof of the vehicle to the rear of the launcher is probably used to allow the mount to be folded into the hull for reloading purposes. Basic specifications of the AT-5 Spandrel ATGW are as follows:

LENGTH	1.3 m
DIAMETER	155 mm
MAX RANGE	4000 m
MIN RANGE	100 m
MAX FLIGHT TIME	about 20 seconds

In East Germany it has been observed that on the BRDM-2/AT-5 Spandrel vehicles, the outer launch position has been fitted with the AT-4 Spigot ATGW. This arrangement allows the carriage of an increased missile load, believed to be six AT-5 Spandrels plus eight AT-4 Spigots rather than two AT-5s.

SA-9 (Gaskin) System

This entered service with the Soviet Army in 1972 and is issued on the scale of four per Soviet Motorised Rifle Division and a similar number in each tank division, or a total of 16 per division.

BRDM-2 with AT-5 Spandrel ATGWs from above showing hatch behind launcher which is probably for reloading purposes

101

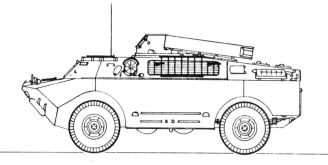

SA-9 Gaskin SAM system based on BRDM-2 chassis, with launching arms and missiles in travelling position

The system consists of a BRDM-2 with the turret removed and replaced by a new turret with four ready-to-launch missiles which are normally lowered to the horizontal alongside the turret when travelling to reduce the overall height of the vehicle. The missile itself is 1.829 metres long, can be fitted with an infra-red seeker and is believed to have an effective slant range of about 8000 metres and a maximum engagement altitude of 4000 metres. The system is capable of clear weather operations only. It is possible that a further two missiles in their launcher boxes are carried on the light steel gratings either side of the hull. These are loaded manually onto the launcher.

More recently some vehicles have been observed fitted with a Gun Dish radar in front of the turret to give the system all-weather capability. This radar is already installed on the ZSU-23-4 self-propelled anti-aircraft gun and is also known as the B-76. It has both target acquisition capabilities and can pick targets up at a maximum range of 20 km. It operates in the J-band and is equipped with an MTI facility and a computer.

Some SA-9 Gaskin SAM systems have been observed fitted with the Hat Box antenna pack either side of the turret and either side of the vehicle above the front road wheel. It is believed that this is a radar data link between the B-76 Gun Dish radar on the ZSU-23-4 self-propelled anti-aircraft gun system or with other divisional air defence radars.

SA-9 Gaskin SAM system on BRDM-2 vehicle with only two missiles in ready to launch position. Note the Hat Box antenna pack above front road wheel and on left side of missile launcher

BRDM-2 with turret removed as used by Israeli Army (Israeli Army)

Model	BRDM-2	BRDM-2 (Sagger)	Model	BRDM-2	BRDM-2 (Sagger)
CREW	4	2–3	TYRES	13.00 × 18	13.00 × 18
CONFIGURATION	4 × 4	4 × 4	ELECTRICAL SYSTEM	24 V	24 V
COMBAT WEIGHT	7000 kg	7000 kg	ARMAMENT		
POWER-TO-WEIGHT			(main)	1 × 14.5 mm MG	6 Sagger ATGWs
RATIO	20 hp/tonne	20 hp/tonne	(coaxial)	1 × 7.62 mm MG	n/app
LENGTH	5.75 m	5.75 m	AMMUNITION		
WIDTH	2.35 m	2.35 m	(main)	500	14 Saggers (total)
HEIGHT OVERALL	2.31 m	2.01 m	(coaxial)	2000	n/app
FIRING HEIGHT	2.13 m	n/app	FIRE-CONTROL SYSTEM		
GROUND CLEARANCE	0.43 m	0.43 m	Turret power control	manual	n/app
TRACK	1.84 m	1.84 m	Gun elevation/depression	+30°/−5°	n/app
WHEELBASE	3.1 m	3.1 m	ARMOUR (max)		
MAX SPEED			Hull front upper	5 mm at 80°	5 mm at 80°
(road)	100 km/h	100 km/h	Hull front lower	7 mm at 45°	7 mm at 45°
(water)	10 km/h	10 km/h	Hull nose plate	14 mm at 14°	14 mm at 14°
FUEL CAPACITY	290 litres	290 litres	Hull sides upper	7 mm at 18°	7 mm at 18°
MAX RANGE (road)	750 km	750 km	Hull sides lower	7 mm at 0°	7 mm at 0°
FUEL CONSUMPTION (road)	0.35 – 0.45 litre/km	0.35 – 0.45 litre/km	Hull rear upper	7 mm at 0°	7 mm at 0°
FORDING	amphibious	amphibious	Hull rear lower	7 mm at 0°	7 mm at 0°
GRADIENT	60%	60%	Hull top	7 mm at 0°	7 mm at 0°
VERTICAL OBSTACLE	0.4 m	0.4 m	Belly front	2 mm	2 mm
TRENCH	1.25 m	1.25 m	Belly rear	3 mm	3 mm
ENGINE	GAZ-41 V-8 water-cooled petrol developing 140 hp at 3400 rpm		Turret front	7 mm at 43°	n/app
TRANSMISSION	both have manual with 4 forward and 1 reverse gears		Turret sides	7 mm at 36°	n/app
SUSPENSION	semi-elliptical springs with hydraulic shock absorbers		Turret rear	7 mm at 36°	n/app
			Turret top	7 mm	n/app

Status: Probably still in production. In service with Algeria (including Sagger and SA-9), Angola (including SA-9), Benin, Bulgaria, Cape-Verde Islands, Central African Republic, Chad, Congo, East Germany (including Spandrel), Egypt (including Sagger), Equatorial Guinea, Ethiopia, Guinea, Guinea-Bissau, Hungary (Sagger and SA-9 only), Iraq (including Sagger and SA-9), Israel, Jibuti, Libya (including Sagger and SA-9), Madagascar, Malawi, Mali, Mozambique, Peru, Poland (including Sagger and SA-9), Romania (including Sagger), Sao-Tome Principe, Seychelles, Somalia, Sudan, Syria (including Sagger and SA-9), Tanzania, USSR (including all variants), Viet-Nam (including SA-9), Yemen, People's Democratic Republic (South) (including SA-9), Yugoslavia (Sagger and SA-9), Zambia and Zimbabwe.

BRDM-1 Amphibious Scout Car

Development

The BRDM-1 amphibious scout car first appeared in the spring of 1959 and was subsequently issued to most members of the Warsaw Pact. Czechoslovakia and Poland also use the Hungarian-designed FUG which is designed to fulfil a similar role to the BRDM-1 but has its engine at the rear rather than the front as in the case of the BRDM-1. In most Soviet front-line units the BRDM-1 has now been replaced by the BRDM-2 which has a higher road speed and is fitted with a turret armed with a 14.5 mm and a 7.62 mm machine gun rather than weapons on unprotected mounts as fitted to the BRDM-1.

Description

The hull of the BRDM-1 is made of all-welded steel with the engine at the front and the crew compartment at the rear. The driver is seated at the front of the vehicle on the left with the commander to his right. Both are provided with a hatch to their front that is hinged at the top and opens forwards, and a windscreen with a wiper blade. The hatch cover has a vision block for when the hatch is closed. A vision slit protected by a vision block is provided to the left of the driver and right of the commander. There are two firing ports in each side of the hull and two large hatches in the forward part of the roof that open to the rear. The rear of the crew compartment slopes at an angle of about 30 degrees and is fitted with a two-piece hatch that opens either side of the superstructure. There is a firing port in each hatch.

On either side of the vehicle, between the front and rear wheels, are two belly wheels, which are lowered by the driver and give the BRDM-1 improved cross-country performance and also allow it to cross ditches. The BRDM-1 is fully

Basic BRDM-1 amphibious scout car armed with 12.7 mm DShKM machine gun

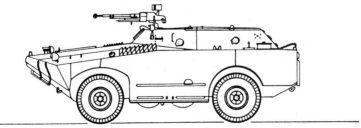

Two BRDM-1s fording armed with 7.62 mm machine gun and showing trim vane erected at front of hull

amphibious being propelled in the water by a single water jet at the rear of the hull. Before entering the water a trim board, which is stowed folded under the nose of the vehicle when not in use, is erected at the front of the hull. Standard equipment includes a system that allows the driver to adjust the tyre pressures to suit the type of ground being crossed. The vehicle is not fitted with an NBC system and when introduced was not fitted with any night vision equipment. A white light searchlight mounted on the left side of the hull is operated by the driver. A communications reel and wire is mounted on the left side of the superstructure towards the rear.

The vehicle is normally armed with a 7.62 mm SGMB machine gun pintle-mounted on the forward part of the roof, which has a limited traverse of 45 degrees left and right and can be elevated from −6 to +23.5 degrees. Some vehicles are fitted with a 12.7 mm DShKM heavy machine gun mounted at the forward part of the roof with a 7.62 mm SGMB machine gun being mounted at the rear.

Variants

Command Vehicle (BRDM-U)
This can be distinguished from the basic vehicle as it has a radio antenna on each side of the hull and two radio antennas at the rear whereas the basic vehicle has only a single radio antenna on the right side of the hull.

Radiological-Chemical Reconnaissance Vehicle (BRDM-RKh)
This is easily distinguishable from the basic vehicle as on either side of the hull at the rear of the vehicle are two rectangular racks which contain lane marking poles with pennants. The racks are normally covered with a canvas

BRDM-1 command vehicle with antenna erected

BRDM-1 with Snapper ATGWs raised ready to launch

cover and when required are swung through 90 degrees so that they are vertical over the rear of the vehicle. The poles are used to mark lanes through contaminated areas.

BRDM-1 with Snapper ATGWs

This system is basically a BRDM-1 vehicle with its superstructure extended to the rear of the hull and carrying a triple launcher for the Snapper AT-1 ATGW. The Soviet designation for the Snapper is the 3M6 or Shmel. The missiles are mounted under the launcher arms and before the launcher can be raised into the open the four hatch covers over the missile compartment are swung clear, two to either side of the hull. The missiles can be launched from within the vehicle or away from it with the aid of a separation sight. Spare missiles carried within the vehicle have to be loaded from outside. As far as it is known this model is no longer in front-line service

AT-2a Swatter ATGW as carried in the BRDM-1 (Snapper) ATGW vehicle (US Department of Defense)

BRDM-1 with Swatter ATGWs in raised position ready for launching (US Department of Defense)

Close-up of Swatter ATGW launcher on BRDM-1 vehicle (US Department of Defense)

Basic man-portable version of the Sagger with sight and joystick controller on left and missile on right (US Department of Defense)

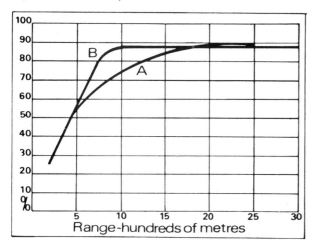

First-round hit probability of Snapper (A) and Sagger (B) ATGWs from stationary vehicle at stationary target

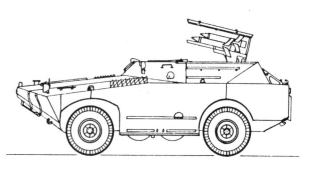

BRDM-1 armed with six ready to launch Sagger ATGWs

BRDM-1 with Sagger ATGWs raised ready to launch (US Department of Defense)

with the Soviet Union. Details of the missile are given in the specifications table.

BRDM-1 with Swatter ATGWs

This model is similar to the previous model but has a quadruple rather than a triple launcher with the missiles being mounted above the long launcher rails. In addition to the hatch covers that open either side of the vehicle there is also a cover that opens to the rear of the launcher. This model has been seen in service only with Soviet units. Details of the missile are given in the specifications table.

BRDM-1 with Sagger ATGWs

This model was first seen during a parade held in Moscow in May 1965 and differs from the other models in that the sextuple launcher is raised into the launch position complete with the overhead cover. The missiles can be launched from inside the vehicle or up to 80 metres away from it with the aid of a separation sight. Details of the missile are given in the specifications table. The Soviet designation for the Sagger is the 9M14M or Malyutka. The basic vehicle is called the 2P27 by the Soviets.

SPECIFICATIONS

Model	BRDM-1	BRDM-1 (Snapper)	BRDM-1 (Swatter)	BRDM-1 (Sagger)
CREW	5	2–3	2–3	2–3
CONFIGURATION	4 × 4	4 × 4	4 × 4	4 × 4
UNLOADED WEIGHT	5600 kg	5600 kg	5600 kg	5600 kg
LENGTH	5.7 m	5.7 m	5.7 m	5.7 m
WIDTH	2.25 m	2.25 m	2.25 m	2.25 m
HEIGHT*	1.9 m	1.9 m	2 m	2 m
GROUND CLEARANCE	0.315 m	0.315 m	0.315 m	0.315 m .
TRACK	1.6 m	1.6 m	1.6 m	1.6 m
WHEELBASE	2.8 m	2.8 m	2.8 m	2.8 m
MAX SPEED				
(road)	80 km/h	80 km/h	80 km/h	80 km/h
(water)	9 km/h	9 km/h	9 km/h	9 km/h
FUEL CAPACITY	150 litres	150 litres	150 litres	150 litres
MAX CRUISING RANGE				
(road)	500 km	500 km	500 km	500 km
FUEL CONSUMPTION	0.3 litre/km	0.3 litre/km	0.3 litre/km	0.3 litre/km
FORDING	amphibious	amphibious	amphibious	amphibious
GRADIENT	60%	60%	60%	60%
VERTICAL OBSTACLE	0.4 m	0.4 m	0.4 m	0.4 m
TRENCH	1.22 m	1.22 m	1.22 m	1.22 m
ENGINE	GAZ-40P 6-cylinder in-line petrol, water-cooled developing 90 hp at 3400 rpm			
TRANSMISSION	manual with 4 forward and 1 reverse gears			
TRANSFER CASE	2-speed	2-speed	2-speed	2-speed
CLUTCH	single dry plate for all models			
SUSPENSION	semi-elliptical springs and hydraulic shock absorbers			

Model	BRDM-1	BRDM-1 (Snapper)	BRDM-1 (Swatter)	BRDM-1 (Sagger)
TYRES	12.00 × 18	12.00 × 18	12.00 × 18	12.00 × 18
ELECTRICAL SYSTEM	24 V	24 V	24 V	24 V
ARMAMENT (main)	1 × 7.62 mm MG	Snapper ATGW	Swatter ATGW	Sagger ATGW
AMMUNITION	1250	n/app	n/app	n/app
READY TO LAUNCH MISSILES	n/app	3	4	6
ARMOUR (max)	10 mm	10 mm	10 mm	10 mm

* Without armament (BRDM-1), with missiles retracted (BRDM-1 ATGW)

	BRDM-1 (Snapper)	BRDM-1 (Swatter)	BRDM-1 (Sagger)
NATO name	Snapper	Swatter	Sagger
NATO designation	AT-1	AT-2a	AT-3
WEIGHT	24.26 kg	29.48 kg	11.29 kg
LENGTH	1.148 m	1.163 m	0.863 m
DIAMETER	134 mm	132 mm	119 mm
RANGE			
(minimum)	500 m	500 m	500 m
(maximum)	2500 m	3000 m	3000 m
GUIDANCE	wire	radio	wire
FLIGHT TIME TO MAX RANGE	19 s	23 s	27 s
AVERAGE VELOCITY	105 m/s	150 m/s	120 m/s
WARHEAD	HEAT	HEAT	HEAT
ARMOUR PENETRATION 0°	380 mm	510 mm	410 mm

Status: Production complete. In service with Albania, Algeria, Angola, Bulgaria, Congo, Cuba, Czechoslovakia, Ethiopia, East Germany, Guinea, Mozambique, Poland, Romania, USSR, Yugoslavia and Zambia.

Manufacturer: Soviet state arsenals.

UNITED KINGDOM

Alvis Saladin Armoured Car

Development

In January 1946 the British Army issued a requirement for a new armoured car as a replacement for the Daimler Mk II and AEC Mk III armoured cars which were developed during the Second World War. Design work on this new vehicle, called the FV601(A), began in the same year at the Fighting Vehicles Design Department (later to become the FVRDE and now the MVEE). In many respects the vehicle is very similar to the American M38 (T38) Chevrolet Wolfhound (6 × 6) armoured car which was built only in very small numbers and did not enter service with the United States Army.

As originally conceived the FV601(A) was to have had a crew of four and be armed with a 2-pounder gun fitted with a Littlejohn Adaptor to increase the muzzle velocity. But in February 1948 it was decided that the 2-pounder was not powerful enough so a new weapon, the 76 mm gun L5, was designed by the Armament Design Establishment at Fort Halstead (now RARDE), but was not ready until 1953. In 1947 a contract was awarded to Alvis Limited of Coventry to build two prototypes of the FV601 which were completed in 1953. The first mock-up, fitted with a 2-pounder gun, was completed in 1948.

At the same time as Alvis was building the prototypes of the FV601 it was also building the FV603 armoured personnel carrier which eventually became known as the Saracen. As the Saracen was urgently required for operations in Malaya it was decided to let Alvis concentrate on this vehicle and that the six pre-production vehicles, the FV601(B), would be built by Crossley Motors at Stockport in Cheshire.

Alvis Saladin armoured car with commander's and gunner's hatches open (Christopher F Foss)

The six pre-production vehicles were completed in 1955 and had a slightly different shaped turret from those of prototype vehicles as well as different vision equipment and different hatches for the commander and gunner.

Production was authorised in 1956 and the vehicle entered production at Coventry in 1958 with first vehicles being delivered to the Army the following year. Production continued until 1972 by which time 1177 vehicles had been built. The vehicle was succeeded by the Alvis Scorpion CVR(T) which is armed with a new and lighter version of the 76 mm gun of the Saladin called the L23. The Saladin is officially known as the FV601(C) Armoured Car 76 mm Gun (Alvis Saladin Mk 2 6 × 6).

The Saladin has been replaced in all front-line British units by the Alvis Scorpion CVR(T). A small number are, however, used in Cyprus and some are still used for training drivers. War reserve stocks of the Saladin are also maintained by the United Kingdom.

Description

The all-welded steel hull of the Saladin is divided into three compartments: driver's at the front, fighting in the centre and engine at the rear.

The driver is seated at the front of the vehicle and is provided with a single-piece hatch cover that folds forwards onto the glacis plate for improved visibility. The driver has three No 17 periscopes, one in the hatch cover and one on either side of his position.

The all-welded turret is in the centre of the hull with the gunner seated on the left and the commander, who also acts as the loader, on the right, both with a single-piece hatch cover that opens to the rear. The commander has four No 17 periscopes arranged around the forward part of his hatch and a single swivelling periscope to the rear. The gunner has a

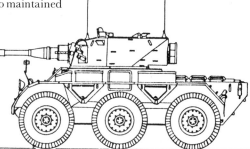

Alvis Saladin armoured car

Alvis Saladin armoured car from rear showing external stowage
(Christopher F Foss)

periscope forward of his hatch cover, the lower part with a magnification of ×6 for fire-control and the upper part with a ×1 magnification for observation. On the left side of the turret, just to the rear of the mantlet, is an extractor fan. A small rectangular observation hatch is provided in the rear of the fighting compartment, just below the turret ring. Either side of the turret below the turret ring is a crew escape hatch.

The engine compartment at the rear of the hull is separated from the crew compartment by a fireproof bulkhead and is fitted with a fire warning system and a fire-extinguishing system, the latter being operated by the driver.

Air for the engine compartment is drawn in via six louvred engine covers by two fans and then passes through the radiator and is expelled through grilles at the very rear of the hull.

The engine is coupled to a Daimler fluid coupling which in turn is coupled to a Daimler epicyclic pre-selective gearbox which transmits power to the transfer box consisting of a bevel and helical gear, incorporating reverse and a differential and enabling the five gears to be used in both directions. This transfers the drive direct to each centre bevel box and thence via transmission shafts to the front and rear axles. Each wheel houses epicyclic reduction gears and is connected to the bevel box by a transmission shaft and two universal joints.

The suspension at each wheel station consists of an upper and lower link, with the upper attached to a longitudinal torsion bar which is splined to a tube which in turn is secured to the hull. Steering is hydraulically power-assisted on the front and centre road wheels.

The Saladin has no amphibious capability although a kit is available which enables the vehicle to ford to a depth of 2.13

Alvis Saladin armoured car with driver's hatch open (Christopher F Foss) metres. For trials purposes a Saladin was fitted with a collapsible flotation screen similar to that fitted to the CVR(T) Scorpion, but this was never adopted by the British Army.

The Saladin does not have an NBC system or night vision equipment.

Main armament of the Saladin consists of a 76 mm L5A1 gun with a vertical sliding breech-block and a hydro-spring recoil mechanism. A 7.62 mm (0.30) machine gun model M1919A4(L3A3/L3A4) is mounted coaxially to the left of the main armament and a similar anti-aircraft weapon is mounted on the right of the commander's hatch. Six smoke dischargers fitted on either side of the turret are electrically fired from within the vehicle. The 76 mm gun fires the following types of ammunition:

Type DESIGNATION	Canister L33A3	HESH L29A3/L29A5	HE L24A4	HE/PRAC L25A4	SH/P L40A1	SMK/BE L32A5	ILL L42A1
WEIGHT OF COMPLETE ROUND	7.76 kg	7.41 kg	7.17 kg	7.38 kg	7.41 kg	10.04 kg	11.5 kg
WEIGHT OF PROJECTILE	n/app	5.39 kg	5.35 kg	5.24 kg	5.39 kg	8.0 kg	8.0 kg

The 42 rounds of ammunition are stowed vertically: 11 between the commander and the gunner, 12 on the left and 11 on the right behind the driver and eight at the left rear of the hull.

Variants

The only variant of the Saladin in service is designated the FV601(D). It was built for the Federal German Border Police (Bundesgrenzschutz), who call it the Geschützer Sonderwagen III(SW III)(Kfz 93), has no coaxial machine gun and is fitted with West German smoke dischargers and driving lights. It is reported that 97 Saladins originally delivered to the Federal German Border Police were subsequently supplied to Sudan in the early 1960s.

The British Aircraft Corporation Guided Weapon Division (now British Aerospace Dynamics Group) fitted a Saladin with a Swingfire ATGW either side of the turret but this was not adopted for service. There was also a project to fit the turret of the Fox armoured car to the Saladin but this did not reach even the mock-up stage.

Saladins were also used by the Australian Army and when they were withdrawn from service their turrets were removed and fitted to M113A1 APCs, which were then called M113A1 Fire Support Vehicles.

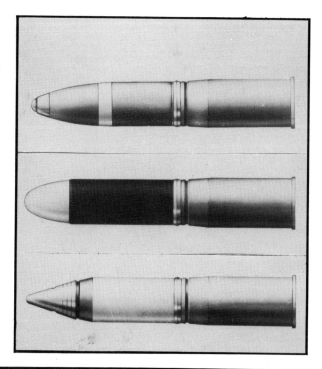

76 mm fixed ammunition for L5 gun of Saladin and L23 gun of Scorpion. Top to bottom; High Explosive, High Explosive Squash Head and Smoke (Base Ejection) (Royal Ordnance Factories)

SPECIFICATIONS

CREW	3	VERTICAL OBSTACLE	0.46 m	AMMUNITION	
CONFIGURATION	6 × 6	TRENCH	1.52 m	(main)	42
COMBAT WEIGHT	11 590 kg	TURNING RADIUS	7.31 m	(machine gun)	2750
UNLOADED WEIGHT	10 500 kg	ENGINE	Rolls-Royce B80 Mk 6A	FIRE-CONTROL SYSTEM	
POWER-TO-WEIGHT			8-cylinder petrol	Turret power control	electric/manual
RATIO	14.66 hp/tonne		developing 170 bhp at	By commander	yes
GROUND PRESSURE	1.21 kg/cm²		3750 rpm	By gunner	yes
LENGTH GUN FORWARD	5.284 m	TRANSMISSION	pre-selector 5-speed	Gun elevation/	
LENGTH HULL	4.93 m	STEERING	recirculating ball,	depression	+20°/−10°
WIDTH	2.54 m		hydraulic assisted	Gun stabiliser	
HEIGHT		CLUTCH	fluid coupling	(vertical)	no
(to top of gunner's		SUSPENSION	independent, double	(horizontal)	no
periscope)	2.93 m		wishbone and torsion	Range setting device	yes
(to turret roof)	2.19 m		bar, hydraulic shock	Traverse indicator	yes
FIRING HEIGHT	1.854 m		absorbers	ARMOUR	
GROUND CLEARANCE	0.426 m	TYRES	12.00 × 20	Hull glacis	12 mm at 45°
TRACK	2.038 m	BRAKES		Hull nose	14 mm at 42°
WHEELBASE	1.524 m + 1.524 m	(main)	hydraulic disc all wheels	Hull sides	16 mm at 20°
ANGLE OF APPROACH/		(parking)	mechanical all wheels	Hull top	10–12 mm
DEPARTURE	60°/50°	ELECTRICAL SYSTEM	24 V	Hull floor	8–12 mm
MAX SPEED FORWARDS		BATTERIES	2 × 12 V, 60 Ah	Hull rear	16 mm
(road)	72 km/h	ARMAMENT		Turret front	32 mm at 15°
FUEL CAPACITY	241 litres	(main)	1 × 76 mm	Hull sides	16 mm
MAX RANGE	400 km	(coaxial)	1 × 7.62 mm MG	Hull rear	16 mm
FORDING	1.07 m	(anti-aircraft)	1 × 7.62 mm MG	Hull top	10 mm
(with kit)	2.13 m	SMOKE-LAYING			
GRADIENT	46%	EQUIPMENT	2 × 6 smoke dischargers		

Status: Production complete. In service with Bahrain, Federal German Border Police, Ghana, Indonesia, Jordan, Kenya, Kuwait, Lebanon, Libya, Oman, Nigeria, Portugal, Sierra Leone, Sri Lanka, Sudan, Tunisia, United Arab Emirates, United Kingdom, Yemen Arab Republic (North), People's Democratic Republic of Yemen (South). They were also used by Uganda but these are now non-operational.

Manufacturer: Alvis Limited, Holyhead Road, Coventry, West Midlands CV5 8JH, England. (A member of the United Scientific Group).

Alvis Sagitar

Alvis Limited has submitted three studies to the United States Army Tank Automotive Command for the Mobile Protected Weapon System (MPWS) and one for the Mobile Protected Gun System (MPGS). For the MPWS the company has put forwards the Sagitar chassis which is a further development of the Stormer APC of which 25 have been delivered to Malaysia, with a two-man turret armed with a Royal Ordnance Factories 76 mm L23A1 gun (as installed in the Scorpion) and a twin TOW ATGW launcher, another armed with a 75 mm ARES gun and a conceptual design armed with a Royal Ordnance Factories low pressure gun. For the MPGS requirement the 105 mm low pressure gun and the West German Rheinmetall Rh 105-11 super low recoil gun have been proposed.

Status: Project.

Manufacturer: Alvis Limited, Holyhead Road, coventry, West Midlands CV5 8JH, England. (A member of the United Scientific Group.)

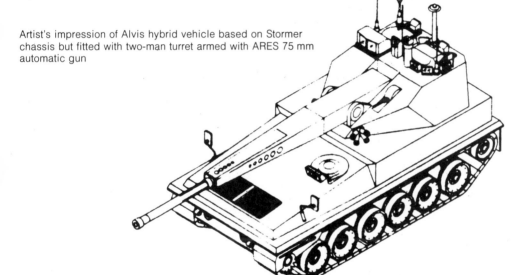

Artist's impression of Alvis hybrid vehicle based on Stormer chassis but fitted with two-man turret armed with ARES 75 mm automatic gun

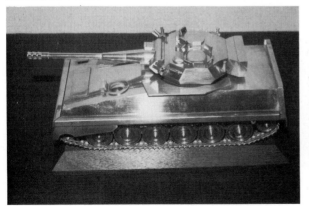

Model of Alvis hybrid vehicle based on Stormer chassis but fitted with two-man turret armed with Cockerill 90 mm Mk III gun (Christopher F Foss)

Model of Alvis hybrid vehicle based on Stormer chassis but fitted with two-man turret armed with 76 mm L23A1 gun and twin launcher for Hughes TOW ATGW (Christopher F Foss)

Alvis Scorpion Reconnaissance Vehicle

Development

In the late 1950s the British Army issued a requirement for an Armoured Vehicle Reconnaissance (AVR) to undertake the roles of reconnaissance, fire support and anti-tank. After studying a variety of proposals the Fighting Vehicles Research and Development Establishment (now the Military Vehicles and Engineering Establishment) came to the conclusion that two vehicles would be required to carry out these roles. These became the Combat Vehicle Reconnaissance (Tracked) Scorpion range and the Combat Vehicle Reconnaissance (Wheeled) Fox vehicle, both of which use the same Jaguar engine.

The Scorpion was preceded by a test rig known as the TV 15000, which was made of aluminium armour, powered by a Rolls-Royce B60 petrol engine which developed 130 hp (replaced in 1966 by the more powerful Jaguar XK petrol engine), and had a hydro-pneumatic suspension. The TV 15000 was followed in 1966 by two test rigs, one of which was static and was used to test the cooling system and other components and the second, called the Mobile Test Rig, tested automotive features. The latter did not have the hydro-pneumatic suspension as fitted to the TV 15000 but

Combat Vehicle Reconnaissance (Tracked) Scorpion (FV101)

Alvis Scorpion CVR(T) of British Army with flotation screen removed (Christopher F Foss)

had a new TN15 transmission which is essentially a scaled-down version of that installed in the Chieftain MBT.

In September 1967 Alvis Limited of Coventry, which was at that time building the FV600 range of 6 × 6 armoured vehicles, was awarded a contract to build 17 prototypes. The first prototype was completed in January 1969 and the first official announcement of the vehicle was made in September the same year. All 17 prototypes were completed by the middle of 1970 and in May 1970 the Scorpion was accepted for service with the British Army. In October 1970 the Belgian Army placed an order for 701 Scorpions and variants, which were assembled at a British Leyland facility at Malines in Belgium. Some of the components of the British and Belgian vehicles were made in Belgium.

It is believed that Egypt is considering manufacturing the CVR(T) Scorpion family of vehicles under licence.

The first production Scorpions were delivered to the British Army in January 1972 with first deliveries being made to the Belgian Army in February 1973.

In July 1977 it was stated that production for both the Belgian and British Armies would be completed by 1980 when the number of vehicles deployed would be over 2000 (including variants). At the same time it was said that export sales had reached 400 vehicles. Since then further export orders for the Scorpion series have been won and it is estimated that at least 3300 vehicles have now been ordered (including those delivered).

It was announced early in 1979 that the Royal Air Force Regiment had ordered 150 members of the Scorpion family (including Scorpion, Spartan, Sultan and Samson) for the defence of Royal Air Force airfields in West Germany. In November 1981 the Royal Air Force Regiment at Catterick formally took delivery of its first Alvis CVR(T) Scorpions for airfield defence. Each RAF Regiment Squadron will be equipped with six Scorpions, 15 Spartan APCs, one Sultan command vehicle and one Samson ARV. Number 1 Squadron, Royal Air Force Regiment is deployed in West Germany to defend the Harrier Force, while the other three squadrons are based in the United Kingdom but will deploy to West Germany in time of war to defend Laarbruch, Brüggen and Wildenrath.

Scorpion has been designed to operate in temperatures from −30° to +50°C and a Lockheed C-130 Hercules transport can carry two of them. In the British Army of the Rhine Scorpion is centralised in the division reconnaissance regiments for medium reconnaissance. Each armoured reconnaissance regiment has 32 Scorpions, 40 Scimitars, 12 Spartans (five with ZB 298 radars), 7 Sultans, 4 Samsons, and 3 Samaritans.

During the 1982 Falklands campaign, the British Army deployed two Scorpions, four Scimitars and one Samson armoured recovery vehicle. The official British government report on the Falklands had this to say about the Scorpion: "Mobility. The ground forces were heavily dependent on helicopters and tracked vehicles for mobility. The tracked reconnaissance vehicles, Scorpion and Scimitar, performed very well in boggy conditions, covering an average of 350 miles each. One vehicle withstood a shell which landed 1½ metres away; another ran over a mine which severely damaged the vehicle but left the crew unharmed."

113

Belgian Army Combat Vehicle Reconnaissance (Tracked) with flotation screen erected (C R Zwart)

Description

The hull of the Scorpion is made of all-welded aluminium armour and provides the crew with protection against attack over its frontal area from 14.5 mm projectiles and against 7.62 mm armour-piercing rounds over the remainder of the vehicle. The hull is divided into three compartments: driver's at the front on the left, engine at the front on the right and the fighting compartment at the rear.

The driver has a single-piece hatch cover that swings to the left, in front of which is a single wide-angle periscope which can be replaced by a Pilkington passive periscope for night driving.

The Scorpion is powered by a de-rated (from 265 to 190 bhp) and militarised Jaguar 4.2-litre engine with a Solex carburetter and a compression ratio reduced from 9:1 to 7.75:1, which permits the use of military fuels. The transmission, which is at the front of the vehicle, has been developed on the same principles as that used for the Chieftain MBT. It is a hot-shift, foot-operated, seven-speed gearbox with a controlled differential steering system. For engine cooling a single mixed flow fan draws in air through the radiator over the gearbox, over the engine and out through the louvres.

The other two crew members are seated in the all-welded aluminium armour turret with the commander on the left and the gunner on the right, both with a single-piece hatch cover that opens to the rear. The commander has seven periscopes and a roof-mounted sight in front of his hatch cover with a magnification of ×1 and ×10. The roof-mounted sight is capable of limited rotation allowing approximately an 85-degree horizontal field of view. The gunner has two periscopes and a roof-mounted sight with a magnification of ×1 and ×10. Mounted to the right of the main armament is a Rank Precision Industries passive night sight with a

Cutaway drawing of CVR(T) Scorpion

The Scorpion can ford to a depth of 1.067 metres without preparation. A flotation screen carried collapsed around the top of the hull can be erected by the crew in five minutes and the vehicle is then propelled and steered across the stream or river by its tracks at a speed of 6.44 km/h. A propeller kit has also been developed and when fitted with it the Scorpion has a maximum water speed of 9.65 km/h.

The Scorpion is armed with a 76 mm L23 gun which is a lighter version of the L5 used in the Saladin armoured car. This weapon has a vertical sliding breech and is loaded with fixed ammunition. It has a recoil of approximately 280 mm and is returned to the firing position by a hydro-pneumatic recuperator. During runout the breech is opened by a semi-automatic cam, the empty cartridge case is ejected and the breech then remains open ready for reloading. The gun has an elevation of +35 degrees and a depression of -10 degrees, turret traverse being 360 degrees. Elevation and traverse are both manual but if required the vehicle can be delivered with powered traverse. The following types of ammunition can be fired:

Belgian Army Alvis CVR(T) Scorpion with special cab used for driver training (C R Zwart)

Type	Canister	HESH	HE	HE/PRAC	SH/P	SMK/BE	ILL
DESIGNATION	L33A3	L29A3/L29A5	L24A4	L25A4	L40A1	L32A5	L42A1
WEIGHT OF COMPLETE ROUND	7.76 kg	7.41 kg	7.17 kg	7.38 kg	7.41 kg	10.04 kg	11.5 kg
WEIGHT OF PROJECTILE	n/app	5.39 kg	5.35 kg	5.24 kg	5.39 kg	8.0 kg	8.0 kg
MAX RANGE DIRECT	150 m	2200 m	2200 m	2200 m	2200 m	n/app	n/app
MAX RANGE INDIRECT	290 m	5000 m	5000 m	5000 m	5000 m	3700 m	n/app
MUZZLE VELOCITY	290 m/s	533 m/s	514 m/s	514 m/s	533 m/s	n/app	n/app

magnification of ×5.8 (8-degree field of view) and a low magnification of ×1.6 (28-degree field of view). There can be no confusion between the two as when the high magnification is being used a shutter isolates the low magnification objective. The image intensifier diaphragm isolates the high magnification objective. The image intensifier tube is protected from the effect of gun muzzle flash by a flash shutter that is operated electrically from the gun firing circuit. When high magnification is selected an illuminated ballistic graticule with brightness control is automatically injected into the optical system. The exposed objective window is cleaned by a wiper and washer and the sight is protected by an armoured cover with a door which is kept closed when the sight is not in use. The sight will detect infra-red devices.

The radios are in the turret bustle and a light metal stowage box is mounted externally at the rear of the hull. British Army Scorpions now have a stowage box on the left side of the hull.

The torsion bar suspension consists of five rubber-tyred aluminium road wheels with the drive sprocket at the front and the idler at the rear. There are no track return rollers.

Hydraulic lever type shock absorbers are provided for the first and last road wheel stations either side. The tracks are of light steel with rubber bushes and pads, and have a life of over 5000 km of mixed road and cross-country running.

British Army Scorpions have an NBC system at the rear of the hull, but if it is not installed an additional five rounds of 76 mm ammunition can be carried. Optional equipment includes an NBC detector kit, vehicle navigation system and a Normalair-Garrett air-conditioning system which has already been fitted on the vehicles supplied to the United Arab Emirates.

A 7.62 mm machine gun mounted coaxially to the left of the main armament can be used as a ranging machine gun. Mounted each side of the turret is a four-barrelled electrically-operated smoke discharger.

Scorpion 90

For the export market Alvis has fitted a Scorpion with a 90 mm Mk III Cockerill gun. The weapon fires the following types of fixed ammunition which has been designed and produced by PRB:

Type	Canister	HE-T	HEAT-T	HEAT-TP-T	HEAT-T-HVY	HESH-T	Smoke-WP-T	HE-APERS-FRAG
DESIGNATION	NR 125	NR 501	NR 478	NR 479	NR 220	NR 503	NR 502	NR 219
WEIGHT								
(complete round)	6.2 kg	8.3 kg	7.3 kg	7.5 kg	8.2 kg	7.7 kg	8.6 kg	11 kg
(projectile)	n/app	5.1 kg	4.1 kg	4.1 kg	5.1 kg	4.3 kg	5.4 kg	8.5 kg
(propellant)	0.4 kg	0.9 kg	1 kg	1.2 kg	0.9 kg	1 kg	0.9 kg	0.3 kg
(primed cartridge case)	2.3 kg	2.3 kg	2.2 kg	2.2 kg	2.2 kg	2.3 kg	2.3 kg	2.2 kg
EFFECTIVE RANGE	200 m	2000 m	1500 m	1500 m	1500 m	1200 m	2000 m	1000 m
COMBAT RANGE WITH MAX TRAJECTORY HEIGHT OF 2.3 m	n/app	800 m	1000 m	1000 m	800 m	800 m	800 m	n/app
MUZZLE VELOCITY	200 m/s	700 m/s	890 m/s	900 m/s	700 m/s	800 m/s	695 m/s	320 m/s

Notes
Canister projectile contains 1400 balls with a total weight of 2.42 kg, which at 50 m range have a 4 m spread, at 100 m 8 m spread, at 150 m 12 m spread, at 200 m 16 m spread and at 250 m 20 m spread
HEAT-T projectile will penetrate 300 mm of armour at 0 degrees incidence at 1000 m range
HEAT-T-HY projectile will penetrate 330 mm of armour at 0 degrees incidence

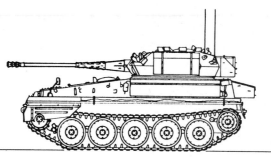

Scorpion 90 with Cockerill Mk III 90 mm gun

The turret of the Scorpion 90 is designated the AC 90 and is almost identical to that fitted to the basic vehicle.

The 90 mm gun has an elevation of +30 degrees and a depression of −8 degrees which is almost the same as that of the basic Scorpion. The first production orders are fitted with the American Cadillac Gage power traverse and elevation system.

The basic Scorpion carries 40 rounds of 76 mm ammunition and the Scorpion 90 carries 35 rounds. When fitted with the 90 mm Cockerill gun the vehicle can deal with all types of target and can inflict severe damage on MBTs. Late in 1981 Malaysia ordered 26 Scorpion 90s fitted with the Perkins diesel engine. Production commenced in 1982 with first deliveries due in 1983. Alvis supplied one Scorpion 90 with a Perkins diesel model T6-3544 engine, developing 200 bhp at 2700 rpm, to the USA for evaluation in the USMC Light Armored Vehicle project.

The Malaysian vehicles also have West German Wegmann 76 mm smoke/fragmentation grenade dischargers fitted to give 360 degree coverage. In early 1983 it was confirmed that 33 Nigerian Scorpions were to be fitted with the Belgian OIP-5 fire control system and have the original 76 mm gun replaced by a Cockerill 90 mm Mk III weapon.

Scorpion with diesel engine

In 1980 Alvis announced that a Scorpion with its Jaguar XK petrol engine replaced by a Perkins turbo-charged six-cylinder diesel model T6-3544 would be offered for export. This model entered production for Malaysia in 1982 with first deliveries due in 1983. The engine, for this application, develops 200 bhp at 2700 rpm and is already in production. Performance comparison between the diesel engine and the basic petrol engined versions is given below:

Model	Diesel	Petrol
WEIGHT	8260 kg	8073 kg
GROUND PRESSURE	0.384 kg/cm²	0.376 kg/cm²
ROAD RANGE	over 840 km	over 640 km
ACCELERATION TO 48.3 km/h	18.5 s	16 s

Scorpion with Laser Rangefinder

At least three British companies, Avimo, Barr and Stroud, and Rank Pullin Controls, have already developed laser rangefinders for the Scorpion. The Avimo model is called the LV10 and is an integrated laser rangefinder/gunner's sight which can be fitted into the Scorpion without modification to the vehicle. Barr and Stroud has developed the LF11 laser rangefinder which has already been adopted by two countries

for installation in the Scorpion and is suitable for installation in other AFVs such as the Vickers MBT. Rank Pullin Controls has developed the SS125/126 Argus day/night sight which can be installed at either the commander's or gunner's position and can be fitted with a laser rangefinder as can the Avimo NVL53 day/night sight, if required. The Omani Scorpions have the Vickers Instruments L20 sight which has a Ferranti laser rangefinder fitted.

Some of the Scorpions used by the United Arab Emirates have been fitted with a Barr and Stroud Tank Laser Sight similar to the one fitted to the Chieftain MBT but with a neodymium-YAG laser in place of the original ruby laser and a graticule for a 76 mm instead of 120 mm gun.

Marconi Radar has also developed a version of its SFCS 600 tank fire-control system for the Scorpion as well as a powered traverse system. A system with both powered elevation and traverse has been developed by Marconi.

In addition to the Avimo (LV10) and Barr and Stroud laser rangefinders the Scorpion can be fitted with the Belgian OIP LRS-5 laser sight and the Vickers Instruments L20 sight laser rangefinder which is interchangeable with the existing Vickers No. 54 Mark 1 gunner's sight used in the Scorpion.

Scorpion with Swingfire ATGWs

British Aerospace Dynamics Group has proposed that a Swingfire ATGW could be mounted either side of the turret to give the vehicle a long-range anti-tank capability.

Alvis CVR(T) Scorpion fitted with Belgian Cockerill 90 mm Mk III gun

Belgian Army Striker with launcher for five British Aerospace Swingfire ATGWs in elevated position (C R Zwart)

Striker Anti-tank Guided Weapon Vehicle (FV102)

The first production Striker was delivered to the British Army in June 1975 and it entered service with the BAOR in 1976. First deliveries to the Belgian Army were made in June 1976.

The Striker is based on the hull of the Spartan APC with the driver at the front on the left, commander to the rear of the driver and the missile controller to the right of the commander. The commander has a No. 26 cupola which has eight periscopes, monocular sight with a magnification of ×1 or ×10 with the line of sight elevating with the machine gun. The ×1 mirror assembly can be replaced by a ×1.8 image intensifier. Mounted on the right side of the cupola is a 7.62 mm machine gun which can be aimed and fired from within the vehicle and the cupola has a single-piece hatch cover that opens to the left.

The missile controller has a split-view monocular sight with magnification of ×1 and ×10 which can be traversed through 55 degrees left and right, and a single-piece hatch cover that opens to the right is provided to the rear of his sight.

On the roof at the rear of the vehicle is a launcher box with five British Aerospace Swingfire ATGWs. A further five missiles carried inside the vehicle are loaded manually and one of the crew has to leave the vehicle to accomplish this. The launcher box is pivoted at the rear and is elevated to an angle of about 40 degrees before the missiles are launched.

The Swingfire missile weighs 28 kg and has a HEAT warhead. Minimum range is between 150 and 300 metres depending on the distance of the vehicle and the controller when being used in the separated mode. Maximum range of the Swingfire is 4000 metres. An advantage of the Swingfire ATGW system over other systems is that the missiles can be launched from behind a crest or cover so that the launcher position cannot be seen by the enemy. The missiles can be launched by the controller in the vehicle, or with the controller at a vantage point (up to 100 metres from the launcher)

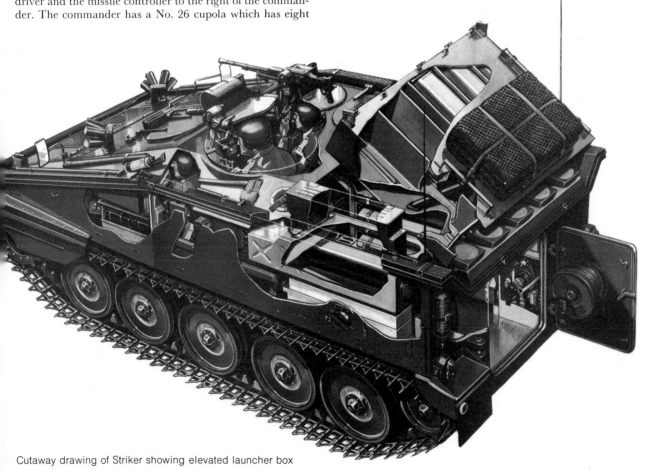

Cutaway drawing of Striker showing elevated launcher box

British Army Striker launching a British Aerospace Dynamics Swingfire ATGW (Simon Dunstan)

separated from the launcher giving him protection from counter fire.

Mounted at the front of the vehicle are two four-barrel smoke dischargers which are operated from within the vehicle.

Spartan Armoured Personnel Carrier (FV103)

This entered service with the BAOR in 1978 and is used for a variety of roles such as carrying Royal Artillery Blowpipe SAM teams, missile resupply carrier for the Striker and for carrying Royal Engineer assault teams. It is not the replacement for the FV432 APC.

The Spartan has a similar hull to that of the Striker and can carry four infantrymen in addition to the driver, vehicle commander/gunner and section commander/radio operator.

The driver is seated at the front of the hull on the left and has a single-piece hatch cover that opens forwards. He is provided with a single wide-angle periscope which can be replaced with a passive periscope for night driving.

The vehicle commander/gunner is seated behind the driver and has a No. 16 cupola with eight periscopes, monocular sight with a magnification of ×1 or ×10 with the line of sight elevating with the machine gun. The ×1 mirror assembly can be replaced by a ×1.8 image intensifier. Mounted on the right side of the cupola is a 7.62 mm machine gun which can be aimed and fired from inside the vehicle. The cupola has a single-piece hatch cover that opens to the left.

To the right of the commander/gunner is the section commander/radio operator who is provided with three observation periscopes and a single-piece hatch cover that opens to the right.

Entry to the personnel compartment at the rear of the vehicle is by a single door in the rear of the hull hinged on the right side, which has an integral vision block. Over the top of

the troop compartment are two roof hatches that open either side of the vehicle. Two periscopes are provided in the left side and one in the right side of the troop compartment but there is no provision for the crew to fire their weapons from inside the vehicle. Three infantrymen are seated on the left side of the vehicle and a fourth to the rear of the vehicle commander/gunner and section commander/radio operator, facing the rear. A ZB 298 ground surveillance radar can be mounted on the roof of the vehicle if required.

Spartan Anti-aircraft Vehicle

It has been proposed that the Spartan could be fitted with the French ESD TA 20 turret armed with twin 20 mm cannon, which has a depression of −5 degrees and an elevation of +85 degrees, turret traverse being 360 degrees. Elevation and

Spartan APC with all hatches open (Simon Dunstan)

Cutaway drawing of Spartan APC showing crew positions and fitted with ZB 298 ground surveillance radar

traverse are both electro/hydraulic. Mounted on the rear of the turret is a pulse-Doppler radar with a maximum detection range of 8 km, which carries out surveillance of the surrounding air space, allocates targets to the weapons and supplies selected target trajectory characteristics to the fire-control computer.

Spartan with Hughes TOW ATGW System

In 1973 Alvis proposed that the Spartan could be fitted with a Hughes TOW launcher on the roof and carry nine missiles in the rear of the vehicle. A tripod would also be carried enabling the missile to be used in the ground role.

Spartan with Euromissile HOT ATGW System

For trials purposes a Spartan APC has been fitted with a Euromissile HOT HCT turret with four HOT 4000 metre ATGWs in the ready to launch position. This was fitted on a plinth above the troop compartment at the rear of the vehicle.

Spartan with Euromissile MILAN ATGW System

Shown for the first time in 1980 was an Alvis Spartan APC fitted with a Euromissile MILAN MCT compact turret over the roof with two missiles in the ready to launch position. This turret can be installed on the Spartan during manufacture or retrospectively fitted to existing vehicles without major modification. Maximum range of the MILAN ATGW

Alvis Spartan APC fitted with Euromissile HOT HCT turret with four HOT long range ATGWs in ready to launch position

Spartan APC with Euromissile MILAN MCT turret with two ready-to-launch missiles

Samaritan armoured ambulance in travelling order (Ministry of Defence)

is 2000 metres. In addition to the two ready-to-launch missiles a minimum of eight missiles would be carried internally. This model has been evaluated by the British Army.

Spartan with Blowpipe SAMs
Shorts is designing a new turret which will be suitable for

Cutaway drawing of Samaritan armoured ambulance

installation on APCs such as the Spartan and M113. This will carry four Blowpipe SAMs which will be raised from their travelling position prior to launch.

Samaritan Armoured Ambulance (FV104)
This model entered production early in 1978 and has the same hull as the Sultan command vehicle and has a crew of two: commander/medical orderly and driver. It is unarmed and can carry four stretcher cases, or five sitting cases, or two stretcher and three sitting cases. There is a large door at the rear of the hull, hinged on the right, with an integral vision block. The commander has five periscopes for all-round observation, plus a single wide-angle periscope with a forward-sloping window with an interchangeable passive night sight. The single-piece hatch cover opens to the left. Medical supplies can be carried on the top of the hull and at the rear of the vehicle.

Sultan Armoured Command Vehicle (FV105)
First production Sultans were delivered to the British Army in April 1977 and have replaced the Saracen vehicles as command vehicles (eg FV604 and FV610). The vehicle has a similar hull to the Samaritan and has a crew of five or six: commander/radio operator, radio operator, driver plus two or three additional crew members. The command area is at the rear of the vehicle and to increase the amount of working

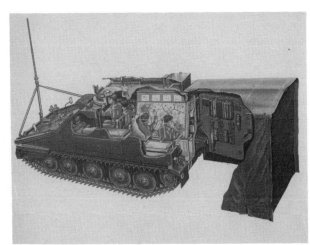

Cutaway drawing of Sultan command vehicle with tent and radio antenna erected

Belgian Army Alvis Sultan command vehicle in travelling configuration (C R Zwart)

space a tent can be quickly erected at the rear of the vehicle. The vehicle is normally equipped with at least two radios (one forwards and one rearwards), and mapboards. A radio antenna can be erected at the front of the vehicle when it is being used in the static role. The commander has a Number 27 cupola with five periscopes for all-round observation, plus a single wide-angle periscope with a forward-sloping window with an interchangeable passive night sight. The single-piece hatch cover opens to the left. Armament consists of a pintle-mounted 7.62 mm machine gun and four smoke dischargers mounted on either side of the vehicle towards the front.

Samson Armoured Recovery Vehicle (FV106)

This entered service with the British Army in 1978 and has a hull similar to that of the Spartan APC. The driver is seated at the front of the vehicle on the left and has a single-piece hatch cover that opens forwards and a single wide-angle periscope which can be replaced by a passive night periscope. The commander's No. 27 cupola has a single wide-angle periscope which can be replaced with a passive night periscope, five periscopes for all-round observation plus a single-piece hatch cover that opens to the left.

The heavy-duty winch fitted inside the hull is driven from the main engine and has a variable speed of up to 122 metres a minute on the 229 metres of wire rope. Maximum pull, with a 4:1 snatch block, is 12 000 kg. The winch leads to the rear of the vehicle and when being used for recovery operations two spades are lowered manually at the rear of the vehicle. An A-frame can be erected at the rear of the hull. Tools, a bench, tow bars and tow cables are fitted as standard. Armament comprises a pintle-mounted 7.62 mm machine gun and four smoke dischargers mounted on either side of the vehicle towards the front.

Samson carrying out recovery operation with spade lowered at rear

Alvis Scimitar armed with 30 mm Rarden cannon (Simon Dunstan)

Cutaway drawing of Scimitar armed with 30 mm Rarden cannon

Belgian Army Alvis Scimitar with 30 mm Rarden cannon at maximum elevation (C R Zwart)

Scimitar Reconnaissance Vehicle (FV107)

The first prototype of the Scimitar was completed in July 1971 and accepted for service in June 1973. First deliveries were made to the British Army in March 1974 with first deliveries being made to the Belgian Army in April 1974. In the British Army, Scimitar is centralised in division armoured reconnaissance regiments but deploys to battalions in the division as their close reconnaissance force. It

has the same hull and turret as the Scorpion but is armed with a 30 mm Rarden cannon instead of the 76 mm gun.

The 30 mm cannon was designed by the Royal Armament Research and Development Establishment at Fort Halstead and the Royal Small Arms Factory at Enfield. It fires all types of 30 mm Oerlikon ammunition as well as a number of British rounds. In addition the 30 mm Rarden cannon fires a new

APDS-T round developed jointly by the Royal Ordnance Factories and PATEC of the United States. This will penetrate 40 mm of armour at an angle of 45 degrees at ranges in excess of 1500 metres with approximately half the dispersion of current HE-T ammunition. The projectile has a muzzle velocity of 1175 metres a second and weighs 300 grams with the complete round weighing 822 grams. The tracer burns to ranges in excess 2000 metres.

| | British | | | Swiss | | |
Ammunition type	APSE-T	HE-T	PRAC-T	HE	AP	PRAC
DESIGNATION	L5A2	L8A2	L7A4	UIAT	RINT	ET
WEIGHT OF PROJECTILE	357 g	357 g	357 g	360 g	360 g	360 g
WEIGHT OF FILLING	29 g	25.6 g	26.5 g	25 g	n/app	n/app
WEIGHT OF CARTRIDGE CASE	365 g	365 g	365 g	350 g	350 g	350 g
WEIGHT OF COMPLETE ROUND	904 g	904 g	904 g	870 g	870 g	870 g
MUZZLE VELOCITY	1070 m/s	1070 m/s	1070 m/s	1080 m/s	1080 m/s	1080 m/s

The gun is fired in rapid single shots but bursts of up to six rounds can be fired if required. The empty cartridge cases are automatically ejected outside the turret.

A 7.62 mm machine gun is mounted coaxially to the left of the main armament and four smoke dischargers are mounted either side of the front of the turret. The main armament, coaxial machine gun and smoke dischargers are electrically operated, with the main armament and coaxial machine gun having manual overriding control.

30 mm ammunition manufactured for the RARDEN cannon by the British Manufacture and Research Company of Grantham, Lincolnshire

Streaker HMLC

Late in 1982 Alvis completed the prototype of the private venture Streaker high mobility load carrier which is based on the chassis of the Spartan APC. This is powered by the standard 4.2 litre petrol engine which could however be replaced by the Perkins T6/3544 200 bhp turbo-charged diesel coupled to an automatic transmission. Maximum road speed is 72 km/h, road range 483 km, the unloaded weight is 5465 kg and it has a payload of 3000 kg.

The baseline vehicle has two possible rear configurations; one a flat bed, the other with a recessed deck. It also offers two front configurations, one with a lightweight cab structure which is unarmoured, the other with the driver and engine compartment having full armour protection.

Prototype of Alvis Streaker high mobility load carrier with driver's and engine compartments under full armoured protection

Status: In production. In service, or ordered by Belgium, Brunei (16 Scorpion, 2 Sultan and 1 Samson), Honduras, Iran, Ireland (14 Scorpion and 2 Sultan), Kuwait, Malaysia (in late 1981 26 Scorpion 90s with the Perkins diesel engine were ordered for delivery from 1983), New Zealand (in August 1980 26 Scorpions were ordered at a cost of £8.2 million, to replace M41 light tanks), Nigeria, Oman, Tanzania, Thailand, Philippines, United Arab Emirates and the United Kingdom (Army and Air Force).

Manufacturer: Alvis Limited, Holyhead Road, Coventry, West Midlands CV5 8JH, England. (A member of the United Scientific Group.)

SPECIFICATIONS

Model	Scorpion	Scorpion 90	Striker	Spartan	Samaritan	Sultan	Samson	Scimitar
DESIGNATION	FV101	n/app	FV102	FV103	FV104	FV105	FV106	FV107
CREW	3	3	3	3 + 4	2	5 – 6	3	3
COMBAT WEIGHT	8073 kg	8573 kg	8346 kg	8172 kg	8664 kg	8664 kg	8738 kg	7756 kg
POWER-TO-WEIGHT RATIO	23.54 bhp/tonne	22.16 bhp/tonne	22.77 bhp/tonne	23.25 bhp/tonne	21.93 bhp/tonne	21.93 bhp/tonne	21.74 bhp/tonne	24.50 bhp/tonne
GROUND PRESSURE	0.36 kg/cm²	0.39 kg/cm²	0.345 kg/cm²	0.338 kg/cm²	0.358 kg/cm²	0.358 kg/cm²	0.358 kg/cm²	0.338 kg/cm²
LENGTH GUN FORWARDS	n/app	5.283 m	n/app	n/app	n/app	n/app	n/app	4.985 m
LENGTH HULL (inc stowage boxes where applicable)	4.794 m	4.794 m	4.826 m	5.125 m	5.067 m	4.8 m	4.788 m	4.794 m
WIDTH	2.235 m	2.235 m	2.28 m	2.257 m	2.242 m	2.254 m	2.43 m	2.235 m
(over tracks)	2.134 m	2.134 m	2.134 m	2.134 m	2.134 m	2.134 m	2.134 m	2.134 m
HEIGHT (overall)	2.102 m	2.102 m	2.28 m	2.28 m	2.416 m	2.559 m	2.254 m	2.102 m
GROUND CLEARANCE	0.356 m	0.356 m	0.356 m	0.356 m	0.356 m	0.356 m	0.356 m	0.356 m
TRACK	1.708 m	1.708 m	1.708 m	1.708 m	1.708 m	1.708 m	1.708 m	1.708 m
TRACK WIDTH	432 mm	432 mm	432 mm	432 mm	432 mm	432 mm	432 mm	432 mm
NUMBER OF LINKS (per track)	79	79	82/84	84	84	82/84	84	79
MAX SPEED (road)	80.5 km/h	72.5 km/h	80.5 km/h	80.5 km/h	72.5 km/h	72.5 km/h	72.5 km/h	80.5 km/h
FUEL CAPACITY	423 litres	423 litres	350 litres	386 litres	395 litres	395 litres	404 litres	423 litres
MAX RANGE (road)	644 km	644 km	483 km	483 km	483 km	483 km	483 km	644 km
FORDING	1.067 m	1.067 m	1.067 m	1.067 m	1.067 m	1.067 m	1.067 m	1.067 m
	all members of Scorpion family are amphibious with preparation							
FREEBOARD (forward with screen erected)	0.965 m	0.98 m	0.89 m	0.914 m	0.832 m	0.883 m	0.965 m	0.965 m
(aft with screen erected)	0.711 m	0.72 m	0.813 m	1.168 m	0.559 m	0.457 m	0.815 m	0.711 m
GRADIENT	60%	60%	60%	60%	60%	60%	60%	60%
VERTICAL OBSTACLE	0.5 m	0.5 m	0.5 m	0.5 m	0.5 m	0.5 m	0.5 m	0.5 m
TRENCH	2.057 m	2.057 m	2.057 m	2.057 m	2.057 m	2.057 m	2.057 m	2.057 m
TURNING RADIUS	all members can pivot turn in neutral							
(in 1st gear)	1.71 m	1.71 m	1.84 m	1.84 m	1.84 m	1.84 m	1.84 m	1.71 m
(in 7th gear)	33.22 m	33.22 m	35.9 m	35.9 m	35.97 m	35.97 m	35.97 m	33.22 m
ENGINE	Jaguar J60 No 1 Mk 100B 4.2-litre 6-cylinder petrol developing 190 hp at 4750 rpm							
TRANSMISSION	TN15 crossdrive, semi-automatic hot-shift type, providing 7 speeds in each direction and pivot turns							
STEERING	Merritt system incorporated in transmission							
SUSPENSION	torsion bar on all members of Scorpion family							
ELECTRICAL SYSTEM	28.5 V	28.5 V	28.5 V	28.5 V	28.5 V	28.5 V	28.5 V	28.5 V
BATTERIES	4	4	4	4	4	8	4	4
MAIN ARMAMENT	76 mm	90 mm	Swingfire ATGWs	n/app	none	n/app	n/app	30 mm
MACHINE GUN	7.62 mm	7.62 mm	7.62 mm	7.62 mm	none	7.62 mm	7.62 mm	7.62 mm
SMOKE DISCHARGERS	2 × 4	2 × 4	2 × 4	2 × 4	2 × 4	2 × 4	2 × 4	2 × 4
AMMUNITION (main)	40	35	10	n/app	none	n/app	n/app	165
(MG)	3000	3000	3000	3000	none	2000	2000	3000
FIRE-CONTROL SYSTEM	manual	powered	n/app	n/app	none	n/app	n/app	manual
Gun elevation/depression	+35°/−10°	+30°/−8°	n/app	n/app	none	n/app	n/app	+35°/−10°

Fox Light Armoured Car

Development

In the 1960s the Fighting Vehicles Research and Development Establishment (now the Military Vehicles and Engineering Establishment) designed two reconnaissance vehicles, the Combat Vehicle Reconnaissance (Tracked) Scorpion (FV101) and the Combat Vehicle Reconnaissance (Wheeled) Fox (FV721), both of which use the same Jaguar engine.

Development of the Fox began in 1965 and the following year the Daimler company of Coventry, which was building the Ferret scout car at the time, was awarded a contract to build 15 prototype vehicles. The first was completed in November 1967 and the last in April 1969. User trials began in 1968 and the first official announcement concerning the Fox was made in October 1969. The following year the Fox was accepted for service with the British Army and a production order was placed with the Royal Ordnance Factory at Leeds. Production began in 1972 and the first vehicle was completed in May 1973.

Daimler completed production of the Ferret in 1971 and then closed down its armoured vehicle production facility.

The Fox is used by both regular and reserve (TA) units of the British Army, but has not replaced the Ferret which was to have been replaced by a development of the Fox known as the Vixen (FV722). This was however cancelled in 1974 owing to a shortage of funds.

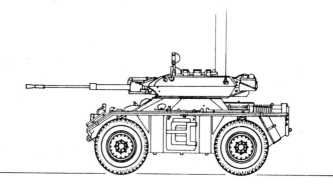

Fox light armoured car

CVR(W) Fox with driver's hatch open. This model is not fitted with flotation screen (Ministry of Defence)

Description

The Fox is a further development of the late production Ferret light scout car and has an all-welded aluminium armour hull and turret which gives protection against medium and heavy machine gun fire and field artillery splinters.

The driver is seated at the front of the vehicle and is provided with a hatch cover that lifts and opens to the right with an integral wide-angle periscope that can be quickly replaced by a passive night periscope.

The turret is in the centre of the vehicle with the commander/loader on the left and the gunner on the right, both with a single-piece hatch cover that opens to the rear. The commander has a periscopic binocular surveillance instrument in a rotating mount with a magnification of ×1 and ×10 and seven observation periscopes. The gunner has a periscopic binocular daylight sight linked to the main armament, with a magnification of ×1 and ×10, and two observation periscopes.

Mounted to the right of the main armament is a Rank Precision Industries SPAV L2A1 passive night sight with a high magnification of ×5.8 (8-degree field of view) and a low magnification of ×1.6 (28-degree field of view), the first for gunnery and the second for surveillance. There can be no confusion between the two as when the high magnification is being used a shutter isolates the low magnification, and when the other is being used an iris diaphragm isolates the high magnification objective. The image intensifier tube is protected from the effect of gun muzzle flash by a flash shutter that is operated electrically from the gun firing circuit. When high magnification is selected an illuminated ballistic graticule with brightness control is automatically injected into the optical system. The exposed objective window is

cleared by a wiper and washer and the sight is protected by an armoured cowl with a door which is kept closed when the sight is not in use. The L2A1 night sight will also detect infra-red devices.

The radios are in the rear of the turret and the batteries are mounted externally on the left side.

The engine compartment is at the rear of the hull and the engine and its auxiliaries including the main and transfer gear boxes are mounted as a powerpack which can be removed through the rear of the hull. The engine is a militar-

CVR(W) Fox fitted with flotation screen around top of hull (Ministry of Defence)

125

CVR(W) Fox from rear showing external stowage (T J Gander)

ised 4.2-litre Jaguar XK with a reduced compression ratio (7.75 to 1) in order to use military petrol. The valve gear is lead-proofed and a single two-choke Solex carburetter is fitted, as is a Ki-gas cold starting system.

The cooling system has twin radiators horizontally disposed across the top and to the rear of the engine, and, sealed to the radiator, a pair of ducted centrifugal fans. An oil/water heat exchanger unit serves both the engine and the transmission.

Power is transmitted from the engine to the wheels through a fluid coupling, a five-speed pre-selecting epicyclic gearbox, and a transfer box providing reversal of all five speeds.

The independent suspension comprises in each case an upper and lower wishbone, coil spring and a hydraulic telescopic damper. The upper and lower wishbone linkages incorporate lubrication reservoirs and the dampers are enclosed in the recoil springs. The independent suspension allows wheel movements of 0.279 metre and the tyres are of the run-flat type.

The Fox can ford to a depth of one metre without preparation. A flotation screen carried collapsed around the top of the hull can be erected by the crew in two minutes and the vehicle is then propelled and steered across the river or stream by its wheels. The front of the flotation screen con-

ROF Leeds Panga armoured reconnaissance vehicle with Helio FVT 800 one-man turret armed with 12.7 mm (0.50) M2 HB machine gun and 8 electrically operated smoke dischargers either side (Royal Ordnance Factories)

tains transparent panels for viewing and a bilge pump with a capacity of 205 litres a minute is fitted as standard on all vehicles. The Fox can travel down or up river banks with a gradient of up to 46 per cent. British Army CVR(W) Foxes have had their flotation screens removed as have the CVR(T) Scorpions.

Fox has been designed to operate in temperatures from −25 to +50° C and is air transportable. A Lockheed C-130 Hercules can carry three Fox vehicles or two for parachute dropping.

Standard equipment on British Army vehicles includes infra-red filters for the white light headlamps, spotlight for the commander, external stowage boxes either side of the hull

ROF Leeds Panga armoured reconnaissance vehicle from front showing trench crossing channels at front of hull (Royal Ordnance Factories)

coaxial machine gun and smoke dischargers are electrically operated with the main armament and coaxial machine gun having manual overriding control.

Variants

Panga Armoured Reconnaissance Vehicle

The Panga armoured reconnaissance vehicle has been developed specifically for the export market by the Royal Ordnance Factory Leeds and is basically a modified Fox hull with a new one-man turret armed with a 12.7 mm M2 HB machine gun.

The first prototype was completed in January 1980 and was subsequently shipped to Malaysia for trials. This vehicle was fitted with a Peak Engineering one-man turret armed with a 12.7 mm (0.50) M2 HB machine gun.

The current model of the Panga has a redesigned hull with a spare wheel and tyre being carried on the right side of the hull, additional escape hatch in both sides of the hull, additional external stowage, additional periscope either side of the driver's hatch cover, vapour-cycle air-cooling system with manual and automatic control, hub winching equipment for self-recovery, electronic ignition and engine speed governor, automatic locking differential, improved vehicle lighting, engine fire-extinguishing system, dual circuit brakes, electrically operated tyre pump, trench crossing channels at the front of the hull, flashing lights, public address system and a Helio FVT 800 one-man turret which in this application has a 12.7 mm (0.50) M2 HB and a L37A2 machine gun. Mounted either side of the turret are eight electrically operated smoke dischargers.

Automotive characteristics of the Panga are identical to the Fox except for the following:

CREW	2
COMBAT WEIGHT	5840 kg
LENGTH	4.22 m
WIDTH	2.13 m
HEIGHT	
(sight)	2.34 m
(turret roof)	2.13 m
AMMUNITION	
(machine gun)	1200
(smoke grenades)	16
FIRE-CONTROL SYSTEM	
Turret power control	manual
Gun elevation/	
depression	+40°/−10°

Fox/25 mm Hughes Chain Gun

The prototype of the Fox/25 mm Hughes Chain Gun was shown at the 1982 British Army Equipment Exhibition. This is the basic Fox fitted with the FMC one-man electric driven turret which is armed with a Hughes Helicopters 25 mm M242 Chain Gun with a 7.62 mm machine gun (for example a GPMG or a Chain Gun) being mounted coaxially to the left of the main armament. Turret traverse is a full 360 degrees with the weapons having a maximum elevation of +50 degrees. A minimum of 250 rounds of 25 mm and 1500 rounds of 7.62 mm ammunition are carried. As an option an electric stabilisation system can be fitted to give a fire-on-the-move capability.

Optional equipment includes escape hatches, limited slip differential, air cooling for the crew and increased fuel capacity for increased operational range.

between the wheels, drinking water tank containing 13.6 litres and a hull electric distribution box with a cooking vessel socket, inspection socket, inter-vehicle starting socket and a master switch. Optional equipment includes navigation aids, powered traverse, nuclear and chemical detection equipment and a ZB 298 surveillance radar mounted on the left side of the turret.

Main armament of the Fox is a 30 mm Rarden cannon designed by the Royal Armament Research and Development Establishment at Fort Halstead and the Royal Small Arms Factory at Enfield. This fires all types of 30 mm Oerlikon ammunition. In addition the 30 mm Rarden cannon fires a new APDS-T round developed jointly by the Royal Ordnance Factories and PATEC of the United States. This will penetrate 40 mm of armour at an angle of 45 degrees at ranges in excess of 1500 metres with approximately half the dispersion of current HE-T ammunition. The projectile has a muzzle velocity of 1175 metres a second and weighs 300 grams with the complete round weighing 822 grams. The tracer burns to ranges in excess of 2000 metres.

	British		Swiss			
Type	APSE-T	HE-T	PRAC-T	HE	AP	Practice
DESIGNATION	L5A2	L8A2	L7A4	UIAT	RINT	ET
WEIGHT						
projectile (g)	357	357	357	360	360	360
filling (g)	29	25.6	26.5	25	n/app	n/app
cartridge case (g)	365	365	365	350	350	350
complete round (g)	904	904	904	870	870	870
MUZZLE VELOCITY (m/s)	1070	1070	1070	1080	1080	1080

The gun is fired in rapid single shots but bursts of up to six rounds can be fired. The empty cartridge cases are automatically ejected outside the turret.

A 7.62 mm machine gun is mounted coaxially to the left of the main armament and four smoke dischargers are mounted either side of the front of the turret. The main armament,

Basic specifications are identical to the Fox except for:

CREW	2
COMBAT WEIGHT	6297 kg
LENGTH	4.22 m
WIDTH	2.13 m
HEIGHT (to turret top)	2.23 m

Fox/MILAN

The prototype of the Fox/MILAN was shown at the 1982 British Army Equipment Exhibition and early in 1983 went on a sales tour of the Middle East. This is the basic Fox fitted with a new one-man all-welded steel turret designed by Royal Ordnance Factory Leeds. Mounted in the forward part of the turret is a 7.62 mm Hughes Chain Gun or a GPMG for which a total of 2600 rounds of ammunition are carried. Mounted on the roof of the turret on the left side is a twin launcher for the Euromissile MILAN 2000-metre ATGW with a minimum of four missiles being carried in reserve. The MILAN launcher and its integral sight can be elevated and traversed independently of the turret. Mounted either side of the forward part of the turret is a bank of four electrically-operated smoke dischargers. The commander/gunner has one periscopic sight for aiming the machine gun and four vision blocks.

Optional equipment includes escape hatches, limited slip differential, air cooling for the crew, 16 grenade launcher configuration and increased fuel capacity. Basic specifications are identical to the Fox except:

Fox/Scout fitted with one-man turret armed with one 7.62 mm Hughes Helicopters Chain Gun (Royal Ordnance Factories)

Fox/25 mm Hughes Chain Gun (Royal Ordnance Factory Leeds)

CREW	2
COMBAT WEIGHT	6136 kg
LENGTH	4.22 m
WIDTH	2.13 m
HEIGHT (top of	
missile tubes)	2.40 m

Fox/Scout

This is essentially the Fox/MILAN with the MILAN installation removed and the hole blanked out. Main armament consists of a Hughes Helicopters 7.62 mm Chain Gun with 4500 rounds of ammunition being carried. Four smoke dischargers are mounted either side of the turret firing forwards. Vision equipment for the commander consists of one sight periscope with ×1 magnification and four vision blocks.

Fox/MILAN with 7.62 mm GPMG (Royal Ordnance Factory Leeds)

SPECIFICATIONS

		GRADIENT	58%	ELECTRICAL SYSTEM	24 V
		VERTICAL OBSTACLE	0.5 m	BATTERIES	2 × 6TN, 100 Ah
CREW	3	TRENCH (with channels)	1.22 m	ARMAMENT	
CONFIGURATION	4 × 4	TURNING RADIUS	6.1 m	(main)	1 × 30 mm
COMBAT WEIGHT	6120 kg	ENGINE	Jaguar XK 4.2-litre	(coaxial)	1 × 7.62 mm MG
UNLOADED WEIGHT	5733 kg		6-cylinder petrol	SMOKE-LAYING	
POWER-TO-WEIGHT			developing 190 bhp at	EQUIPMENT	2 × 4 smoke
RATIO	30.04 bhp/tonne		4500 rpm		dischargers
LENGTH GUN		TRANSMISSION	Daimler pre-selective	AMMUNITION	
FORWARDS	5.08 m		5-speed unit	(main)	99
LENGTH GUN REAR	4.242 m	TRANSFER CASE	Daimler spiral bevel	(coaxial)	2600
WIDTH	2.134 m		directional control	(smoke grenades)	16
HEIGHT			gears and double helical	FIRE-CONTROL SYSTEM	
(to turret top)	1.981 m		drop down gear to	Turret power control	manual, 2-speed
(overall)	2.2 m		differential provide, in	By commander	yes
GROUND CLEARANCE	0.3 m		combination with gear	By gunner	yes
TRACK	1.753 m		box, 5 forward and 5	Gun elevation/	
WHEELBASE	2.464 m		reverse speeds	depression	+40°/−14°
MAX SPEED		STEERING	power-assisted	Gun stabiliser	
(road)	104 km/h	CLUTCH	fluid flywheel	(vertical)	no
(water)	5.23 km/h	SUSPENSION	independent	(horizontal)	no
ACCELERATION		TYRES	11.00 × 20,		
(0–48 km/h)	9 s		run flat		
FUEL CAPACITY	145.47 litres	BRAKES			
MAX RANGE (road)	434 km	(main)	hydraulic disc all wheels		
FORDING (amphibious	with	(parking)	contracting band on front		
preparation)	1 m		bevel box input		

Status: Production as required. In service with Iran, Kenya, Malawi, Nigeria, Saudi Arabia and the United Kingdom.

Manufacturer: Royal Ordnance Factory, Leeds, England.
Enquiries to Ministry of Defence, Royal Ordnance Factories, Sales and Marketing Division, St Christopher House, Southwark Street, London SE1 0TD.

Alvis Ferret 80 Scout Car

Development

At the 1982 British Army Equipment Exhibition Alvis announced that it had designed a new version of the Ferret (of which 4409 were produced by the Daimler company between 1952 and 1971) under the name of Ferret 80. It uses basic Ferret components but incorporates up-to-date refinements improved protection, performance, stability and capability.

Description

The hull of the Ferret 80 is of all-welded aluminium armour and well sloped to give maximum possible protection within the weight limits of the vehicle. Complete protection against 7.62 mm ball at point blank range and all angles of attack is given.

The driver is seated at the front of the vehicle with the commander/gunner in the centre and the engine at the rear.

The driver has three splinter-proof windscreens to his front and sides. Armoured visors are provided with integral observation periscopes. A separate driver's access hatch is fitted.

The Ferret 80 can be fitted with a wide range of armament installations including the following:
Helio FVT 900 turret with Oerlikon 20 mm cannon and coaxial 7.62 mm MG
Helio FVT 800 turret with Browning 12.7 mm and 7.62 mm MG
Helio FVT 700 turret with twin 7.62 mm MG

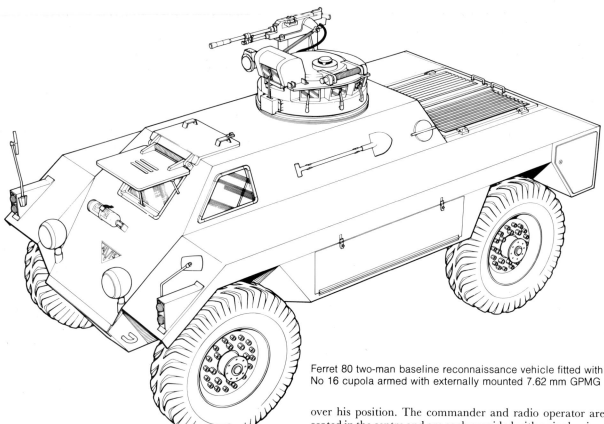

Ferret 80 two-man baseline reconnaissance vehicle fitted with No 16 cupola armed with externally mounted 7.62 mm GPMG

Euromissile MILAN MCT turret with two MILAN ATGWs in ready-to-launch position

The Ferret 80 is powered by a Perkins T6/3544 six-cylinder turbo-charged diesel developing 155 bhp which has already been proved in the Alvis Scorpion and Stormer vehicles while rated at 250 bhp.

Power is transmitted through a three-speed automatic gearbox and transfer box connected to each wheel hub by propeller shafts and bevel boxes. A reduction gear is located in each wheel hub. The two-speed transfer box provides for a road range and a cross-country range. The cooling system is an adaptation of the standard system already proven in the Scorpion series.

Steering is dual circuit, power-assisted, eliminating the awkward wheel location and size in the original Ferret. Independent suspension, wheels and braking system are identical to those of the big-wheeled Ferret Mk 4. Hydraulic disc brakes are fitted to all wheels and a parking brake operates on the transmission. Flat divided disc road wheels with run-flat cross-country tyres are fitted as standard.

The electric system is 24 V with the 2×12 V batteries being contained in the baseline hull.

Variants

In addition to the basic two-man Ferret 80, Alvis has proposed a three-man model. This has a slightly different hull top with the driver being provided with bullet-proof windscreens to his front and sides and a single hatch cover over his position. The commander and radio operator are seated in the centre and are each provided with a single-piece hatch cover, with the commander having a cupola with fixed periscopes that can be traversed through a full 360 degrees. A 7.62 mm machine gun can be externally-mounted on this position. Vision blocks mounted in the upper part of the hull give all round observation.

Status: Prototype.

Manufacturer: Alvis Limited, Holyhead Road, Coventry CV5 8JH, England. (A member of the United Scientific Group.)

Ferret 80 fitted with Helio FVT 900 turret armed with 20 mm Oerlikon cannon and 7.62 mm coaxial MG (not to 1/76th scale)

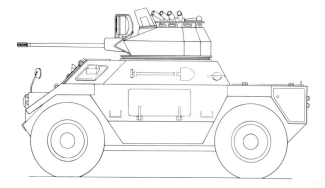

Daimler Ferret Scout Car

Development

In 1947 the British Army issued a requirement for a scout car to replace the Daimler Dingo scout car used during the Second World War. Late in 1948 Daimler was awarded a contract to design and build prototypes of a new scout car under the designation FV701. The first prototype was completed in 1949 and delivered to the Army for trials the following year. After trials it was adopted for service with the British Army and was named the Ferret.

The first production Ferret, the Mk 2, was completed in mid-1952 and the first production Mk 1 was completed late

Daimler Ferret Mk 1 scout car

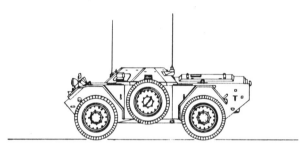

Ferret Mk 1/2 without armament installed (Ministry of Defence)

the same year. Throughout its production life the basic hull of the Ferret remained unchanged although slightly more powerful engines were installed as well as different turrets fitted to meet different requirements. Production of the Ferret was finally completed in 1971 by which time 4409 vehicles of all types had been built.

In 1966 the Daimler company was awarded a contract to build 15 prototypes of a new vehicle called the FV721 (or Fox as it later became known), which were completed between 1967 and 1969. The Fox was accepted for service with the British Army in 1970 but the production order was placed with the Royal Ordnance Factory at Leeds rather than Daimler at Coventry. When production of the Ferret was completed Daimler closed down its production line for wheeled armoured vehicles although it still supplies some automotive components for the Fox light armoured car. The Fox is based on experience obtained with the rebuilt Ferret Mk 4 and Mk 5.

The Ferret was to have been replaced in the British Army by a development of the Fox called the FV722 Vixen, but this was cancelled in 1974 as a defence economy and Ferrets will therefore remain in service until the 1990s. It is probable that some form of NBC system will be fitted to British Army Ferrets in the future as well as night driving equipment and a new turret in the case of the Mk 2.

Alvis is now the design authority for the Ferret and supplies the spare parts for it.

Description (Mk 2)

The all-welded steel hull of the Ferret is divided into three compartments: driver's at the front, fighting in the centre and the engine at the rear.

The driver has three hatches, one to his front and one to each side, each of which contains an integral No 17 observation periscope. The front hatch can be folded down onto the glacis plate for increased visibility and can then be fitted with a splinter-proof windscreen with wiper blade and electric motor. The two side hatches can be opened upwards on the outside for increased visibility when not in a combat area.

The manually-operated turret in the centre of the hull has a single-piece hatch cover in the rear part of the roof which can be locked in three different positions, and the rear part of the turret folds down to the horizontal to enable it to be used as a seat. Mounted in the forward part of the turret roof is a sight periscope AFV No 3 Mk 1 which is used for aiming the turret-mounted machine gun.

Mounted in either side of the hull below the turret ring is a vision slit protected by a glass block. At the rear of the fighting compartment are two hatches which can be opened for increased observation. On each side of the hull, between the front and rear road wheels, is a hull escape hatch. The left one is covered by the spare wheel and the right by a stowage box.

The engine is at the rear of the hull and is fully waterproofed and will operate when completely submerged without any preparation other than venting the crankcase breather pipe. Drive is transmitted to all four road wheels through a fluid coupling, five-speed pre-selecting epicyclic gearbox and a transfer box, incorporating a forward and reverse mechanism and a differential unit to give five speeds in each direction.

The suspension at each wheel station consists of a single coil spring which encloses a double-acting shock absorber and is mounted on a stabiliser bracket at the bottom and carried in a bracket at the top attached to the hull plates. The tyres are of the run-flat type.

The Mk 2 is armed with a turret-mounted 7.62 mm (0.30) Browning machine gun which can be elevated manually from −15 to +45 degrees, turret traverse being a full 360 degrees. A total of 2500 rounds of machine gun ammunition are carried. Mounted either side of the hull at the front of the vehicle are three smoke dischargers which are electrically fired from within the vehicle.

The basic Ferret has no NBC system, no night vision equipment and no amphibious capability. A deep fording kit available consists of a collapsible bellows type collar fitted around the top of the commander's hatch and another fitted at the very rear of the hull. Ferrets Mk 3 and 4 are fitted with a collapsible screen around the top of their hulls which, when erected, enables them to propel themselves across lakes and rivers with their wheels. To enable the vehicle to cross trenches Ferrets Mks 1, 2 and 3 have provision for carrying steel channels on the front of their hulls.

Early production vehicles had BSF threads, different gear ratios and were powered by a Rolls-Royce B60 MkIIIA six-cylinder petrol engine developing 120 bhp at 3750 rpm. Later production vehicles had UNF threads and the B60 MkVIA six-cylinder engine which develops 129 bhp at 3750 rpm.

Ferret Mk 2/3 from rear showing external stowage (Ministry of Defence)

British Army Ferret Mk 1 with all driver's hatches open and without machine gun (Ministry of Defence)

Variants

Ferret Mk 1

This is called Car Scout 4 × 4 Liaison (Ferret Mk 1) FV701(C) and has an open top which can be covered by a canvas cover. It is armed with a 7.62 mm Bren LMG or a 7.62 mm (0.30) Browning machine gun, with 450 rounds of machine gun ammunition being carried. Later production models are known as the Ferret Mk 1/1, FV701(J). Some Mk1/1s have been fitted with a flotation screen similar to that fitted to the Ferret Mk 4.

Ferret Mk 1/2 (FV704)

This is identical to the Mk 1 but has a crew of three and is used by infantry units as a light reconnaissance vehicle in forward areas. Its official designation is Car Scout Liaison (Ferret) Mk 1/2. It has an armoured roof with a hatch and is armed with a 7.62 mm pintle-mounted Bren LMG. The single-piece hatch cover opens to the rear and periscopes and vision blocks are provided for observation by the commander.

Ferret Mk 2

This is basically a Mk 1 fitted with a turret and is officially known as the Car Scout 4 × 4, Reconnaissance (Ferret) Mk 2 FV701(E).

Ferret Mk 2/2

This was a local modification carried out in the Far East and is basically the Ferret Mk 2 with an extension collar fitted between the top of the hull and the machine gun turret and enables the commander/gunner to have a better field of fire.

Ferret Mk 2/3

This is a later production model of the basic Mk 2 and is officially known as the Scout Car Reconnaissance Mk 2/3 (Daimler Ferret 4 × 4) FV701(H). The description in this entry relates to this model.

Ferret Mk 2/4

This is a Ferret Mk 2/3 with additional armour.

Ferret Mk 2/5

This is a Ferret Mk 2 brought up to Ferret Mk 2/4 standard.

Ferret Mk 2/6 (FV703)

The full designation of this model is the Scout Car Reconnaissance/Guided Weapon Mk 2/6. It is basically a Mk 2/3 with a single British Aircraft Corporation (Guided Weapons Division) (now British Aerospace Dynamics) Vigilant ATGW in its launcher box mounted on either side of the turret. A further two missiles are carried in their launcher boxes on the left side of the hull in place of the spare wheel.

The two ready-to-launch missiles have a common elevating mechanism and can be launched from inside the vehicle or away from it with the aid of a combined sight/controller and separation cable. The 7.62 mm (0.30) machine gun is retained. The Vigilant ATGW is wire guided and has a minimum range of 200 metres and a maximum range of 1375 metres, weighs 14 kg and has a HEAT warhead. The Ferret Mk 2/6 is used only by Libya and the United Arab Emirates.

Ferret Mk 2/7

This is a Ferret Mk 2/6 with the missile system removed and is therefore basically a Ferret Mk 2/3.

Ferret Mk 3

This is the Ferret Mk 1/1 brought up to the same standards as the Mk 4 but with the machine gun turret.

British Army Ferret Mk 2/3 scout car (Christopher F Foss)

Ferret Mk 2/6 with Vigilant ATGWs either side of turret

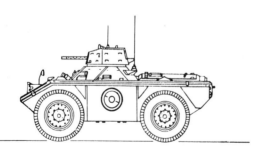

Daimler Ferret Mk 4 scout car

Ferret Mk 4 (FV711)

This model, like the Mk 5, is used only by the British Army and is basically an early Ferret rebuilt with stronger suspension units, original 330 mm diameter drum brakes replaced by vacuum-assisted 381 mm diameter disc brakes, and large wheels and tyres. A flotation screen is carried collapsed around the top of the hull and when erected the vehicle can propel itself across lakes and rivers by its wheels. There are watertight stowage containers either side of the hull, and the number of servicing points has been reduced.

Ferret Mk 5 (FV712)

This model is no longer in service and was used only by the British Army. It was essentially a Mk 4 with turret mounting four British Aerospace Swingfire ATGWs fitted.

Ferret Mk 4 in Belize (Ministry of Defence)

SPECIFICATIONS

Model	Mk 1/1	Mk 1/2	Mk 2/3	Mk 2/6	Mk 4
CREW	2–3	3	2	2	2
CONFIGURATION	4 × 4	4 × 4	4 × 4	4 × 4	4 × 4
COMBAT WEIGHT	4210 kg	4370 kg	4400 kg	4560 kg	5400 kg
UNLOADED WEIGHT	3510 kg	3660 kg	3640 kg	3680 kg	4725 kg
POWER-TO-WEIGHT RATIO	30.64 bhp/tonne	29.51 bhp/tonne	29.35 bhp/tonne	28.28 bhp/tonne	23.88 bhp/tonne
LENGTH	3.835 m	3.835 m	3.835 m	3.835 m	3.96 m
WIDTH	1.905 m	1.905 m	1.905 m	1.905 m	2.134 m
HEIGHT OVERALL	1.448 m	1.651 m	1.879 m	1.879 m	2.03 m
GROUND CLEARANCE	0.33 m	0.33 m	0.33 m	0.33 m	0.432 m
TRACK	1.539 m	1.539 m	1.539 m	1.539 m	1.75 m
WHEELBASE	2.286 m	2.286 m	2.286 m	2.286 m	2.286 m
MAX SPEED (road)	93 km/h	93 km/h	93 km/h	93 km/h	80 km/h
FUEL CAPACITY	96 litres	96 litres	96 litres	96 litres	96 litres
MAX RANGE (road)	306 km	306 km	306 km	306 km	306 km
(cross country)	160 km	160 km	160 km	160 km	160 km
FUEL CONSUMPTION (road)	0.31 litre/km	0.31 litre/km	0.31 litre/km	0.31 litre/km	0.31 litre/km
(cross country)	0.6 litre/km	0.6 litre/km	0.6 litre/km	0.6 litre/km	0.6 litre/km
FORDING	0.914 m	0.914 m	0.914 m	0.914 m	0.914 m
(with preparation)	1.524 m	1.524 m	1.524 m	1.524 m	amphibious
GRADIENT	46%	46%	46%	46%	46%
VERTICAL OBSTACLE	0.406 m	0.406 m	0.406 m	0.406 m	0.406 m
TRENCH (with channels)	1.22 m	1.22 m	1.22 m	1.22 m	1.22 m
TURNING RADIUS	5.795 m	5.795 m	5.795 m	5.795 m	5.795 m
ENGINE	Rolls-Royce B60 Mk 6A 6-cylinder in-line water-cooled petrol developing 129 bhp at 3750 rpm				
TRANSMISSION	Daimler pre-selective epicyclic, 5-speed				
STEERING	re-circulating ball (not power-assisted)				
CLUTCH	Daimler fluid coupling				
SUSPENSION	independent, coil spring and double-acting shock absorber at each wheel station				
TYRES	9.00 × 16	9.00 × 16	9.00 × 16	9.00 × 16	11.00 × 20
BRAKES (main)	hydraulic on all wheels				
(parking)	hand-operated, mechanical on transmission				
ELECTRICAL SYSTEM	24 V	24 V	24 V	24 V	24 V
BATTERIES	2 × 12 V, 60 Ah	2 × 12 V, 60 Ah	2 × 12 V, 60 Ah	2 × 12 V, 60 Ah	2 × 12 V, 60 Ah
ARMAMENT (MG)	1 × 7.62 mm	1 × 7.62 mm	1 × 7.62 mm	1 × 7.62 mm	1 × 7.62 mm
(missile)	n/app	n/app	n/app	Vigilant	n/app
(ready use missiles)	n/app	n/app	n/app	2	n/app
(reserve missiles)	n/app	n/app	n/app	2	n/app
SMOKE-LAYING EQUIPMENT	all Ferret models have 2 × 3 smoke dischargers				
ARMOUR Hull front	12 mm at 50° and 16 mm at 35° all models				
Hull sides	12 mm at 10°, 15°, 40°; 16 mm at 20° all models				
Hull floor	10 mm driver's position, 6 mm remainder of vehicle all models				
Hull rear	12 mm and 6 mm at 45° all models				
Turret front	n/app	16 mm	16 mm at 15°	16 mm at 15°	16 mm at 15°
Turret sides	n/app	16 mm	16 mm at 15°	16 mm at 15°	16 mm at 15°
Turret rear	n/app	16 mm	16 mm at 15°	16 mm at 15°	16 mm at 15°
Turret top	n/app	8 mm	8 mm	8 mm	8 mm

Status: Production complete. In service with Bahrain, Burma, Cameroon, Central African Republic, Gambia, Ghana, Indonesia, Jordan, Kuwait, Libya, Madagascar, Malaysia, New Zealand, Nigeria, Portugal, Qatar, Saudi Arabia, Senegal, South Africa, Sri Lanka, Sudan, UAE, United Kingdom, Upper Volta, Yemen Arab Republic (North), People's Democratic Republic of Yemen (South) and Zimbabwe.

Manufacturer: Daimler Company Limited, Coventry. Spare parts and post-design work is now the responsibility of Alvis Limited, Holyhead Road, Coventry, West Midlands CV8 8JH, England. (A member of the United Scientific Group.)

Shorland Armoured Patrol Car

Development

The Shorland armoured patrol car was originally designed in 1965 specifically to meet the requirements of the Royal Ulster Constabulary for use in Northern Ireland. First production vehicles were completed at Short Brothers and Harland's facility at Newtownards in 1965. By 1971 almost 200 vehicles had been built, by 1978 the figure had reached over 500 and by the end of 1982 was over 1000 vehicles. The vehicles used by the Royal Ulster Constabulary have subsequently been taken over by the military authorities and are now used by the Ulster Defence Regiment and the British Army in Northern Ireland. Production of the Shorland is now undertaken at the company's main plant in Belfast.

The first production models, the Mk 1s, were powered by a four-cylinder Rover petrol engine which developed 67 hp at 4000 rpm and their hull armour was 7.25 mm thick. The Mk 2 was based on the Series 2 Land-Rover chassis and was powered by a four-cylinder petrol engine which developed 77 bhp at 4000 rpm. Hull armour on this model was increased to 8.25 mm thickness. The Mk 3 was introduced in

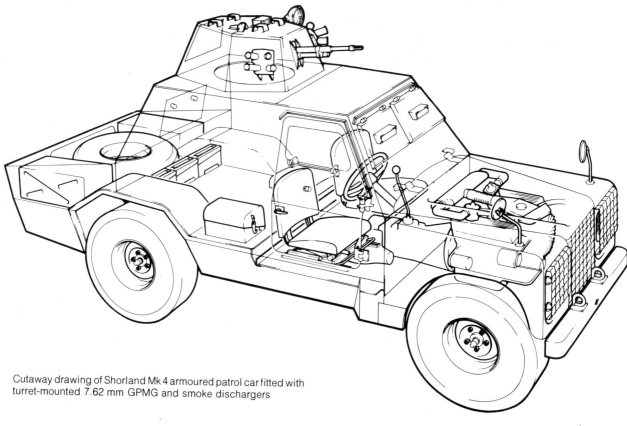

Cutaway drawing of Shorland Mk 4 armoured patrol car fitted with turret-mounted 7.62 mm GPMG and smoke dischargers

1972 and was fitted with a 2.6-litre six-cylinder engine which developed 91 bhp at 4500 rpm. The latest version, the Mk 4, employing the new V-8 engine and increased armour protection, went into production in 1980, this being the replacement for the Mk 3.

The Shorland patrol car is widely used for both internal security operations and border patrol work. In addition Shorts has developed an APC, the latest version of which is called the SB 401, also based on the chassis of the long wheelbase Land-Rover, and built in large numbers.

Description

The Shorland Mk 4 is based on the well-established 2.768-metre (109 inch) long wheelbase Land-Rover chassis strengthened to take the all-welded armour body. Trials carried out by the British Army have shown that the armour cannot be penetrated by fire from a 7.62 mm FN rifle or a 7.62 mm GPMG down to 23 metres firing at right angles to the plate. Servicing and 85 per cent of the spares are identical to the Land-Rover's. Major automotive differences are the stronger axles and different final drives, constant four-wheel drive and hydraulically operated locking differentials controlled by a vacuum switch.

The V-8 engine at the front of the vehicle is protected by armour plate on the front, sides, rear and top, and the bonnet is opened from inside the vehicle. The engine is fitted with an extra capacity radiator for the tropics.

The driver is seated on the left side of the vehicle with the commander to his right (a right-hand drive model is also available with the positions reversed). The windscreens are Triplex safety glass and can quickly be covered by

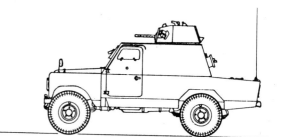

Shorland Mk 4 armoured patrol car

SB401 APC (left) and Shorland armoured patrol car (right) which are both based on a LWB Land Rover chassis (Simon Dunstan)

internally-controlled drop-down armoured visors containing laminated glass observation windows. Both the driver and commander are provided with a side door with a drop-down vision port in the upper part. All doors and openings are locked internally. All openings are seamed and channelled to prevent metal splash entering the interior.

The gunner is seated in the manually-operated turret which can be traversed through 360 degrees by the gunner's feet. The turret is provided with an adjustable seat for the gunner and a mechanical lock prevents rotation while the turret is not in use. The rear part of the turret roof folds forwards and the turret rear folds downwards on the outside to provide a seat for the gunner.

The turret is normally armed with a 7.62 mm GPMG linked to an optical periscope sight fitted in the roof of the turret, but other types of armament can be fitted and a tear-gas discharger, loaded from inside the turret, can be fitted in place of a machine gun. Four electrically-operated smoke/CS dischargers can be mounted either side of the turret and a floodlight mounted to the left of the turret is bore-sighted with the main armament. Gun mounts can be provided as an option to facilitate ground support and anti-aircraft defence.

The gunner is provided with alternative seating behind the commander and there is ample space for other equipment such as radios. An emergency exit in the rear of the hull contains the air extractor fan which is operated electrically by a dashboard switch.

The rear compartment is isolated from the crew compartment and is fitted with a rear armoured port for access to the spare tyre and wheel and also contains the fuel tank, which is filled by an armoured opening locked from the crew compartment.

The heavy duty front axle has hypoid spiral bevel differential for all-wheel drive and the rear axle is a similar type but with floating shafts (Salisbury 8HA).

Standard equipment includes seat belts. The vehicle is internally insulated with washable plastic polyurethane foam and the floor is made of reinforced glass fibre which provides protection against blast, nail and pipe bombs. Optional equipment includes air-conditioning, various radio installations and a loud hailer which is normally mounted at the front of the vehicle.

Variants

Shorland SB 403 Anti-Hijack Vehicle

This has been developed specifically for anti-hijack patrols at airports and other high-risk areas. The driver's and commander's windscreens and side windows are made of armoured glass rather than the Triplex glass covered by armoured visors of the basic vehicle.

The specially-designed turret has a vision block and ball mount which permits an HK33 sniper's rifle to be sighted discreetly on a target while both the rifle and the marksman remain concealed.

Shorland Mk 4 armoured patrol car fitted with turret armed with 7.62 mm GPMG and eight electrically operated smoke dischargers. Windscreen and door flaps in open position

Shorland Mk 4 armoured patrol car from rear with turret and emergency hatch cover in hull rear open

Anti-hijack version of Shorland armoured patrol car

SPECIFICATIONS (Mk 4)						
CREW	3	TURNING RADIUS	8.84 m	ARMAMENT (main)	1 × 7.62 mm MG
CONFIGURATION	4 × 4	ENGINE	Rover 4-stroke V-8, 3528 cc	AMMUNITION (main)	1500
COMBAT WEIGHT	3360 kg		petrol developing 91 bhp at	SMOKE-LAYING	
UNLOADED WEIGHT	2931 kg		3500 rpm	EQUIPMENT	4 smoke dischargers
POWER-TO-WEIGHT		TRANSMISSION	manual with 4 forward		either side of turret
RATIO	28.75 bhp/tonne		and 1 reverse gears		(optional)
LENGTH	4.597 m	TRANSFER CASE	2-speed	ARMOUR	
WIDTH	1.778 m	STEERING	recirculating ball,	Hull front	7.7 mm
HEIGHT	2.286 m		worm and nut	Hull sides	7.7 mm
GROUND CLEARANCE	0.324 m	SUSPENSION	semi-elliptical leaf	Hull top	5 mm
TRACK	1.358 m		springs and hydraulic	Hull rear	7.7 mm
WHEELBASE	2.768 m		shock absorbers,	Turret front	9 mm
MAX SPEED (road)	104.6 km/h		anti-roll bars fitted	Turret sides	7.7 mm
FUEL CAPACITY	128 litres		front and rear	Turret rear	7.7 mm
MAX RANGE (road)	514 km	TYRES	9.00 × 16	Turret top	5 mm
VERTICAL OBSTACLE	0.23 m	ELECTRICAL SYSTEM	12 V (24 V optional)		
		BATTERIES	1 × 12 V, 57 Ah		

Status: In production. In service with 38 countries including Argentina, Botswana, Brunei, Burundi, Guyana, Kenya, Libya, Malaysia, Portugal, Seychelles, Thailand, United Arab Emirates and United Kingdom (Northern Ireland only).

Manufacturer: Short Brothers Limited, Montgomery Road, Belfast BT6 9HN, Northern Ireland.

UNITED STATES OF AMERICA

M41 Light Tank

Development

The standard American light tank at the end of the Second World War was the M24 Chaffee. Shortly after the end of the war design work began on a new light tank called the T37 Phase I. This was armed with a 76 mm gun with a 12.7 mm (0.50) machine gun mounted coaxially with the main armament, a similar anti-aircraft weapon pintle-mounted on top of the turret and remote-controlled 7.62 mm (0.30) machine gun mounted on either side of the turret. The hull and turret were of all-welded armour and the suspension was of the torsion bar type with a total of five road wheels, idler at the front, drive sprocket at the rear, three track return rollers and a tensioning wheel between the drive sprocket and the fifth

road wheel. The T37 Phase I was powered by a 500 hp engine and weighed 21 800 kg. This was followed by the T37 Phase II which was almost identical but had a redesigned turret made of both cast and welded armour with a new mantlet, redesigned ammunition stowage and a new fire-control system which consisted of super-imposed coincidence range-finder integrated with a Vickers stabilisation system (in both the horizontal and vertical planes) and an automatic lead computer. The final development was the T37 Phase III which had a 76 mm automatic gun and an IBM stabiliser.

The T37 Phase II was later designated the T41 light tank and three further prototypes were built under the designation T41. With modifications the T41 became the T41E1 which was standardised in mid-1950 as the M41 tank, or Little

Bulldog, subsequently Walker Bulldog in honour of General W W Walker who was killed in Korea in 1951.

Production of the M41 was undertaken by the Cadillac Motor Car Division of General Motors Corporation at Cleveland Tank Arsenal.

First production M41s were completed in mid-1951 and 1802 were built before production was switched to the later M41A1, which was followed by the M41A2 and finally the M41A3 which differ only in minor details. Total production of the vehicle amounted to about 5500 units. Its full United States Army designation is Tank, Combat, Full-Tracked: 76 mm Gun, M41. It has been replaced in the United States Army by the M551 Sheridan but is still used by many armies. The M41 was a member of a trio of armoured vehicles developed for the United States Army after the end of the war, the others being the M47 (T42) medium tank and the M103 (T43) heavy tank. Many of the components of the M41 are also used in the M42 twin 40 mm self-propelled anti-aircraft gun system (also built at Cleveland), M44 155 mm and M52 105 mm self-propelled howitzers.

Description

The all-welded steel hull of the M41 is divided into three with the driver's compartment at the front, fighting compartment in the centre and the engine at the rear.

The driver is seated at the front of the vehicle on the left side and is provided with a single-piece hatch cover that opens to the right. Three M17 periscopes are mounted for-

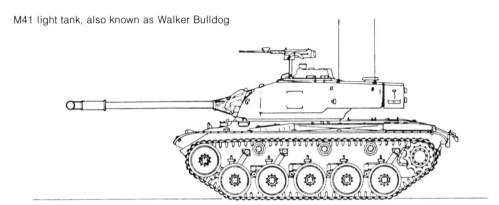

M41 light tank, also known as Walker Bulldog

M41 light tank of Japanese Ground Self-Defence Force (Kensuke Ebata)

Danish Army M41 with mount for infra-red searchlight to left of main armament (S Tunbridge)

ward of his position and a single one to his left. A hull escape hatch is provided beneath the driver's seat.

The turret, which is provided with a basket, is of cast and welded construction with the commander and gunner seated on the right and the loader on the left. The commander's cupola has a single-piece hatch cover that opens forwards and five vision blocks, and an M20A1 periscope that can be traversed through 360 degrees. The gunner has an M97A1 telescopic sight for aiming the 76 mm gun and an M20A1 periscope that can be traversed through 360 degrees. The loader is provided with a single-piece hatch cover that opens forwards and a single M13 periscope. Mounted at the rear of the turret is a light sheet metal stowage box and there is a dome-shaped ventilator in the turret roof towards the rear. The ventilator blower is operated from the driver's position.

The engine compartment is at the rear of the hull and is separated from the fighting compartment by a fireproof bulkhead. It is equipped with a fire extinguisher that is operated by the driver. The engine is mounted towards the front of the engine compartment with the transmission at the rear.

The torsion bar suspension consists of five dual road wheels each side with the drive sprocket at the rear, idler at the front and three track return rollers. The first, second and fifth road wheel stations are provided with a hydraulic shock absorber. The steel tracks, which have 75 or 76 links when new, have detachable rubber pads.

Standard equipment on all tanks includes a heater, deep fording equipment and electric bilge pumps. It is not fitted with an NBC system. The basic model was not fitted with

night vision equipment although the final production model did have provision for an infra-red searchlight over the main armament. A number of countries have fitted the vehicle with infra-red night fighting equipment, for example the Danish M41s have an AEG B30 infra-red searchlight mounted to the left of the main armament and an Electro B8V infra-red sight.

Main armament of the M41 consists of a 76 mm gun M32 (T91E3) in a mount M76 (T138E1), the M41A1 has the M32A1 gun in mount M76A1. The gun has a vertical sliding breech-block, spring actuator and an inertia percussion firing mechanism. The main components of the gun, which has a life of 350 rounds, are the barrel, muzzle brake, bore evacuator chamber and the breech mechanism assembly. The recoil system is of the concentric hydro-spring type.

The gun mount M76 or combination mount M76A1 consists of a shield assembly and a recoil cylinder assembly. The mount supports the barrel and provides attachment for the breech-operating mechanism, firing plunger assembly, manual firing and safety mechanism assembly (M76A1), hand firing control assembly (M76), machine gun mounting bracket, recoil guard, replenisher assembly, elevating cylinder assembly (M76) and the elevating gear box assembly (M76A1).

A 7.62 mm (0.30) Browning M1919A4E1 machine gun is mounted coaxially to the right of the main armament and an anti-aircraft 12.7 mm (0.50) Browning M2 HB machine gun is mounted at the commander's position. This has a traverse of 360 degrees, elevation limits being from −10 to +65 degrees.

The 76 mm gun fires the following types of fixed ammunition:

AP-T (M339), with complete round weighing 12.39 kg, a muzzle velocity of 975.36 metres per second, a range of 4572 metres at an elevation of 2 degrees 16 minutes and at maximum elevation a range of 14 703 metres Blank (M355) used for simulated fire and training

Canister (M363), with complete round weighing 12.33 kg, muzzle velocity of 731.5 metres per second, with an effective range of 155 metres

HE Comp B (M352), with complete round weighing 11.716 kg, a muzzle velocity of 731.52 metres per second and a range of 14 337 metres at maximum elevation

HEAT-T (M496), with complete round weighing 9.253 kg, muzzle velocity of 1082 metres per second and maximum effective range of 2000 metres

HVAP-DS-T (M331A1), with complete round weighing 9.389 kg, a muzzle velocity of 1257.3 metres per second, a range of 4572 metres at an elevation of 2 degrees 28 minutes and at maximum elevation a range of 21 607 metres

HVAP-T (M319), with complete round weighing 8.768 kg, a muzzle velocity of 1260 metres per second, a range of 4572 metres at an elevation of 1 degree 8 minutes and at maximum elevation a range of 9884 metres

HVTP-T (M320), used for target practice, with complete round weighing 8.723 kg, a muzzle velocity of 1260 metres per second, a maximum range of 4572 metres at an elevation of 1 degree 8 minutes and at maximum elevation a range of 9884 metres

TP-T (M340 and M340A1), similar to M339 but without an armour-piercing core, complete round weighing 12.39 kg, a muzzle velocity of 975.36 metres per second and a maximum range of 14 703 metres

WP Smoke (M361), with complete round weighing 11.71 kg, a muzzle velocity of 731.5 metres per second and a maximum range of 14 694 metres.

In 1982 it was revealed that AAI Corporation had developed a new 76 mm APFSDS round for the M32 cannon that would defeat Main Battle Tank frontal armour.

The M41A2 is almost identical to the M41A1 except that it has a simplified turret and gun control system developed by Cadillac. This consists of manual and hydraulic power traverse for the gunner with direct mechanically linked control of oil gear pump in lieu of the electrical control in the M41, dual power traverse by commander, and manual mechanical, rack and pinion type, elevation for the gunner, with slewing elevation control for the gun. This more compact system enabled the tank to carry 65 rounds of 76 mm ammunition compared with 57 of the earlier model. These modifications were also incorporated in the M41A2 and the M41A3 both of which also have the fuel injection engine fitted.

Cadillac Gage TMS

The Cadillac Gage Company, which supplied the weapon control systems for the M48, M60A1, M60A2, M60A3, Leopard 1, Leopard 2, M1, Marder, LVTP-7, V-150 and V-200 Commando, M109, AIFV and special versions of the Centurion, has now developed a Turret Modernisation System for the M41. This can be fitted by the user and gives the following advantages over the existing system: improved low speed tracking and target acquisition, high precision gun positioning capability, improved first round hit capability,

reduced system weight and volume, simplified system operation and maintenance, simplified overall logistical support, readily available spare parts, increased reliability and high system growth potential.

Variants

QM41

This is a remote controlled tank used by the United States Navy for testing air-to-ground missiles. The tank has also been used for a variety of other trials purposes including much of the development work with the turret of the M551 Sheridan light tank/assault vehicle.

Spanish M41 programme

The Spanish Army has 180 M41 light tanks half of which it wants to retain in the original gun version, the remainder being converted to the anti-tank role. For trials purposes one M41 has had its turret replaced by a Euromissile HCT turret with HOT ATGWs, but it is believed that the preferred choice is now the Emerson ITV system as fitted to the M901 Improved TOW Vehicle. The M41 fitted with the Emerson Improved TOW Vehicle turret is known as the Cazador, with conversion work being undertaken by Talbot of Spain. The original petrol engine has been replaced by a GMC Detroit Diesel model 8V-71T developing 450 hp at 2500 rpm which is coupled to the original GMC Allison Division CD-500-3 transmission. The installation of the diesel engine has increased the operating range of the tank from 161 km to 560 km. This vehicle has a four-man crew and a maximum combat weight of 23 tonnes. In addition to the two TOW missiles in the ready to launch position a further ten missiles are carried inside. A 7.62 mm machine gun with 200 rounds of ammunition is provided for local protection.

Brazilian M41 programme

The Bernardini company of Sao Paulo is converting 300 Brazilian Army M41 light tanks into the M41B configuration. The original M32 gun has been replaced by one manufactured by Bernardini which fires the same NR 8500 range of

M41 rebuilt by Talbot of Spain and fitted with Emerson Improved TOW launcher with two TOW missiles in launch position. In this photograph launcher is traversed to rear

Brazilian M41C showing side skirting for additional armour protection

Brazilian Army M41B fitted with new 90 mm gun and Saab-Scania diesel engine with conversion work carried out by Bernardini

ammunition as the Cockerill Mark III gun. The original 500 hp Continental or Lycoming petrol engine has been replaced by a Saab-Scania DS-14 diesel which develops 400 hp coupled to the original CD-500-3 transmission. The M41B has an operational range of 600 km compared to the original model's 161 km. The M41B repower package has been evaluated by a number of other countries including Spain and Thailand. Recently the company has developed the M41C which has a more powerful engine, improved armour with side skirts, the same 90 mm gun and a new fire-control system. It is thought that at a later date Brazilian Army M41Bs will be brought up to the M41C standard.

M41 with New Powerpacks
In addition to the Spanish and Brazilian repowered M41s previously mentioned there are at least three other repower packages being offered.

NAPCO of the United States has designed a powerpack for the M41 that uses the Detroit Diesel 8V-71T engine developing 450 hp at 2500 rpm coupled to the original transmission, so giving an operating range of over 450 km. This vehicle is known to have been tested in Denmark, Spain and Thailand.

Levy Autoparts Company of Canada have designed a powerpack for the M41 that uses the Cummins VTA-903T engine as installed in the FMC Bradley Infantry Fighting Vehicle coupled to the original transmission. This vehicle has

a maximum operating range of 563 km and is known to have been tested in Denmark and Thailand.

FFG of West German have designed a powerpack for the M41 that uses the British Rolls-Royce Military Engine Division Condor CV-8 diesel engine that powers the MCV-80, recently ordered into production by the British Army. This also retains the original transmission and is known to have been tested by Denmark and Thailand.

M41 with Cockerill 90 mm Gun
The Belgian company of Cockerill has replaced the 76 mm gun of the M41 with their new 90 mm gun Mk IV which fires the following types of ammunition: HEAT-T, HESH-T, HE-T, Smoke-WP-T and Canister. This model has already been adopted by Uruguay.

M41 light tank fitted with NAPCO powerpack from rear with loader's hatch open

M41 fitted with Belgian Cockerill 90 mm gun Mk IV

M41 light tank fitted with NAPCO powerpack from front with driver's hatch open

SPECIFICATIONS

CREW	4		
COMBAT WEIGHT	23 495 kg		
UNLOADED WEIGHT	18 457 kg		
POWER-TO-WEIGHT			
RATIO	21.26 bhp/tonne		
GROUND PRESSURE	0.72 kg/cm²		
LENGTH GUN		AUXILIARY ENGINE	GMC model A41-1
FORWARDS	8.212 m	TRANSMISSION	GMC Allison Division
LENGTH HULL	5.819 m		cross-drive model
WIDTH	3.198 m		CD-500-3 with 1
HEIGHT			forward and 1 reverse
(to cupola)	2.726 m		ranges
(including MG)	3.075 m	FINAL REDUCTION	
GROUND CLEARANCE	0.45 m	RATIO	4.25 : 1
TRACK	2.602 m	SUSPENSION	torsion bar
TRACK WIDTH	533 mm	ELECTRICAL SYSTEM	24 V
LENGTH OF TRACK ON		BATTERIES	4 × 6TN, 100 Ah
GROUND	3.251 m	ARMAMENT	
MAX SPEED (road)	72 km/h	(main)	1 × 76 mm
FUEL CAPACITY	530 litres	(coaxial)	1 × 7.62 mm MG
MAX RANGE	161 km	(anti-aircraft)	1 × 12.7 mm MG
FUEL CONSUMPTION	3.29 litres/km	AMMUNITION	
FORDING	1.016 m	(main)	57 rounds M41, 65
(with preparation)	2.44 m		rounds M41A1, M41A2
GRADIENT	60%		and M41A3
SIDE SLOPE	30%	(coaxial)	5000
VERTICAL OBSTACLE	0.711 m	(anti-aircraft)	2175
TRENCH	1.828 m	FIRE-CONTROL SYSTEM	
TURNING RADIUS	skid turns	Turret power control	hydraulic/electric
ENGINE	M41 and M41A1, Conti-		with manual controls
	nental or Lycoming	By commander	yes (only on M41A1
	AOS-895-3, 6-cylinder		and later models)
	air-cooled super-	By gunner	yes

charged petrol devel-	Max rate power	
oping 500 bhp at	traverse	360° in 10 s
2800 rpm. M41A2 and	Gun elevation/	
M41A3 Continental or	depression	+19° 45 min/−9°
Lycoming AOSI-895-5		45 min
with fuel injection also	Gun stabiliser	
developing 500 bhp	(vertical)	none
at 2800 rpm	(horizontal)	none
	Rangefinder	none
	Elevation quadrant	Type M9
	Gunner's sight	M97 telescope with ×8
		magnification and
		7° 24 min field of view

Both commander and gunner have M20A1 periscope with 2 optical systems: ×1 system for observation and ×6 for ranging on targets. Illumination of reticle patterns provided for by Light, Instrument M36

ARMOUR	
Hull front glacis	25.4 mm at 30°
Hull front nose	31.75 mm at 45°
Hull top	12/15 mm
Hull floor	9.25/31.75 mm
Hull rear	19 mm
Turret mantlet	38 mm
Turret front	25.4 mm
Turret sides	25 mm
Turret rear	25 mm
Turret roof	12.7 mm

Status: Production complete. In service with Argentina (few), Brazil, Chile, Denmark, Ethiopia, Greece, Japan, Philippines, Portugal, Spain, Taiwan, Thailand, Tunisia, Turkey, Sudan (53 from Saudi Arabia in 1981), Uruguay and Viet-Nam.

Manufacturer: Cadillac Motor Car Division of General Motors Corporation, Cleveland Tank Arsenal, Ohio, USA.

M551 Light Tank/Reconnaissance Vehicle

Development

Technical feasibility and preliminary concept studies for a new vehicle to replace both the M41 light tank and the M56 self-propelled anti-tank gun began in January 1959. These concepts were subsequently revised in March 1959 when the draft military characteristics were received. In June 1959 the vehicle feasibility studies and the associated technical investigations relative to the design requirement were reviewed and agreements were reached on approaches to satisfy the military characteristics. The major agreements were the establishment of a net weight of 9072 kg, a maximum permissible width of 2.794 metres and the selection of the Shillelagh weapon system as the only weapon system acceptable.

In August 1959 the project for this vehicle, officially called the Armored Reconnaissance/Airborne Assault Vehicle (AR/AAV) was approved with the recording of the military characteristics and approval for building six prototypes.

After evaluating a number of different proposals, in May 1960 the General Motors concept was selected and the com-

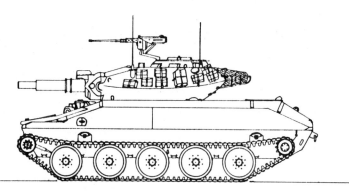

M551 Armored Reconnaissance/Airborne Assault Vehicle

pany was awarded a development contract for the vehicle under the designation XM551. The finalised AR/AAV design was approved at the final mock-up review meeting held in December 1961. The first automotive test bed vehicle ran for the first time in the same month. By this time trials of the XM81E7 gun/launcher for the Shillelagh missile were under way at the Erie Army Depot.

The original intention was to build six prototypes but in fact twelve were built and subjected to extensive trials includ-

ing flotation, durability, hot room, cold room, vibration, firing, swimming, air drop and turret performance. The prototypes differed considerably from production models as they had a box type hull, no flotation screen, and their road wheels were provided with bulbous covers.

In November 1965 approval was given for the type classification of the XM551 as Limited Production and a four-year production contract was awarded to the Allison Motor Car Division of General Motors Corporation. Also

M551 Sheridan with infra-red searchlight mounted to left of main armament (US Army)

M551 modified to resemble Soviet T-72 MBT (US Army National Training Center)

included in the contract was an order for the 155 mm M109 self-propelled howitzer.

In May 1966 the Sheridan was classified as Standard A and by this time production was well under way with the first production vehicle being completed in June 1966. Production continued until 1970 by when 1700 M551s (or General Sheridans) had been built, of which 1570 were still in service with the US Army in 1978.

The M551 was tested by a number of armed forces including Australia and the United Kingdom but no other Army adopted the vehicle. In 1968–69 64 M551s were deployed to Viet-Nam where numerous deficiencies quickly became apparent especially with the engine, transmission, suspension and the conventional round with its combustible cartridge case. Late in 1978 it was announced that the M551 would be phased out of service and replaced by the M60A1 MBT, apart from those vehicles allocated to the 82nd Airborne Division (57) and Arkansas National Guard (12). 330 have been assigned to the National Training Center at Fort Irwin, California. These are essentially basic M551s but with visual modifications to the outside to disguise them as "agressor force" vehicles such as ZSU-23-4 SPAAG, T-72 MBT, BMP MICV and the 122 mm M-1974 self-propelled howitzer.

Description

The all-welded aluminium armour hull of the M551 is divided into three compartments with the driver's at the front, fighting compartment in the centre and the engine at the rear.

The driver is seated at the front of the vehicle and is provided with a single-piece hatch cover which, when he is driving with his head out, is swung inside the vehicle to his rear. The hatch cover has three integral M47 periscopes for day driving, each with a washer and wiper, while the centre periscope can be replaced by an M48 infra-red periscope for night driving.

The turret is of all welded steel armour with the commander and gunner seated on the right and the loader on the left. The commander's cupola is provided with a split hatch cover that opens left and right and ten vision blocks for all-round vision. The commander is also provided with a portable night-vision device with a magnification of ×4.

The gunner is seated to the front and below the commander and has an M129 telescope linked to the main armament with a magnification of ×8 and an 8-degree field of view. For engaging targets at night the gunner has an infra-red roof-mounted sight M44 with a ×9 magnification and a 6-degree field of view through one eyepiece and ×1 daylight viewing window. The loader has a single-piece hatch cover that opens to the left with an M37 periscope which can be traversed through 360 degrees, mounted in the roof forward of his hatch cover.

A large wire stowage basket is provided at the rear of the turret and some machine gun ammunition is stowed in ammunition boxes strapped to the sides of the turret, nine boxes on the left and six on the right.

The engine and transmission are at the rear of the vehicle with the aluminium cross-flow radiator mounted in the forward part of the engine compartment from the fighting compartment. The aluminium and magnesium TG-250 (formerly the XTG-250-1A) transmission consists of a hydraulic torque converter with lock-up clutch. Planetary range gearing is combined with steering and output planetary sets to give four forward and two reverse gears. Pivot turns are possible in first and reverse gears and the brakes are integral with the transmission.

The engine compartment is equipped with a fire suppression system which can be operated by the driver, or from outside the vehicle. No fire warning system is fitted.

The torsion bar suspension consists of five dual road wheels with the idler at the front and the drive sprocket at the rear. There are no track return rollers. The first and last road wheel stations are fitted with a hydraulic shock absorber. Tracks are cast steel with rubber bushes and steel pins. Each track has 102 links when new.

It was originally intended that the Sheridan would be fully amphibious without preparation but in the end a flotation screen was designed and fitted around the top of the hull. This takes about five minutes to erect and the vehicle is then propelled in the water by its tracks.

Night vision equipment is provided for the commander, gunner and driver and most vehicles now have an infra-red searchlight fitted to the left of the main armament. Standard equipment includes a heater, extraction fan in the turret roof, diesel cooker and an NBC system that pipes fresh air to the crew's face masks from a central unit.

M551 modified to resemble Soviet 122 mm M-1974 self-propelled howitzer (US Army National Training Center)

Main armament on the M551 is the M81 (formerly the XM81E12) gun/launcher which can fire the Shillelagh missile or a number of conventional rounds with a combustible cartridge. Its recoil system is of the concentric hydro-spring type.

The Shillelagh missile is designated the MGM-51A and was designed by the United States Army Missile Command and the Philco-Ford Corporation from 1959, with production beginning in 1964. The missile was also launched from the

M551 modified to resemble Soviet ZSU-23-4 self-propelled anti-aircraft gun system (US Army National Training Center)

M60A2 MBT and was to have been the main armament of the MBT-70 which was cancelled in 1970. The missile itself is 1.155 metres long, weighs 26.76 kg and has a maximum velocity of 689 metres per second. Its solid propellant motor burns for 1.18 seconds, its maximum effective range against moving targets is 2500 metres and against stationary targets 3000 metres. The Shillelagh warhead is of the HEAT type.

The missile is guided to its target by the gunner who has to keep the cross-hairs of the sight on the target until the missile impacts. The missile tracker measures the deviation of the missile's flightpath from the line of sight, the signals are converted into commands that are transmitted by the infrared transmitter mounted in the small box over the main armament to the receiver in the missile itself. A well-trained gunner can launch two missiles a minute.

The 152 mm gun/launcher can also fire a number of conventional rounds which have a combustible cartridge case consisting of two parts, a base and a body, which are made of felted nitro-cellulose. The body is attached to the projectile base with epoxy resin and an aluminium locking ring. The following types of conventional type ammunition can be fired:

Type	HEAT-T-MP	WP	TP-T	Canister
DESIGNATION	M409	M410	M411	M625A1
WEIGHT OF COMPLETE ROUND	22 kg	n/av	22.124 kg	21.772 kg
MUZZLE VELOCITY	683 m/s	n/av	683 m/s	683 m/s
MAX RANGE	9000 m	n/av	9000 m	400 m

A well-trained crew can fire a maximum of four rounds of conventional ammunition a minute. The proportion of Shillelagh missiles and conventional ammunition depends on the mission requirement; normally eight Shillelagh and 20 rounds of conventional ammunition are carried.

Mounted coaxially to the main armament is a 7.62 mm M73 machine gun and mounted on the forward part of the commander's cupola is a 12.7 mm (0.50) Browning M2 HB machine gun for anti-aircraft use with an elevation of +70 degrees and a depression of −15 degrees. Many M551s have been provided with a shield to give the commander some protection when he is using the anti-aircraft armament.

M551A1

In 1971 Frankford Arsenal awarded the Hughes Aircraft Corporation a contract worth $8.3 million for initial production of the AN/VVG-1 laser rangefinder for installation in the forward part of the commander's cupola of the M551. The rangefinder consists of a ruby laser, optics and associated panels and electronics, and enables the commander to have accurate range information on the target within seconds. When fitted with the AN/VVG-1 the vehicle is known as the M551A1.

M551 modified to resemble Soviet BMP MICV showing Sagger ATGW over simulated 73 mm gun (US Army National Training Center)

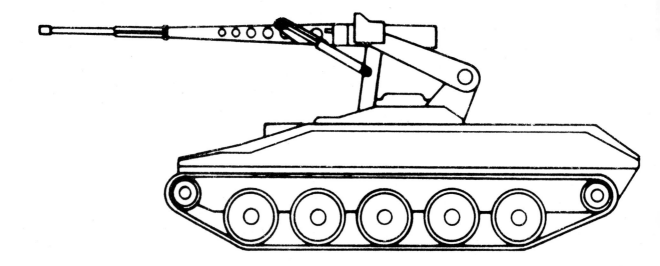

Provisional drawing of M551 Elevated Kinetic-Energy Weapon Test Bed on M551 chassis with mount in raised position (not to 1/76th scale)

M551 for ARMVAL

Ten modified M551s were used for the joint US Army/ Marine Corps Advanced Anti-armor Vehicle Evaluation between September 1978 and December 1980. The programme was sponsored by the Under Secretary of Defense for Research and Engineering with the Marine Corps being the Executive Service as it has a more immediate requirement for a lightweight helicopter transportable vehicle.

For ARMVAL Tank Automotive Research and Development Command rebuilt ten M551s at Warren, Michigan. Each vehicle was reduced to about 11 340 kg by the removal of some armour and the armament. The original 6V-53T engine was replaced by the more powerful 8V-53T as used in the Marine Corps LVTP7s and uprated to give a higher power-to-weight ratio. A new cooling system was installed and the suspension modified to improve cross-country mobility. The vehicle has a maximum road speed (governed) of 72 km/h and can accelerate from 0 to 48 km/h in ten seconds.

The gunner has a fully stabilised West German Pietzsch Staget sighting system which consists of a daylight tv with zoom optics and an integral laser gun simulator fitted to represent the 75 mm cannon. The commander's backup sight is a modified M36E2 optical sight, also fitted with a laser gun simulator.

The commander can also operate the Staget system and has a tv display; his backup is an M20A3 daylight optical sight.

M551 with 75 mm ARES cannon

Under contract to the US Army Tank Automotive Reseach and Development Command, the Pacific Car and Foundry Company has built an Elevated Kinetic-Energy Weapon Test Bed.

It consists of an M551 Sheridan with its turret removed and replaced by a new turret with an elevated mount fitted with a 75 mm ARES automatic cannon fed by a powered ammunition feed system that will convey ammunition up through an elevator tube to the chamber from the storage carousel in the turret.

The cannon will be stabilised in elevation with the turret being stabilised in azimuth. Components from the M551 and M60 series will be used in the turret drives and stabilisation systems.

A modified M36 sight will be mounted on the turret roof and this will follow the cannon at any cannon trunnion elevation. It can be used only when the target is in line of sight with the turret roof, for example when the elevated mounting is in the lowered position.

When the mount is elevated, surveillance and target acquisition will be carried out by a sight using current Improved TOW Vehicle components.

M551 with 105 mm gun

For trials purposes the Vought Corporation is to fit the chassis of the M551 with the West German Rheinmetall Rh 105-11 super low recoil gun as already fitted to the MOWAG Shark (8 × 8) vehicle. The gun would be on an external pedestal mount fitted with an automatic loader designed by Rheinmetall.

Variants

The Sheridan was projected to have been the basis for a whole family of vehicles which would have included an anti-aircraft missile vehicle with the General Dynamics Mauler missile, anti-aircraft gun vehicle, amphibious assault vehicle, cargo carrier, crane, bridgelayer (developed to the prototype stage but cancelled owing to a lack of a military requirement), engineer vehicle, flamethrower, MICV, 107 mm mortar carrier and a 155 mm self-propelled gun. Early in the development of the Sheridan a number of different weapons were installed in prototype vehicles in case of any major problems with the Shillelagh system. These included a 76 mm gun and a 105 mm gun.

CREW	4	TRENCH	2.54 m	AMMUNITION	
COMBAT WEIGHT	15 830 kg	ENGINE	Detroit Diesel Model	(main)	10 missiles and 20
UNLOADED WEIGHT	13 589 kg		6V-53T 6-cylinder		conventional rounds
POWER-TO-WEIGHT			water-cooled turbo-	(coaxial)	3080
RATIO	18.95 bhp/tonne		charged diesel devel-	(anti-aircraft)	1000
GROUND PRESSURE	0.49 kg/cm²		oping 300 bhp at	FIRE-CONTROL SYSTEM	
LENGTH	6.299 m		2800 rpm	Turret power control	electric/manual
WIDTH	2.819 m	AUXILIARY ENGINE	none	By commander	yes
HEIGHT		TRANSMISSION	TG-250 cross-drive	By gunner	yes
(to turret top)	2.272 m		with 4 forward and 2	Max rate power	
(overall)	2.946 m		reverse speeds	traverse	(non stabilised)
GROUND CLEARANCE	0.48 m	FINAL REDUCTION			360° in 10 seconds
TRACK	2.348 m	RATIO	2.22 : 1		(stabilised)
TRACK WIDTH	444 mm	SUSPENSION	torsion bar		360° in 7.5 seconds
LENGTH OF TRACK ON		ELECTRICAL SYSTEM	24 V	Gun elevation/	
GROUND	3.66 m	BATTERIES	2 × 6TN (or 4 in	depression	+19.5°/−8°
MAX SPEED			cold climate)	Gun stabiliser	
(road)	70 km/h			(vertical)	yes
(water)	5.8 km/h	ARMAMENT		(horizontal)	yes
FUEL CAPACITY	598 litres	(main)	1 × 152 mm gun/	Elevation quadrant	M13A1C
MAX RANGE (road)	600 km		launchor	Traverse indicator	M31 MOD
FORDING	amphibious	(coaxial)	1 × 7.62 mm MG		
GRADIENT	60%	(anti-aircraft)	1 × 12.7 mm MG		
SIDE SLOPE	40%	SMOKE-LAYING			
VERTICAL OBSTACLE	0.838 m	EQUIPMENT	4 smoke dischargers		
			either side of turret		

Status: Production complete. In service in limited numbers only with the US Army.

Manufacturer: Allison Division of General Motors Corporation, Cleveland Tank-Automotive Plant, Cleveland, Ohio, USA.

High Survivability Test Vehicle (Lightweight)

Development

The High Survivability Test Vehicle – Lightweight (HSTV-L) was developed under the direction of the TACOM project manager for Armored Combat Vehicle

Technology at the US Army Tank-Automotive Command, Warren, Michigan.

Following the field testing, the HSTV(L) is being used for experiments in fire-control and stabilisation. Stabilisation processing has been converted from analogue to digital. Various stabilization control algorithms are being tried along with different combinations of transducers to determine effects on gun pointing performance and the possibility of eliminating some of the expensive sensors such as gyros. The TACOM Motion Base Simulator, a huge shaker table, is being used to provide terrain input. These tests began in September 1982 and are to continue for a year or more.

Description

The high survivability of this vehicle is derived from the low silhouette, high horsepower per ton, duplication of sights, improved night vision capabilities, and the lack of specific driver and gunner controls. Any crewman can shoot and both hull crewmen can drive.

Although a test vehicle, the HSTV(L) is not a variable parameter test bed but an exercise in system realism for the three-man crew, hunter/killer fire control concept and low silhouette.

Armament for the HSTV(L) consists of a 7.62 mm M240 machine gun for both commander and coaxial position and a 75 mm smooth bore cannon. The cannon employs a revolving breech and telescoping ammunition which enables the automatic loader to load one round per 1½ seconds. The inbattery-firing recoil mechanism has a fixed piston that allows the greater mass of recoil cylinder and breech mechanism parts to recoil during firing. The 75 mm gun and automatic ammunition feeder are designed and made by ARES Inc, Port Clinton, Ohio.

Texas Instruments supplies the fire-control system which uses the hunter/killer concept. The commander uses a stabil-

HSTV(L) undergoing stabilisation/fire-control testing on Motion Base Simulator, TACOM, Warren, Michigan (US Army)

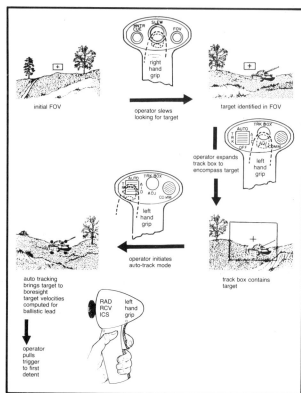

ised hunter sight that revolves independently of the turret. Once a target is selected on this sight, the turret and killer sight can be aligned with it. The gunner can then destroy the selected target while the commander returns to search with his hunter sight. Both direct vision and FLIR (Forward Looking Infra-red) optics are available for either sight. The commander can use either a biocular direct view optic eyepiece for improved clarity and reduced power drain, or a

HSTV(L) with all hatches closed and armoured track skirts fitted

Above: Typical target engagement by HSTV(L)

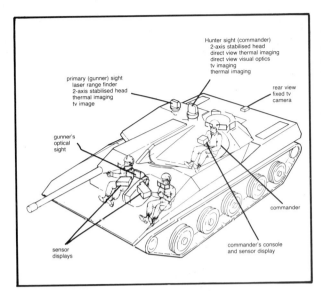

Cutaway drawing of HSTV(L) showing position of main components of Texas Instruments fire-control system

Both elevation and azimuth stabilisation is provided for the 75 mm gun with a slaved killer sight and an independently stabilised hunter sight. Fire-on-the-move capabilities are improved by decoupling the yaw motion of the hull from the turret. Cadillac Gage supplies the gun control and stabilisation system for HSTV(L).

Propulsion for the HSTV(L) comes from a gas turbine engine mounted beside the transmission with a cross-drive gearbox connecting the two. Avco Lycoming supplies the nonregenerative 650 horsepower modified helicopter gas turbine. The transmission is an X-300 Detroit Diesel Allison automatic four-speed with lock-up torque converter. Auxiliary power is provided by two 250 amp generators and a 60 gpm hydraulic pump. The hydraulic pump supplies power for the engine compartment mounted oil cooler fan and through a hydraulic slip ring; it also supplies power to the gun control system and automatic ammunition loader in the turret.

Teledyne supply the fixed height hydro-pneumatic suspension system. A 355.6 mm jounce and 127 mm rebound travel is possible due to the small 558.8 mm diameter road wheels. The track is an improved version of the type found on the M551 Sheridan.

The man-machine interface for the HSTV(L) is of prime importance. The use of the hunter/killer concept allows both the gunner and the commander to contribute as much information as possible towards the neutralisation of the enemy. The use of pressure sensitive isometric rate controller thumb switches allows for more precise gun control while firing on the move. The driver and gunner seating positions are semi-reclined for maximum comfort in a minimum space. The tv screens considerably improve fire-on-the-move sighting clarity.

video screen. In the hull, a video screen visible to both gunner and driver receives transmissions from hunter and killer sights.

The electronic fire control processor uses inputs from the sights, crosswind sensor, muzzle reference, verticle reference system, and an eye-safe CO_2 laser rangefinder to compute proper gun pointing. The laser rangefinder is supplied by Raytheon. Automatic tracking and rate aid tracking can also be accomplished by the fire control processor.

Three-view drawing of HSTV(L)

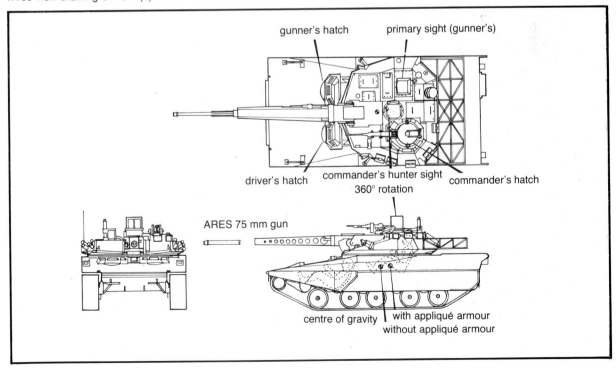

SPECIFICATIONS

CREW	3	TRANSMISSION	GMC Detroit Diesel Allison Division cross drive model X-300-4A with 4 forward and 1 reverse gears, single-stage, multiple-phase torque converter with automatic lock up			+45°/−6° rear +45°/−30° side
TEST VEHICLE WEIGHT (with instrumentation and partial applique armour)	and 20 450 kg			Max rate (power) Max rate (manual) Min rate (power)		elevation/depression 1.0 rad/sec elevation/depression 10 mils/crank elevation/depression 0.2 mils/sec
POWER-TO-WEIGHT RATIO	31.78 hp/tonne					
GROUND PRESSURE	0.7 kg/cm²	STEERING	hydrostatically controlled differential, pivot steer in neutral	Max traverse rate (power)		1.0 rad/sec
LENGTH GUN FORWARDS	8.528 m					
LENGTH HULL	5.918 m	TURNING RADIUS	pivot to infinity	Max traverse rate (manual)		10 mils/crank
WIDTH	2.794 m	BRAKES	multiple wet plate, service and parking, hydrostatically applied with mechanical backup	Min traverse rate (power)		0.2 mils/sec
HEIGHT (overall)	2.414 m					
(to turret top)	1.994 m			Periscopes		driver 3 (×1) gunner 3 (×1) commander 8 (×1)
(to hull top)	1.422 m	SUSPENSION	hydro-pneumatic			
GROUND CLEARANCE	0.508 m	ELECTRICAL SYSTEM	24 V			
TRACK	2.349 m	BATTERIES	6 × 12 V, 300 Ah	Primary engagement sight (turret)		stabilised head, FLIR CO₂ laser rangefinder, tv, 2 FOV linked to all three crew members
TRACK WIDTH	445 mm	ARMAMENT (main)	1 × 75 mm			
MAX SPEED (road)	83.68 km/h	(coaxial)	1 × 7.62 mm MG			
ACCELERATION (0 to 48 km/h)	11.8 sec	(anti-aircraft)	1 × 7.62 mm MG			
FUEL CAPACITY	409 litres	AMMUNITION (main)	26	Hunter sight (turret)		stabilised head, rotates independently of turret; FLIR; direct view optics, tv, 2 FOV linked to all three crew members
MAX CRUISING RANGE	160 km	(MG)	3200			
FORDING	1.0 m	FIRE-CONTROL SYSTEM	powered/manual			
GRADIENT	60%	By commander	yes			
SIDE SLOPE	30%	By gunner	yes	Gunner's sight (hull)		slaved to weapon, direct view optics, 2 FOV gunner's use only
TURNING RADIUS	pivot to infinity	Gun elevation/ depression	+45°/−17° front			
ENGINE	Avco-Lycoming 650 turboshaft developing 650 hp					

Status: Undergoing stabilisation/fire control testing on the Motion Base Simulator, Tank Automotive Command, Warren, Michigan.

Manufacturer: AAI Corporation, Box 6767, Baltimore, Maryland 21204, USA.

Rapid Deployment Force Light Tank (RDF/LT)

Development

The Rapid Deployment Force Light Tank (RDF/LT) has been designed as a private venture by AAI Corporation which has already built the prototype of the High Survivability Test Vehicle (Lightweight) under contract to the United States Army Tank-Automotive Command.

The prototype was shown for the first time in October 1980 when it was said by the company that it could be in service by 1984, if a decision on production was taken in the immediate future.

The vehicle is airportable: the Lockheed C-5B transport aircraft can carry eight RDF/LTs, the C-130 and C-141 could each carry two and the Navy/Marine Corps CH-53E helicopter can carry one slung under its fuselage.

This vehicle, with some changes and improvements in armour protection, is AAI's entry in the MPGS competition.

Description

The hull of the RDF/LT is made of all-welded aluminium armour with the driver sitting at the front of the hull on the left and the commander/gunner to his right. Both crew mem-

Powerpack of AAI RDF/LT slides out for ease of maintenance and field replacement

Prototype of AAI Rapid Deployment Force Light Tank

Rapid Deployment Force Light Tank fitted with Universal One-Man turret armed with 75 mm ARES gun

153

bers have a single-piece hatch cover that opens outwards and has three integrated periscopes. Between the driver and commander/gunner, in the upper part of the glacis plate, is the hull-mounted auxiliary sight.

The main armament consists of a 75 mm ARES cannon mounted in the centre of the hull behind the crew. The 75 mm ARES cannon is fed from an automatic magazine holding 60 rounds of APFSDS and multi-purpose ammunition and when used for indirect fire has a maximum range of 12 000 metres. To the right of the main armament there is a coaxial 7.62 mm machine gun.

Mounted above and behind the main armament is the stabilised rotary head which is the primary sight. The main armament is fully stabilised and the fire-control system includes a digital computer. The fire-control system is similar to that of the HSTV(L) and is fully described in that entry.

The engine and transmission are mounted at the rear of the hull and the complete powerpack is on extensible rails to facilitate maintenance in the field.

The torsion bar suspension consists of five dual rubber-tyred road wheels with a drive sprocket at the rear, idler at the front and one return roller.

Applique steel armour can be fitted to the RDF/LT for increased protection. As an alternative to the 75 mm ARES cannon which is mounted in an unmanned turret and fitted to the prototype vehicle, an AAI Universal One-Man Turret which is also armed with a 75 mm ARES cannon, fed from an automatic loader, can be fitted.

Variants

In 1982 AAI announced a new version of this vehicle fitted with a new one-man turret also armed with the ARES 75 mm automatic cannon. This has a single-piece hatch cover opening to the rear, six periscopes for all round observation and forward and to the right of the hatch is a stabilised sight for target acquisition/firing.

75 mm ARES automatic gun as fitted to the HSTV-L, RDF Light Tank and the High Mobility Agility Test Vehicle (HIMAG)

AAI Rapid Deployment Force Light Tank prototype fitted with new one-man all-cast turret armed with 75 mm ARES automatic gun undergoing trials in 1982

SPECIFICATIONS

(RDF/LT with three man crew and turret mentioned above)

CREW	3
WEIGHT	
(combat)	13 426 kg
(unloaded)	12 247 kg
POWER TO WEIGHT	
RATIO	26.07 hp/tonne
GROUND PRESSURE	0.49 kg/cm²
LENGTH GUN	
FORWARDS	8.235 m
LENGTH HULL	5.569 m
WIDTH	2.54 m
HEIGHT (top of sight)	2.286 m
AXIS OF FIRE	1.562 m
GROUND CLEARANCE	0.50 m
MAX ROAD SPEED	64 km/h
FUEL CAPACITY	378 litres
MAX CRUISING RANGE	500 km
FORDING	1 m
GRADIENT	60%

ENGINE	General Motors 6V53T, turbo-charged, 6-cylinder diesel developing 350 hp
TRANSMISSION	General Motors, Allison Division, X-200 cross drive, automatic
SUSPENSION	torsion bar
ELECTRICAL SYSTEM	24 V
BATTERIES	6 × 12 V, 190 Ah
ARMAMENT	
(main)	1 × 75 mm
(coaxial)	1 × 7.62 mm MG
AMMUNITION	
(main)	60
(coaxial)	2600
FIRE-CONTROL	
turret power control	hydraulic/manual
by commander	yes
by gunner	yes
Gun elevation/	
depression	+40°/−15°
Turret traverse	360°
Turret slew rate	60°/s
Gun elevation rate	60°/s

Status: Prototype. This vehicle has been designed to meet the US requirement for a Mobile Protected Gun System.

Manufacturer: AAI Corporation, PO Box 6767, Baltimore, Maryland, 21204, USA.

13.2 Tonne Rapid Deployment Force Light Tank (RDF/LT)

Development

The original AAI Rapid Deployment Force Light Tank (RDF/T), described in the preceding entry, cannot be exported at present as the ARES 75 mm automatic cannon has not yet completed its US Army funded development.

In 1982 AAI announced that they had built the prototype of a 13.2 tonne RDF/LT fitted with a new two-man turret armed with the same 76 mm M32 gun as the M41 light tank's. This was phased out of US Army service some years ago, although it remains in service with many other countries. The prototype uses the chassis of the original RDF/LT but production vehicles would have a slightly different hull and the description below relates to this. A Lockheed C-130H aircraft can carry two 13.2 tonne RDF/LTs.

Description

The hull of the RDF/LT is of all-welded aluminium construction. The driver is seated at the front of the hull on the left with 30 rounds of 76 mm ammunition stowed horizontally to his right. The driver has a single-piece hatch cover that opens to the left, in the forward part of this are three periscopes the centre one of which can be replaced by a passive periscope for night driving.

The all-welded turret is in the centre of the vehicle with the commander seated on the left and the gunner on the right. Both have a single-piece hatch cover, six periscopes for all round observation and an M32 periscope for aiming the armament. The gunner's M32 periscope incorporates a laser rangefinder.

AAI 13.2 tonne Rapid Deployment Force Light Tank prototype showing new turret armed with 76 mm M32 gun which can fire a new APFSDS-T projectile developed by AAI

Prototype of AAI 13.2 tonne Rapid Deployment Force Light Tank undergoing initial cross-country trials in 1982

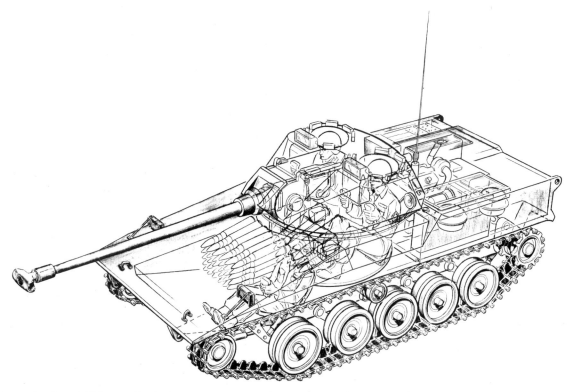

Cutaway drawing of 13.2 tonne Rapid Deployment Force Light Tank showing crew positions and ammunition stowage

Main armament consists of a 76 mm high velocity M32 gun which is installed in the M41 tank. In addition to the range of ammunition originally developed for this weapon, and fully described in the entry for the M41 light tank, AAI have developed a new round of APFSDS-T ammunition based on their experience in developing ammunition for the ARES 75 mm automatic. This has already been tested in Denmark during trials with an M41 light tank. According to AAI, this projectile has three times the probability of killing a T-62 tank at a normal combat range of 1500 metres than the 105 mm M456 HEAT-T round and only slightly less kill probability at a similar range to the 105 mm M735 APFSDS-T round. A 7.62 mm M240 machine gun is mounted coaxially with the main armament.

A Cadillac Gage stabilisation and weapons control system is fitted as standard enabling the vehicle to fire on the move with a high probability of a first round hit. Optional fire-control systems include an M32 sight with an AN/VSG-2 Tank Thermal Sight or a digital tank fire-control system with the AN/VSG-2 Tank Thermal Sight, AN/GVS-5 laser rangefinder and a digital ballistic computer.

The engine and transmission are mounted at the rear of the hull and the complete powerpack is on extensible rails to facilitate maintenance in the field.

The torsion bar suspension consists of five dual rubber tyred road wheels with the drive sprocket at the rear, idler at the front and one return roller which is positioned above the second and third roadwheel stations. Track is the M113.

SPECIFICATIONS

CREW	3	FUEL CAPACITY	378 litres	AMMUNITION	
WEIGHT		MAX CRUISING RANGE	500 km	(main)	50
(combat)	13 200 kg	FORDING	1 m	(coaxial)	2600
(unloaded)	11 800 kg	GRADIENT	60%	FIRE-CONTROL	
POWER TO WEIGHT		ENGINE	General Motors 6V-53T,	turret power control	hydraulic/manual
RATIO	26.5 hp/tonne		turbo-charged, 6-cylinder	by commander	yes
GROUND PRESSURE	0.48 kg/cm²		diesel developing 350 hp	by gunner	yes
LENGTH GUN		TRANSMISSION	General Motors, Allison	GUN ELEVATION/	
FORWARDS	7.34 m		Division, X-200 crossdrive,	DEPRESSION	+22°/−10°
LENGTH HULL	5.569 m		automatic	TURRET TRAVERSE	360°
WIDTH	2.54 m	SUSPENSION	torsion bar		
HEIGHT		ELECTRICAL SYSTEM	24 V		
(overall, M32 sight)	2.235 m	BATTERIES	6 × 12 V, 190 Ah		
(hull top)	1.562 m	ARMAMENT			
GROUND CLEARANCE	0.50 m	(main)	1 × 76 mm		
MAX ROAD SPEED	64 km/h	(coaxial)	1 × 7.62 mm MG		

Status: Prototype.

Manufacturer: AAI Corporation, Box 6767, Baltimore, Maryland 21204, USA.

Mobile Protected Gun System (MPGS)

The United States Marine Corps has a requirement for a highly mobile armoured vehicle which is at present called the Mobile Protected Weapons System (MPWS). It will be an additional anti-armour, anti-material, anti-personnel system complementing, at times replacing (with fewer capabilities) the MBT in combat operations during an amphibious assault and subsequent operations ashore at all levels of combat intensity.

As an integrated part of task organised units, the MPWS will operate with combined arms of infantry, artillery, air and MBTs, and be capable of operating over all types of terrain.

It should be able to deal with a wide variety of battlefield targets including tanks, ATGW carriers and ATGW ground mounts, light armoured vehicles, short-range artillery, motorised and dismounted troops, helicopters, anti-aircraft systems and fixed positions.

MPWS must be airportable in current transport aircraft such as the C-5A, C-130 and C-141, be able to ford rivers, be compatible with current amphibious craft and be fitted with an NBC system. Main armament could be the ARES 75 mm automatic cannon (or a 90 mm version), or the 105 mm Rheinmetall Rh 105-11 super low recoil gun already installed in the Swiss MOWAG Shark (8 × 8) vehicle or a lightweight 105 mm under development by Benet Laboratory.

In December 1981, the Marine Corps agreed to merge its MPWS Program with the Army's Mobile Protected Gun System Program. The Army's requirement is similar to that of the Marine Corps but did not require lift via the CH-53E helicopter. A draft Joint Service Operational Requirement has been developed and is being staffed at this time. The joint system would retain the Marine Corps helicopter lift requirement while incorporating many of the Army's tank-like characteristics.

Although fielding is projected for the early 1990's, it is being reviewed in the context of various armor-antiarmor studies and considerations by the Army to restructure its light forces.

M3 Bradley Cavalry Fighting Vehicle

The M3 Bradley Cavalry Fighting Vehicle is almost identical to the M2 Bradley Infantry Fighting Vehicle but has a five man crew (instead of ten), no firing ports in the rear troop compartment and increased ammunition carrying capability. Main armament comprises a Hughes Helicopters 25 mm Chain Gun, 7.62 mm coaxial machine gun and a twin Hughes TOW ATGW launcher on the left side of the turret. A total of 1500 rounds of 25 mm and 4540 rounds of 7.62 mm ammunition are carried plus 12 TOW ATGW's of which two are in the launcher for ready use.

M3 Bradley Cavalry Fighting Vehicle

Cadillac Gage Commando V-300 Armoured Vehicle Range

Development

The Commando V-300 (6 × 6) range of armoured vehicles has been developed as a private venture by the Cadillac Gage Company which has already designed and built the highly successful Commando V-150 (4 × 4) range of vehicles which are now in service with more than 20 countries. The first two prototypes of the V-300 were completed in 1979 and the vehicle entered production in 1983. Late in 1982 Panama placed an order worth over $6 million for 12 V-300 Commando vehicles in four different configurations including fire support vehicle with 90 mm Cockerill Mk III gun, APC with twin 7.62 mm machine guns and recovery. All of these were

scheduled for delivery by the end of 1983. The company also supplied a number of vehicles for the Light Armored Vehicle competition including models fitted with the two-man Cockerill 90 mm turret, two-man 25 mm Chain Gun turret and two-man 25 mm Chain Gun turret fitted with a stabilisation system.

Description

The hull of the V-300 Commando is of all-welded unitised construction of special high hardness steel ballistic plate that provides the crew with protection from small arms fire and shell splinters.

The driver is seated at the front of the hull on the left side and has a single-piece square hatch cover that opens to the rear. To his front are three periscopes for forward observation

Cadillac Gage V-300 Commando with two-man turret armed with 90 mm Cockerill Mark III gun

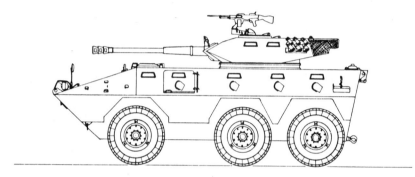

Cadillac Gage V-300 Commando fitted with one-man turret armed with 12.7 mm and 7.62 mm machine guns

Cadillac Gage V-300 Commando fitted with two-man turret armed with 20 mm Oerlikon cannon, 7.62 mm coaxial MG, 7.62 mm anti-aircraft MG and smoke dischargers

and one of these can be replaced by a passive periscope for driving at night. In the side of the hull to the left of the driver is a bullet-proof vision block with a firing port underneath. To the rear of this is a small half-door that opens to the rear, this has a bullet-proof vision block underneath of which is a firing port.

The engine compartment is to the right of the driver with the air inlet and air outlet in the roof and the exhaust pipe in the right side of the hull. Power from the engine is transmitted to the final drives via an Allison MT-643 four-speed automatic gearbox. The transfer box contains a two-speed system with a spline engagement clutch for the axle drive.

On the glacis plate is a receptacle for a shovel and pick axe and under the nose is an internally mounted hydraulic winch which has a maximum capacity of 9072 kg, this is provided with 45 metres of 12.7 mm diameter steel core cable.

The V-300 can be fitted with a number of armament installations, these are mounted in the centre of the hull over the second axle and include:
Cadillac Gage two-man turret with 90 mm Cockerill Mk III gun (described in V-150 entry).
Cadillac Gage two-man turret with 76 mm Royal Ordnance Factories L23A1 gun (described in V-150 entry).
Turret armed with 25 mm M242 Hughes Chain Gun, 7.62 mm coaxial MG, 7.62 mm anti-aircraft MG and smoke dischargers.
Cadillac Gage two-man turret with 20 mm Oerlikon cannon (described in V-150 entry).

Cadillac Gage one-man turret with 20 mm Oerlikon cannon (described in V-150 entry).
Cadillac Gage one-man 1-metre MG turret (described in V-150 entry).
Cadillac Gage one-man MG turret (described in V-150 entry).
Ring mount with 7.62 mm or 12.7 mm MG.

The troop compartment is at the rear of the V-300 and in each side of the hull are three bullet-proof vision blocks each

Cadillac Gage V-300 Commando fitted with turret armed with 20 mm cannon, 7.62 mm coaxial machine gun and 7.62 mm anti-aircraft machine gun

Cadillac Gage V-300 Commando fitted with Cadillac Gage one-metre turret armed with 20 mm Oerlikon cannon and 7.62 mm coaxial machine gun

with a firing port underneath. Over the top of the troop compartment are two rectangular roof hatches hinged on the outside. The infantry enter and leave the vehicle through two doors in the rear of the hull, each of these being provided with a bullet-proof vision block underneath of which is a firing port. As an alternative to the two part hatch cover a circular hatch cover with provision for mounting a 7.62 mm pintle-mounted GPMG can be fitted.

The front suspension is a swing-mounted solid axle with rear suspension being independent with coil springs at each wheel station. The front solid axle is restrained longitudinally by trailing arms and laterally by stabilising rods attached to the axle and hull. The two rear axles consist of short drive shafts extending from the hull-mounted differentials to the independently-sprung trailing-arms mounted wheel stations. The road wheels have a combined wheel travel of 30 cm, a jounce of 17.5 cm and a rebound of 12.5 cm. All the swing mounted axles are of the double-reduction top-mounted type. The front and rear axles have positive No-Spin differentials to maintain traction in off road operations. The central axles contain the inter-axle differential. All wheels have hydraulic brakes with steering being power-assisted on the front wheels. All wheels have run-flat tubeless tyres.

The V-300 is fully amphibious without preparation being propelled in the water by its wheels at a speed of 4.8 km/h.

A wide range of optional equipment is available including night vision devices, heater kit, air-conditioning system, NBC system, wiper kit for the driver and a slave cable.

Ambulance model of V-300 Commando showing raised roof for greater headroom and ramp instead of twin doors in hull rear to facilitate loading of stretchers

Variants

TOW Anti-tank
This would be fitted with the same mount as used in the M901 Improved TOW Vehicle based on the M113 chassis with two missiles in the ready to launch position and additional missiles being carried in reserve in the hull.

TOW Anti-tank
Fitted with an external top-mounted swing-up launcher with an elevation of +30 degrees, depression of −10 degrees and

Cadillac Gage V-300 Commando fitted with turret armed with Hughes Helicopters 25 mm Chain Gun, coaxial 7.62 mm machine gun and smoke dischargers. The 7.62 mm anti-aircraft machine gun is not installed

traverse of 360 degrees. Ten TOW ATGW missiles are carried plus 7.62 mm machine gun and 2000 rounds of ammunition.

81 mm Mortar

Fitted with turntable-mounted 81 mm mortar with elevation from +42 to +85 degrees, total traverse of 360 degrees, range of 150 to 4400 metres with a total of 60 mortar bombs carried. Also fitted with 7.62 mm machine gun for which 2000 rounds of ammunition are carried.

Ambulance

This model would be unarmed and be fitted with a raised roof and ramp in place of twin doors at the rear to facilitate the loading of stretchers and walking wounded.

Others

These could include cargo carrier, command vehicle, recovery vehicle and anti-aircraft with a missile system such as ADATS, or a gun system such as the General Electric 20 mm Vulcan as installed on a number of V-150 Commando 4 × 4 vehicles which have been supplied to Saudi Arabia.

SPECIFICATIONS

CREW	3 + 9 (max)	WHEELBASE	2.209 m + 1.524 m	TRANSFER CASE	2-speed with spline engagement clutch for axle drive
CONFIGURATION	6 × 6	ANGLE OF APPROACH/ DEPARTURE	45°/78°		
COMBAT WEIGHT	13 137 kg	MAX SPEED		STEERING	vario ratio power
POWER-TO-WEIGHT		(road)	92 km/h	SUSPENSION	solid front axle, middle and
RATIO	17.88 bhp/tonne	(water)	5 km/h		rear independent with coil
LENGTH	6.40 m	ACCELERATION			springs, direct acting
WIDTH	2.54 m	(0 to 32 km/h)	8 seconds		telescopic shock absorber
HEIGHT		FUEL CAPACITY	265 litres		acting at each wheel station
(MG turret)	2.59 m	MAX RANGE	700 km	TYRES	14.5 × 21
(20 mm turret)	2.692 m	FORDING	amphibious	BRAKES	
(ITV)	2.756 m	GRADIENT	60%	(main)	hydraulic (all wheels) power
(hull top)	1.981 m	SIDE SLOPE	30%		booster with electric back up
GROUND CLEARANCE		VERTICAL OBSTACLE	0.609 m	(parking)	drum and shoe hand
(hull)	0.533 m	TURNING RADIUS	10 m		operated
(axle)	0.355 m	ENGINE	VT-504 V-8 turbo-charged	ELECTRICAL SYSTEM	24 V
TRACK			diesel, 235 hp at 3000 rpm	BATTERIES	2 × 12 V, 100 Ah
(front)	2.167 m	TRANSMISSION	Allison MT-643 automatic, 4		
(rear)	2.198 m		speeds forwards and 1 reverse		

Status: In production. In service with Panama.

Manufacturer: Cadillac Gage Company, PO Box 1027, Warren, Michigan 48090, USA.

Dragoon 300 Armoured Vehicle Family

Development

The Dragoon 300 armoured vehicle family was originally designed to meet a requirement issued in 1976 by the United States Army Military Police for a vehicle which would be airportable in a Lockheed C-130 Hercules transport aircraft and be suitable for convoy and air base protection.

Although this request subsequently lapsed the Verne Corporation of Detroit went ahead and built two prototypes which made their first public appearance in 1978. Following successful trials, both in the United States and overseas, a pre-production batch of 17 vehicles was built by the Dominion Manufacturing Company, near Washington DC.

Dragoon 300 fitted with two-man Arrowpointe turret armed with 90 mm Cockerill Mk III gun and coaxial 7.62 mm machine gun

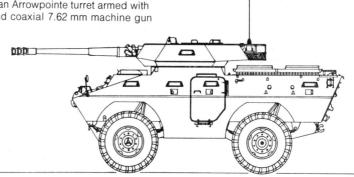

Dragoon 300 in armoured personnel carrier configuration with cupola-mounted 12.7 mm M2 HB machine gun

Dragoon 300 with Arrowpointe designed two-man turret armed with Hughes Helicopters 25 mm M242 Chain Gun, 7.62 mm machine gun coaxial with main armament and two banks of four smoke dischargers

World-wide marketing of the Dragoon 300 armoured vehicle family is undertaken by the Arrowpointe Corporation.

The Dragoon 300 armoured vehicle family has already been evaluated by a number of countries in South America and first production vehicles were completed for the United States Army and Navy in 1982 (see separate entry under Variants).

From the early concept stage, logistics and life-cycle costs were the main criteria in the development of the Dragoon. Some 70 per cent of the components of the vehicle are common to the M113A2 full tracked armoured personnel carrier and the M809 (5 × 5) 5-ton truck. Components of the former include the engine, starter, alternator, cold start, periscopes, bilge pumps, interior and exterior lighting, gauges, switches, electrical and hydraulic system components. M809 components include axles, suspension, brakes, steering, electrical and hydraulic system components.

Description
The all-welded hull of the Dragoon is of XAR-30 high hardness steel ballistic plate which meets the requirements of MIL-A-12560 and is of monocoque construction with welded seams. XAR-30 is approximately 30 per cent superior to US

Specification MIL-A-12560 homogeneous steel armour against small calibre ball and armour piercing ammunition, in addition XAR-30 has threshold penetration velocities in excess of that specified by US Mil.Spec.46100B.

The driver is seated at the front of the vehicle on the left with the vehicle commander/co-driver to his right. The driver has three vision blocks to his front which provide him with a 180-degree field of view, while the commander has one with each being provided with a single-piece hatch cover that opens to the outside and a vision block in the side of the hull. A firing port is provided below the commander's vision block. Both also have a seat which is adjustable front/rear and up/down with the back folding forward for access.

In each side of the hull, between the front and rear axles, is a side door, the lower part folds down to form a step while the upper part, which contains a vision block with a firing port underneath, swings backwards through 180 degrees and can be locked open.

Forward of the side door is a vision block underneath which is a firing port. All vision blocks are fitted with spall shields and crash pads and the firing ports have covers that can be secured from within the vehicle and have quick cam levers for opening and closing.

Dragoon 300 command, control and communications
countermeasures vehicle with 12.7 mm M2 HB machine gun

When being used as an APC, a maximum of eleven fully-equipped men, plus a two-man crew, can be carried, each of the latter being provided with an individual seat with a back rest.

The engine compartment is at the rear of the Dragoon on the right side. Thermal and acoustic insulation are provided between the engine compartment and the personnel area on interchangeable close-out panels. Quick access is provided to the engine compartment from the interior and exterior of the vehicle, the panels do not have to be in place for correct engine running.

The air intake louvres are in top of the hull and the air outlet louvres and exhaust outlet are in the right side of the hull and have been designed to prevent the entry of flaming liquids such as petrol bombs. A counter-balanced tilt hood gives access to the engine compartment and fluid level checks. Access doors are provided for servicing the filters.

Power is transmitted from the engine and gearbox via a chain case and rear propeller shaft to the rear differential, then via an intermediate propeller shaft to the disconnect clutch in the centre of the hull. From then it is transmitted to the front differential and front axle via a forward propeller shaft. All of the drive train components are enclosed. The transmission employs a torque converter active through the

Dragoon 300 with 90 mm Cockerill gun (left), command, control
and countermeasures vehicle (centre with antennas raised) and
12.7 mm APC variant (right)

Dragoon 300 video optical surveillance vehicle as used by US Army's 9th Infantry Division

three lowest forward gear reductions, and direct drive (lock-up) in fourth and fifth forward gears.

The cooling system is at the rear of the engine compartment on the right side and provides the maximum possible engine and transmission cooling and incorporates a hydraulically driven fan.

Both waterproof axles are designed so that in the event of an axle shaft failure, a wheel will not come off.

The Dragoon has power-assisted hydraulic brakes and a separate electrically actuated hydraulic override braking system permits braking in the event of a primary hydraulic system failure. A parking brake is included as part of the primary brake system.

Power-assisted steering is provided and permits manual steering in the event of failure of the hydraulic system, with variable steering ratios for both cross-country and high speed road operations. After a loss of air pressure the tyres are capable of continuing operations for a minimum of 80 km on a concrete road surface at a speed of 56 km/h.

The heavy duty suspension consists of semi-elliptical springs and direct action hydraulic shock absorbers. Special wrap is provided on the second leaf for added safety and the front and rear springs are interchangeable. The shock absorbers have built-in shock valves for good balance between cross-country and high speed road operation. Jounce stops are installed at each spring position to prevent the suspension components from striking the hull. The stops sustain all the imposed loads without damage to the rubber portion.

In the rear of the hull on the left side is another door, the lower part of which folds down to form a step while the upper part, which contains a vision block and a firing port, opens to

the right. In the left side of the hull, towards the rear, is a single vision block.

A tow hook at the rear enables the Dragoon 300 to tow a trailer or other vehicles up to a maximum weight of 11 338 kg. Mounted internally at the front of the hull is a winch with a capacity of 9078 kg, this is operated off the main vehicle hydraulic circuit which enables the vehicle to be in gear while winching and during recovery operations. This has 52 metres of cable.

The Dragoon is fully amphibious being propelled in the water by its wheels, when afloat steering is by turning the front wheels as on land. Three bilge pumps, each with a capacity of 190 litres, expel any water that seeps into the hull through the rubber door seals.

Standard equipment on all vehicles includes a heater, run-flat tyres and a dry fire extinguisher. A wide range of optional equipment is available including active or passive night vision equipment, air conditioning, smoke dischargers, infra-red firewire detection/fire suppression system, NBC system and various spotlights.

Variants

There are four distinct groups of Dragoon 300 vehicles:
Personnel carrier may be outfitted as a basic APC, reconnaissance, command, recovery, security, escort or a command/communications vehicle. Each of these may be fitted with ring or pintle-mounted machine guns up to 12.7 mm in calibre, and a variety of communications systems. Command version could have a raised roof with additional vision blocks.
Light weapons carrier may be fitted with a single machine gun up to 12.7 mm calibre, twin machine guns up to 12.7 mm

calibre, or machine guns in combination such as 7.62 mm/12.7 mm.

Special weapons carrier such as 81 mm mortar, TOW missile carrier (with Improved TOW system), Dragon ATGW carrier and anti-personnel rocket launcher.

Heavy weapons carrier which may be equipped with various armament installations including turret-mounted 20 mm or 25 mm cannon, 76 mm or 90 mm gun, all of which may have a coaxial, ring or pintle-mounted machine guns. The other turrets have been designed specifically for the Dragoon although they can be fitted to other vehicles such as the M113A2. The two-man Arrowpointe designed turrets have the same degree of protection as the basic vehicle with the commander seated on the left and the gunner on the right, both with an individual hatch cover that opens to the rear, two periscopes, one facing the front and the other the rear, and a vision block in each side of the turret. The gunner has a M36 sight, also used in the M60 MBT, with ×1 and ×7 optics with provision for active or passive night vision equipment.

Turret power is provided by the primary vehicle hydraulic system and is supported by a secondary manual back-up. The turret has an independent 24 V dc power source to prevent draw on the vehicle's power system in silent watch and to ensure turret and weapon operations in case the basic vehicle becomes disabled or there is a failure in the primary hydraulic or electrical system. Exhaust blowers are fitted in the turret to expel fumes.

Control of turret and weapons operations is provided by a single cyclic control grip. This self-contained grip includes elevation, depression, traverse, weapon selection (main or coaxial), cyclic rate of fire and firing. All functions of the weapon system are provided with emergency back up.

Brief details of the turrets are given below. When fitted with any of these two-man turrets the Dragoon has a nine-man crew, commander, gunner, driver and six fully-equipped infantrymen.

For the Light Armored Vehicle competition, Arrowpointe proposed the following models of the Dragoon 300 vehicle: Basic vehicle with pintle-mounted 7.62 mm M60 machine gun

MAIN ARMAMENT	Cockerill Mk.III	Mecar	M139A2	Rh 202
CALIBRE	90 mm	90 mm	20 mm	20 mm
SECONDARY ARMAMENT				
(optional)	7.62 mm	7.62 mm	7.62 mm	7.62 mm
AMMUNITION				
(main)	50	50	n/a	n/a
(coaxial)	4000	4000	4000	4000
GUN ELEVATION	+32°	+32°	+60°	+60°
GUN DEPRESSION	−4°	−4°	−10°	−10°
TURRET TRAVERSE	360°	360°	360°	360°
ELEVATION SPEED	40°/s	40°/s	60°/s	60°/s
WEIGHT				
(empty)	1640 kg	1453 kg	1433 kg	1433 kg
(loaded)	1876 kg	1666 kg	1679 kg	1679 kg
DIAMETER				
(outer)	1.6 m	1.6 m	1.6 m	1.6 m
(ring)	1.372 m	1.372 m	1.372 m	1.372 m
(basket)	1.32 m	1.32 m	1.32 m	1.32 m
HEIGHT				
(o/a inc basket)	1.651 m	1.651 m	1.651 m	1.651 m
(turret)	0.607 m	0.607 m	0.607 m	0.607 m

Dragoon 300 with Arrowpointe designed two-man turret armed with 90 mm Cockerill Mark III gun, 7.62 mm coaxial machine gun and two banks of four smoke dischargers

Fitted with one-man turret armed with 7.62 mm and 12.7 mm machine guns

Fitted with two-man turret armed with 20 mm or 25 mm cannon and 7.62 mm coaxial machine gun, weapons have elevation of +60 degrees and depression of −10 degrees

Fitted with two-man turret armed with 90 mm Cockerill Mark III gun and 7.62 mm coaxial machine gun, weapons have elevation of +35 degrees and depression of −8 degrees

Fitted with two-man turret armed with 90 mm Mecar gun and 7.62 mm coaxial machine gun, weapons have elevation of +45 degrees and depression of −8 degrees

Command and control vehicle equipped with various antenna and communications equipment

Service and control vehicle with barricade ram/debris blade at front of hull, 7.62 mm or 12.7 mm machine gun at front and 7.62 mm machine gun at rear of hull

Ambulance or utility vehicle, unarmed

Mortar carrier with 7.62 mm machine gun

Self-loading logistics vehicle with boom with capacity of 2268 kg

Maintenance, recovery and engineer vehicle with boom crane and front mounted dozer blade or scoop bucket

US Army and US Navy vehicles

Between March and November 1982 the Dragoon was in production to meet contracts placed by the US Army and Navy.

Six Dragoons were supplied for the 9th Infantry Division High Technology Test Bed (HTTB) with two provided for the electronic warfare role, each fitted with the Emerson AN/MSQ-103A Teampack and a video optical surveillance vehicle.

The EW variant carries out advanced battlefield direction finding and high speed communications jamming and is fitted with an antenna that can be quickly raised well above the vehicle. The video optical surveillance vehicle has a modified Arrowpointe 25 mm two-man turret which in its forward part has been fitted with a long range day/night surveillance system that can be retracted quickly under armour protection. This provides the field commander with a high mobile, armour protected observation capability, which, when connected to an on-board data link, gives a clear, front line view of the battlefield for rear area commanders. The Teampack electronic detection system is normally carried in the horizontal position on the left side of the vehicle at the rear protected by a brush guard and a weather shield. When required for action it can be erected quickly into the vertical position. A 7.62 mm M60 machine gun is mounted on the forward part of the roof on the right side.

The US Navy versions are used to patrol three nuclear weapon storage facilities on the east coast of the USA and at one facility in Alaska. These are fitted with a 7.62 mm MG with a ballistic shield and a floodlight above. This model also has a double width door each side which in three parts, the lower part dropping down to form a step and the upper parts, each with a vision block with a firing port underneath, opening either side. This enables personnel to be disembarked quickly.

SPECIFICATIONS

CREW	3 + 6	VERTICAL OBSTACLE	
CONFIGURATION	4 × 4	(forwards)	0.99 m
COMBAT WEIGHT	12 700 kg	(reverse)	0.61 m
UNLOADED WEIGHT	9430 kg	TURNING RADIUS	
POWER-TO-WEIGHT		(land)	8.788 m
RATIO	23.62 bhp/tonne	(water)	8.839 m
LENGTH	5.588 m	ENGINE	Detroit Diesel Allison 6V-53T
WIDTH	2.438 m		6-cylinder, liquid-cooled,
HEIGHT			turbo-charged diesel
(over turret periscopes)	2.642 m		developing 300 bhp at
(hull top)	2.133 m		2800 rpm
GROUND CLEARANCE		TRANSMISSION	Allison MT-653 DR
(hull centre)	0.692 m		automatic, 5 forward and 1
(axles)	0.381 m		reverse gears
TRACK	1.981 m	TRANSFER CASE	single-speed
WHEELBASE	2.794 m	STEERING	hydraulic
ANGLE OF APPROACH/		SUSPENSION	semi-elliptical springs and
DEPARTURE	60°/45°		hydraulic shock absorbers
ACCELERATION		TYRES	14.00 × 20
(0 to 35 km/h)	4.5 seconds	BRAKES	
MAX SPEED (road)		(main)	Alien internal expanding
(5th gear)	115.9 km/h		shoe
(4th gear)	83.7 km/h	(parking)	integral
(3rd gear)	37.0 km/h	ELECTRICAL SYSTEM	24 V
(2nd gear)	22.5 km/h	BATTERIES	2 × 12 V, 100 Ah
(1st gear)	11.3 km/h	ARMAMENT	
MAX SPEED (water)	4.83 km/h	(main)	1 × 20 mm
FUEL CAPACITY	341 litres	(coaxial)	1 × 7.62 mm MG
MAX RANGE (road)	1045 km	SMOKE-LAYING	
FORDING	fully amphibious	EQUIPMENT	optional
GRADIENT	60%	FIRE-CONTROL SYSTEM	
SIDE SLOPE	30%	Turret power control	hydraulic/manual
		Gun elevation/	
		depression	+60°/−10°
		Turret traverse	360°

Status: Production. In service with US Army and Navy.

Manufacturer: Dominion Manufacturing Company, marketed by The Arrowpointe Corporation, 4000 Town Center, Southfield, Michigan 48075, USA.

Cadillac Gage Commando V-150 Armoured Vehicle Range

Development

In 1962 the Cadillac Gage Company, as a private venture, started design work on a 4 × 4 armoured vehicle which could undertake a wide range of roles such as armoured personnel carrier, convoy escort vehicle or reconnaissance vehicle. The first prototype of the vehicle, called the V-100 Commando, was completed in March 1963 and the first production vehicles the following year.

The V-100 was widely used in Viet-Nam for both convoy escort work and for patrolling air bases and other high value targets. The V-100 was powered by a Chrysler 361 V-8 petrol engine which developed 200 hp and gave the vehicle a maximum road speed of 100 km/h. Gross vehicle weight was 7370 kg and a maximum of twelve men including the crew could be carried. The V-100 was supplemented in production by the larger V-200, which was powered by a Chrysler 440 CID engine which developed 275 hp and gave the vehicle a maximum road speed of 96 km/h. Gross vehicle weight of the V-200 is 12 730 kg. The V-200 is believed to have been sold only to Singapore and is no longer being produced.

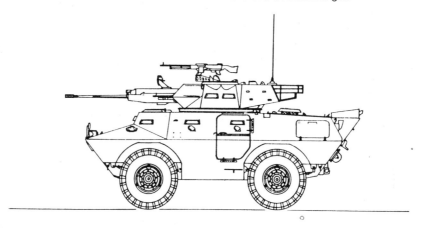

V-150 Commando fitted with two-man turret armed with 20 mm Oerlikon cannon, 7.62 mm coaxial machine gun and 7.62 mm anti-aircraft machine gun

V-150 Commando fitted with turret armed with 20 mm Oerlikon cannon, 7.62 mm coaxial machine gun and 7.62 mm anti-aircraft machine gun. Six smoke dischargers are fitted to turret side

V-100 Commando with turret armed with 0.30 and 0.50 machine guns

The United States Air Force still uses a number of original V-100 Commando vehicles at the Tactical Fighter Weapons Centre at Nellis Air Force Base in Nevada. Typical roles include simulating the Soviet SA-9 SAM system and command and control systems associated with the Soviet air defence systems.

In October 1971 the V-150 was introduced and has now replaced the V-100 and V-200 in production. Production of the V-100, V-150 and V-200 has now reached well over 4000 units.

The vehicles have been exported to over 20 countries and have been used in some numbers both by the United States Army and the United States Air Force. As a result of experience in use the vehicle has been constantly updated and improved.

There is a separate entry for the Cadillac Gage V-300 (6 × 6) armoured vehicle range.

There are two other vehicles on the market today which are very similar in appearance to the Commando, the American Dragoon 300 series and the Portuguese Chaimite, which is known to be in service with Lebanon, Libya, Peru, Philippines and Portugal.

Cadillac Gage has delivered two V-150 S Commando vehicles for evaluation in the LAV competition. One is fitted with a two-man turret armed with a 90 mm Cockerill Mark III gun, 7.62 mm, coaxial and 7.62 mm anti-aircraft machine gun, with the second being armed with a 25 mm M242 Chain Gun, 7.62 mm coaxial and 7.62 mm anti-aircraft machine guns.

Description

The all-welded hull of the V-150 Commando armoured personnel carrier protects the crew from small arms fire up to 7.62 mm in calibre, overhead blast, shell splinters and Molotov cocktails.

The driver is seated at the front of the hull on the left side and has two vision blocks in front of him and one on his left. The vehicle commander sits on the driver's right and has one vision block to his front and one on his right. Both crew members have a single-piece hatch cover over their position that opens to the outside. Early production vehicles had a firing port just behind the driver's and commander's side vision block, but current vehicles do not.

The troop compartment is behind the commander's and driver's position with three infantrymen seated down each side of the hull and one to the rear of the machine gunner's position. They enter and leave the vehicle by two doors in the side of the hull, one on each side. The lower part of the door folds downwards and the upper part, which contains the vision block and firing port, opens to the rear. In each side of the hull, forward of the side door, is a firing port with a vision block over the top. All vision blocks in the V-150 have crash pads and spall shields for additional protection.

In centre of the troop compartment roof is a cupola which can be traversed manually through 360 degrees and has a single-piece hatch cover that opens to the rear. On the forward part of the cupola, which has no observation devices, is a pintle-mounted 7.62 mm machine gun with 200 rounds of ready-use ammunition and another 3000 rounds in reserve in the hull.

There is also an entrance at the rear of the hull on the right side, with the lower part folding downwards and the upper part, which contains the firing port and vision block, opening upwards. Over the top of the passageway that connects the troop compartment with the rear door is a single-piece circular hatch that opens forwards. A further two seats are provided in this passageway.

The engine compartment is at the rear of the hull on the left side with access panels in the top and side of the hull. The engine cooling system is a conventional automotive water-cooled system utilising a fin and tubed radiator with an additional surge tank for reserve capacity. The engine fan and venturi are designed for maximum air flow efficiency and minimum horsepower draw. The cooling system is capable of operating in ambient temperatures of 130° F. The engine compartment has a fire-extinguishing system that is manually operated by the driver.

Wherever possible, standard military automotive components are used in the V-150 Commando, such as the engine, transmission and axles. When originally introduced the Commando V-150 was powered by a Chrysler 361 V-8 petrol engine developing 200 hp at 4000 rpm coupled to a manual transmission with five forward and one reverse gears and a single-speed transfer case. Current production vehicles have a V-8 diesel that develops 202 hp at 3300 rpm coupled to an automatic transmission and a two-speed transfer case.

The solid axles have silent locking differentials and the suspension consists of semi-elliptical springs and hydraulic

V-200 Commando of Singapore Army fitted with two-man Cadillac Gage turret armed with 20 mm Oerlikon cannon and two 7.62 mm machine guns

V-200 Commando 120 mm mortar carrier of Singapore Army with roof hatches, side and rear doors open

double-acting shock absorbers with rebound control at each wheel station. Jounce control is by hollow rubber springs at each wheel station. The run-flat tyres, which are capable of operation for a distance of 40 km, have self-cleaning treads. Mounted internally at the front of the hull is a winch with a capacity of 4536 kg, which has 48.76 metres of 9.5 mm diameter cable. All members of the Commando family are fully amphibious being propelled in the water by their wheels.

Standard equipment on all vehicles includes fuel and water can, two hand-held fire extinguishers, pioneer tool set, tow cable, breaker bar and lug wrench, first aid kit, snatch block, vehicle tool kit (including 8000 kg hydraulic jack stowed inside the vehicle), pamphlet bag, oddment box, slave cable, wiper kit, spare vision blocks and an air compressor with hose.

Optional equipment for the Commando includes smoke or smoke/fragmentation launchers, fixed pintle socket for rear, rear ring mount with 7.62 mm pintle and cradle, ring mount and cradle for 0.30 calibre, 0.50 calibre machine guns or 40 mm automatic grenade launcher, gun shield for fixed pintle socket or ring mount weapon, spotlight for fixed pintle socket or ring mount weapon with or without shield, night vision equipment, periscope for ring mount (standard on 20 mm, 76 mm and 90 mm turret ring mounts), spare periscope and stowage, weapons (where applicable), extra spare barrel stowage, hand held weapon stowage, M26 hand grenade stowage, smoke hand grenade stowage, binocular stowage, radios and associated mountings, canopy with poles (pod type vehicles only), vision blocks in pod (standard on Police ERV), gun ports in pod (standard on police ERV),

sight M28C × 5.6 power (MG turret vehicles only), land navigation system and /or vehicle heading reference system, NBC system, public address system (standard on Police ERV), heater kit, air-conditioning system, wiper kit for driver, blackout covers, handbrake warning light, cooker kit and lifting boom.

Variants

Commando with MG Turret

Basic vehicle fitted with Cadillac Gage one-man turret which can mount twin 7.62 mm or twin 0.30 calibre machine guns or a combination of 7.62 mm/0.50 calibre machine guns or 0.30/0.50 calibre machine guns. Laying and control of the weapons are mechanical with a hand-operated gearbox that allows 360 degrees continuous traverse, and a gunner's handle at the rear of the balanced gun cradle which allows elevation from −13 degrees to +55 degrees. The turret has a single-piece hatch cover that opens to the rear, eight vision blocks and an M28C sight with a magnification of ×1.5. Mounted coaxially with the weapon is a 500 000 candlepower spotlight. When fitted with twin 7.62 mm machine guns 3800 rounds of ammunition are carried of which 800 rounds are in the turret for ready use and 3000 in the hull. This model has a crew of three and can carry seven infantrymen. Height to top of turret is 2.54 metres and gross vehicle weight is 8981 kg.

Commando with 1-metre MG Turret

Basic vehicle fitted with Cadillac Gage one-metre turret which can be armed with twin 7.62 mm, twin 0.30 calibre or

170

twin 0.50 calibre machine guns, or a combination of these weapons. The turret has a manual traverse through 360 degrees and the guns have an elevation of +55 degrees and a depression of −10 degrees. The turret has a single-piece hatch cover that opens to the rear, an M28C sight with a magnification of ×1.5, eight vision blocks and a 500 000 candlepower spotlight. Depending on the armament installed 1400 rounds of 0.50 calibre ammunition are carried, of which 400 are for ready use in the turret, or 3800 rounds of 0.30 or 7.62 mm ammunition of which 800 are for ready use in the turret. This model has a crew of three and can carry seven infantrymen. Height to the top of turret is 2.59 metres and gross vehicle weight is 8754 kg.

Commando with 1-metre 20 mm Turret

Basic vehicle with one-man turret armed with 20 mm Oerlikon 204 GK cannon with provision for coaxial 7.62 mm machine gun. Gun can be elevated from −8 to +55 degrees at 40 degrees a second and turret traversed through 360 degrees at 60 degrees a second. Traverse is electro-hydraulic with manual back up. Turret has eight vision blocks and a sight with a magnification of ×8 and ×1, and a 500 000 candlepower searchlight that moves in elevation with the armament and a blower for removing turret fumes.

A total of 400 rounds of 20 mm ammunition are carried, 200 in the turret ready to use and 200 in hull, and 3200 rounds of 7.62 mm ammunition, 220 for ready use and the remainder in hull.

This model has a three-man crew consisting of commander, gunner and driver and can carry five men, a loaded weight of 9072 kg and a height of 2.895 metres.

Commando with 20 mm Turret

Basic vehicle fitted with a two-man turret armed with a 20 mm Oerlikon 204 GK cannon, with a 7.62 mm machine gun mounted coaxially to the left of the main armament and a 7.62 mm anti-aircraft machine gun mounted on the turret roof. The cannon has an internally controlled hydraulic charger, emergency firing trigger for the commander and rate controller which allows firing of one, two or four rounds per

V-150 S fitted with two-man turret armed with 25 mm Hughes Helicopters M242 Chain Gun and 7.62 mm M240 coaxial machine gun

V-150 fitted with one-man turret armed with 40 mm Mk 19 grenade launcher and 12.7 mm M2 HB machine gun

second or fully automatic. Turret traverse is a full 360 degrees at 60 degrees a second with elevation from −8 to +60 degrees at 40 degrees a second. The electro-hydraulic controls are the same as in the 76 mm and 90 mm turrets and are scaled down versions of the Cadillac Gage system used in the M60 and Leopard 1 MBTs. Either the commander or the gunner can aim and fire the armament. Turret vision equipment consists of four vision blocks (two in each side of the turret), commander's periscope that can be traversed through a full 360 degrees and a gunner's sight with a magnification of ×8 and a periscope with a projected reticle. In addition to the main sights the turret has an external anti-aircraft sight. It is also provided with a 500 000 candlepower spotlight and a turret blower. Of 400 rounds of 20 mm ammunition carried 200 are for ready use and of 3200 rounds of 7.62 mm ammunition 400 are in the turret for ready use and 200 at the anti-aircraft gun for ready use. This model has a crew of three and can carry two infantrymen. The gross vehicle weight is 9888 kg and the height to the top of the turret is 2.54 metres.

Commando with 25 mm turret

This turret was installed on the V-150 S Commando entered in the Light Armored Vehicle competition. It is armed with a 25 mm M242 Hughes Helicopters Chain Gun, 7.62 mm M240 coaxial MG and a similar weapon on the turret roof for anti-aircraft defence. Two hundred and thirty 25 mm ready rounds (170 HE and 60 AP) are carried in the turret with a further 400 in the vehicle. There are 400 rounds of 7.62 mm ready use ammunition in the turret, 200 at the anti-aircraft station and a further 1000 rounds in the vehicle.

The turret has powered traverse (360 degrees at 30 degrees at second) and elevation (from −8 degrees to +60 degrees at 30 degrees a second). Vision equipment includes an M36E1 day/night sight for the gunner and eight periscopes for the commander. The commander can also have an M36E1 day/night sight but only six periscopes are then fitted.

Commando with 40 mm/12.7 mm turret

This is fitted with a one-man turret armed with a 40 mm Mk 19 Mod 3 grenade launcher on the left and a 12.7 mm M2 HB machine gun on the right and four smoke dischargers mounted either side of the turret at the rear. The weapon can be elevated from −8 degrees to +45 degrees and turret traverse is a full 360 degrees.

171

Cadillac Gage 20 mm Vulcan air defence vehicle in firing position with outriggers deployed

Commando V-150 S

This was announced in 1981 with two vehicles being de-livered for evaluation in the LAV competition late in the same year. Both vehicles had a two-man turret, one armed with a 90 mm Cockerill Mk III gun and the second with a 25 mm M242 Hughes Chain Gun, both having a 7.62 mm coaxial and a 7.62 mm anti-aircraft machine gun. The V-150 S is very similar to the V-150 but is slightly heavier, has a longer hull and longer wheelbase.

Commando Air Defence Vehicle

This is the basic vehicle fitted with the same turret as mounted on the 20 mm M167 towed system. Of 1300 rounds of 20 mm ammunition carried 500 are for ready use. The six-barrelled 20 mm cannon has an elevation of +80 degrees and a depression of −5 degrees at a speed of 45 degrees a second and a traverse through a full 360 degrees at a speed of 60 degrees a second. This model has a crew of four: driver, gunner, commander and radio operator. To provide a more stable firing platform stabilisers are lowered to the ground when the system is deployed. This entered production for Saudi Arabia in 1981.

Commando with 76 mm Turret-mounted Gun

This model is fitted with a two-man power-operated turret armed with the 76 mm L23A1 gun as installed on the British

Scorpion CVR(T), with a 7.62 mm machine gun mounted coaxially to the left of the main armament and a 7.62 mm anti-aircraft machine gun on the turret roof. Turret traverse is a full 360 degrees at 45 degrees a second and elevation is from −10 degrees to +30 degrees at 45 degrees a second. The electro-hydraulic control system is identical to that installed in the 20 mm turret. Vision equipment consists of three vision blocks (two in the left side of the turret and one in the right), a commander's periscope that can be traversed through a full 360 degrees, gunner's periscope with a magnification of ×8 and a unity periscope with a projected reticle. A 500 000 candlepower spotlight is mounted co-axially with the main armament. Of 41 rounds of 76 mm ammunition carried ten rounds are in the turret for ready use and of 3200 rounds of 7.62 mm ammunition 400 are in the turret for ready use and 200 at the anti-aircraft position. This model has a crew of three and can carry three infantrymen. Gross vehicle weight is 9888 kg. As of early 1983 the 76 mm version had not been placed in production.

Commando with 90 mm Turret-mounted Gun

This was originally armed with the Belgian Mecar gun but is now offered with the Cockerill Mk III gun. Mounted co-axially with the main armament is a 7.62 mm machine gun and a similar weapon is fitted on the turret roof for anti-aircraft defence. Turret traverse is a full 360 degrees at 30

V-150 fitted with two-man turret armed with 76 mm L23A1 gun, 7.62 mm coaxial and 7.62 mm anti-aircraft machine guns

degrees a second, and elevation is from −8 to +28 degrees at 30 degrees a second. The electro-hydraulic control equipment is identical to that installed in the 20 mm turret. Vision equipment consists of three vision blocks (two in left and one in right side of the turret), commander's periscope that can be traversed through 360 degrees, gunner's periscope with a magnification of ×8 and a unity periscope with projected reticle. A 500 000 candlepower spotlight is mounted coaxially with the main armament. Of 39 rounds of 90 mm

ammunition carried, eight are for ready use in the turret and of 3200 rounds of 7.62 mm machine gun ammunition 400 are for ready use in the turret and 200 for the anti-aircraft machine gun. This model has a crew of three and can carry four infantrymen, gross vehicle weight being 9888 kg. In 1983 the V-150 Commando with the Marconi Space and Defence Systems Digital Fire Control System was successfully demonstrated. This gives a high first round hit probability and is suitable for installation in a wide range of other tracked and wheeled vehicles.

Commando with 81 mm Mortar

This is armed with an 81 mm M29 turntable-mounted mortar that fires through the roof of the vehicle, and can be traversed through a full 360 degrees and elevated from +42 degrees to +85 degrees. Its minimum range is 150 metres and maximum range 4400 metres. When not in action the roof is covered by concertina doors that open either side of the vehicle. Provision is made for mounting a 7.62 mm machine gun at any one of four positions around the top of the hull and 2000 rounds of ammunition are carried for it. A total of 62 81 mm mortar bombs are carried and if required the mortar can be removed from the vehicle and fired from the ground. This model has a five-man crew and a gross vehicle weight of 8845 kg.

Commando with TOW ATGW System

This is almost identical to the above model but is fitted with a Hughes TOW ATGW system which has an elevation of +30 degrees, a depression of −10 degrees and 360-degree traverse. A total of seven TOW missiles are carried. When

V-150 fitted with two-man Cadillac Gage turret armed with 90 mm Mecar gun, 7.62 mm coaxial and 7.62 mm anti-aircraft machine guns and smoke dischargers at turret rear

V-150 S with two-man turret armed with 90 mm Cockerill Mk III gun with externally mounted laser rangefinder, 7.62 mm coaxial and 7.62 mm anti-aircraft machine guns

not in action the top of the vehicle is covered by hatches that open to the front and rear. Provision is made for mounting a 7.62 mm machine gun at any one of four positions around the top of the hull and 2000 rounds of ammunition are carried for this weapon. This model has a four-man crew and can also carry two infantrymen. Gross vehicle weight is 8958 kg.

Commando Command Vehicle
This is the standard vehicle fitted with a fixed armoured pod mounted at the roof opening. In each of the four sides of the pod is a firing port and in the roof is a single-piece hatch cover

that opens to the rear, forward of which is a 7.62 mm pintle-mounted machine gun. Of 2000 rounds of 7.62 mm ammunition carried, 200 are for ready use. Internally the vehicle has a mapboard, table and additional communications equipment. In addition to the three-man crew seven staff members are carried. Overall height without the machine gun is 2.311 metres.

Base Security Vehicle
This was originally developed for the United States Air Force and like the mortar carrier has concertina hatch covers that

V-150 armed with turret-mounted Belgian Cockerill Mk III 90 mm gun, 7.62 mm coaxial and 7.62 mm anti-aircraft machine guns and smoke dischargers on turret rear

V-150 Commando fitted with 81 mm mortar with roof hatches open

V-150 Commando fitted with command pod and externally-mounted 7.62 mm machine gun

Police Emergency Rescue Vehicle (ERV) with fixed pod

Cadillac Gage V-150 recovery vehicle armed with 12.7 mm M2 HB machine gun with A frame stowed to rear

SPECIFICATIONS (Commando V-150 with turret-mounted 20 mm cannon. Specifications in brackets relate to V-150 S Commando)

CREW	3 + 9	SIDE SLOPE	30%	ELECTRICAL SYSTEM	24 V
CONFIGURATION	4 × 4	VERTICAL OBSTACLE	0.609 (0.91) m	BATTERIES	2 × 12 V, 100 Ah
COMBAT WEIGHT	9888 (10 433) kg	TURNING RADIUS	8.382 (8.5) m	ARMAMENT	
POWER-TO-WEIGHT		ENGINE	V-8 diesel developing	(main)	1 × 20 mm
RATIO	20.42 hp/tonne		202 bhp at 3300 rpm	(coaxial)	1 × 7.62 mm MG
LENGTH	5.689 (6.14) m	TRANSMISSION	automatic, 4	(anti-aircraft)	1 × 7.62 mm MG
WIDTH	2.26 m		forward, 1	SMOKE-LAYING	
HEIGHT			reverse gears	EQUIPMENT	optional
(to turret roof)	2.54 m	CLUTCH	single plate,	AMMUNITION	
(to hull top)	1.981 m		hydraulically actuated	(main)	400
GROUND CLEARANCE		TRANSFER CASE	2-speed (with	(7.62 mm)	3200
(axles)	0.381 m		spline engagement for	FIRE-CONTROL SYSTEM	
(hull)	0.648 m		front axle drive)	Turret power control	electro-hydraulic/
TRACK		STEERING	power-assisted		manual
(front)	1.914 m	SUSPENSION	semi-elliptical springs	By commander	yes
(rear)	1.943 m		and double-acting	By gunner	yes
WHEELBASE	2.667 (3.12) m		hydraulic shock	Max rate power	
MAX SPEED			absorbers	traverse	60°/s
(road)	88.54 km/h	TYRES	14.50 × 21	Max rate power	
(water)	4.828 km/h	BRAKES		elevation	40°/s
ACCELERATION	0–32.2 km/h/10 s	(main)	hydraulic, dual	Gun elevation/	
FUEL CAPACITY	303 litres		circuit	depression	+60°/−8°
MAX RANGE	643 km	(parking)	drum acting on	Turret traverse	360 degrees
FORDING	amphibious		output shaft of		
GRADIENT	60%		transmission		

In 1982 Cadillac Gage announced that they had developed a Cummins V-6 diesel conversion kit as a direct replacement for the V-8 diesel installed in the V-150. When fitted with this engine the V-150 has an operational range of 800 km compared to the standard V-8 model with 644 km, with an acceleration of 0 to 32 km/h in nine seconds. This kit can be installed with no special tools or other equipment at base workshop level.

Status: In production. In service with Bolivia (V-100), Botswana (11 delivered in 1980), Cameroon (V-150 additional 24 ordered in 1983 at a cost of $13.1 million), Domican Republic, Ethiopia (V-150)*, Haiti (V-150), Gabon (V-150), Guatemala (V-150), Indonesia (V-150), Jamaica (V-150), Malaysia (V-150), Oman (V-150), Philippines (V-150), Saudi Arabia (ambulance, APC, ARV, 20 mm anti-aircraft, 81 mm mortar, 90 mm gun and Hughes TOW), Singapore (V-150 and V-200), Somalia (V-150)*, Sudan (V-150), Taiwan, Thailand (V-150), Tunisia (V-150), Turkey (V-150), USA (V-100) Venezuela, and Viet-Nam (V-100). Note: the United States Army designation for the V-100 is the M706.

Manufacturer: Cadillac Gage Company, Post Office Box 1027, Warren, Michigan 48090, USA.

*probably out of service

open either side of the vehicle. Provision is made for mounting 7.62 mm machine guns or 40 mm grenade launchers in four positions at the front, sides and rear. A total of 3000 rounds of 7.62 mm ammunition are carried. This model has a crew of three and can carry eight fully-equipped infantrymen, weighs 9072 kg and is 2.311 metres high.

Police Emergency Rescue Vehicle (ERV)
This model has a fixed pod with six vision blocks and eight vertical gun ports. In the roof is a single-piece hatch cover that opens to the rear and in front of which is a 7.62 mm or a 12.7 mm machine gun. This model has a three-man crew and can carry nine additional men and weighs 9162 kg. It is used by a number of police authorities and a large number was purchased by Turkey.

Recovery Vehicle
This is fitted with a heavy-duty winch with a maximum capacity of 11 340 kg which is provided with 60.9 metres of 19 mm diameter cable. The boom is pivoted at the front of the vehicle and when required hinges forward to the front of the vehicle. When it is being used two stabilisers are lowered at the front. The boom has a maximum capacity of 4536 kg with the stabilisers in position. Armament consists of a 7.62 mm or a 12.7 mm machine gun with 2200 rounds of ammunition.

Lynx (or M113) Command and Reconnaissance Vehicle

Development
This Command and Reconnaissance Vehicle was developed as a private venture by the FMC Corporation with the first prototype being completed in 1963. Although tested by the United States Army it was not adopted by them as they had already selected the M114 Command and Reconnaissance Carrier which is itself very similar in appearance to the FMC

Lynx command and reconnaissance vehicle

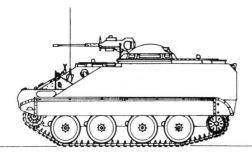

vehicle. The M114 has now been phased out of service with the United States Army.

The vehicle shares many common automotive components with the M113A1 armoured personnel carrier but is much lower, has its engine at the back instead of the front and has one fewer road wheel each side. The vehicle has so far been bought by two countries, Canada and the Netherlands. Canada calls the vehicle the Lynx and the first of 174 vehicles was completed in May 1968. The Dutch Army ordered 250 vehicles, the first of which was completed in September 1966. The Dutch call the vehicle the M113 C & R.

Description (Lynx)
The all-welded aluminium armour hull of the Lynx provides the crew with protection from small arms fire, flash burns and shell fragments.

The driver is seated at the front of the vehicle on the left side and has a single-piece hatch cover that opens to the rear with an integral M19 infra-red periscope mounted in its roof and five M17 periscopes arranged around the forward part in the roof.

The commander, who also operates the main armament, is seated to the right and rear of the driver and is provided with an M26 turret that can be traversed manually through 360 degrees, and has eight vision blocks for all-round observation.

The third crew member, the radio operator/observer, is seated to the left rear of the commander/gunner and is provided with a single-piece hatch cover that opens to the rear.

Canadian Armed Forces Lynx command and reconnaissance vehicle showing position of two machine guns (Canadian Armed Forces)

Canadian Armed Forces Lynx command and reconnaissance vehicle

Three M17 and one M17C periscopes are mounted in the roof of the vehicle around the hatch cover.

Access to the engine at the rear of the hull on the right side is by a large hatch in the roof that opens to the right. In addition there is an access door in the hull rear which opens to the left. The GMC 6V-53 diesel is coupled to an Allison TX100 transmission, which transmits power via a propeller shaft to the FMC DS200 controlled differential at the front of the hull, to which access is by an opening in the glacis plate.

The torsion bar suspension consists of four dual road wheels each side with the drive sprocket at the front and the idler wheel at the rear. There are no track return rollers. The tops of the tracks are covered by a rubber cover which can be removed to reduce the overall width of the vehicle.

The Lynx is fully amphibious, being propelled in the water by its tracks. Before entering the water a trim vane is erected at the front of the hull and rectangular covers are erected around the air inlet and exhaust louvres on the top of the hull.

Standard equipment includes infra-red driving lights and a fire extinguisher mounted in the engine compartment that can be operated by the driver or from outside the vehicle.

Optional equipment includes an NBC detection and alarm system, heater, windscreen and a capstan drum which, when attached to the drive sprockets and used in conjunction with an anchor and cables, can be used for self-recovery.

The M26 turret is armed with a 12.7 mm (0.50) M2 HB machine gun that can be aimed and fired from within the vehicle. Turret traverse and elevation of the main armament are manual. A 7.62 mm (0.30) machine gun is mounted at the radio-operator/observer's station at the rear of the hull and three smoke dischargers are mounted on either side of the hull at the front.

Variants

Dutch Vehicle

The Dutch vehicle has a layout slightly different from that of the Canadian Lynx. The driver is seated at the front of the vehicle on the left and has a single-piece hatch cover that opens to the rear with an integral M19 infra-red periscope mounted in its roof and four M17 periscopes arranged around the forward part in the roof. The radio-operator/gunner is seated to the right of the driver and has a hatch cover that opens to the rear and four M17 periscopes arranged around the forward part of the hatch cover. A 7.62 mm machine gun can be mounted forward of this hatch cover if required. There is an entry door in the right side of the hull, to the rear of the radio-operator/gunner.

When originally delivered the Dutch vehicles were armed with a 12.7 mm (0.50) machine gun but in May 1974 the Dutch Army ordered 266 Oerlikon GBD-AOA turrets armed with a 25 mm Oerlikon KBA-B cannon for installation on the vehicles. The 25 mm cannon has three rates of fire, single shot, 175 or 570 rounds per minute, and has 120 rounds of HE and 80 rounds of APDS-T ready-use ammunition. The turret

178

Dutch Army command and reconnaissance vehicle fitted with Oerlikon GBD-AOA turret armed with 25 mm cannon

has manual traverse and elevation, traverse a full 360 degrees and elevation limits from −12 to +52 degrees. The gunner is provided with a forward facing periscope adjustable in height, six vision blocks and a monocular sight for engaging both ground and air targets and a mechanical auxiliary sight.

Model of FMC C & R vehicle with one-man weapon station armed with 25 mm Hughes Chain Gun and 7.62 mm MAG-58 coaxial machine gun. This model would have M113A2 suspension, 300 hp engine coupled to Detroit Allison X200 transmission. Loaded weight would be less than 9980 kg

Optional Armament Installations

FMC also offers the following armament installations: Model 100-E cupola with a 7.62 mm (0.30) M73 machine gun, Model 74 cupola with twin 7.62 mm M73 or twin 0.30 (7.62 mm) M37 machine guns, XM27 cupola (modified M26) with 20 mm Oerlikon cannon, M113 cupola with 12.7 mm (0.30), 7.62 mm (0.50) or 7.62 mm machine gun pintle-mounted, FMC Pedestal Mount with 7.62 mm (0.30),

Systematic drawing of engine, transmission, differential and suspension of Lynx command and reconnaissance vehicle

Oerlikon-Bührle 25 mm KBA cannon as installed in GBD-AOA turret fitted on Dutch Army command and reconnaissance vehicles

12.7 mm (0.50), 20 mm or 25 mm cannon that can be loaded, aimed and fired from within the vehicle, ATGWs mounted in launcher boxes on the roof of the vehicle, 106 mm M40 recoilless rifle mounted on the roof, and other types of turret as requested by the user.

Product Improved Vehicle
For trials purposes FMC has fitted a vehicle with a new tube-over-bar suspension system, similiar to that fitted to its AIFV (as used by the Dutch Army) and a more powerful turbo-charged diesel engine. These modifications give the vehicle improved cross-country performance and a higher road speed.

SPECIFICATIONS
(Dutch vehicle specifications relate to model before conversion with new turret)

Model	Dutch C & R	Canadian Lynx
CREW	3	3
COMBAT WEIGHT	8477 kg	8775 kg
UNLOADED WEIGHT	7409 kg	7725 kg
POWER-TO-WEIGHT RATIO	25.36 hp/tonne	24.5 hp/tonne
GROUND PRESSURE	0.46 kg/cm²	0.48 kg/cm²
LENGTH	4.597 m	4.597 m
WIDTH	2.413 m	2.413 m
(reduced)	2.266 m	2.266 m
HEIGHT		
(to hull top)	1.651 m	1.651 m
(with armament)	2.108 m	2.171 m
GROUND CLEARANCE	0.406 m	0.406 m
TRACK	1.885 m	1.885 m
TRACK WIDTH	381 mm	381 mm
LENGTH OF TRACK ON GROUND	2.39 m	2.39 m
MAX SPEED		
(road)	70.8 km/h	70.8 km/h
(water)	6.6 km/h	5.6 km/h
ACCELERATION		
(0–48 km/h)	18.5 s	18.5 s
FUEL CAPACITY	330 litres	303 litres

Model	Dutch C & R	Canadian Lynx
MAX CRUISING RANGE	523 km	523 km
FORDING	amphibious	amphibious
GRADIENT	60%	60%
SIDE SLOPE	30%	30%
VERTICAL OBSTACLE	0.609 m	0.609 m
TRENCH	1.473 m	1.524 m
ENGINE	GMC Detroit Diesel 6V-53, 6-cylinder, 2-stroke, water-cooled diesel developing 215 hp at 2800 rpm	
TRANSMISSION	Allison TX100 with torque converter, 3 forward and 1 reverse gears	
SUSPENSION	torsion bar	torsion bar
ELECTRICAL SYSTEM	24 V	24 V
BATTERIES	2 × 12 V	2 × 12 V
ARMAMENT		
(main)	1 × 12.7 mm MG	1 × 12.7 mm MG
(secondary)	1 × 7.62 mm MG	1 × 7.62 mm MG (optional)
SMOKE-LAYING EQUIPMENT	2 × 3 smoke dischargers	2 × 3 smoke dischargers
AMMUNITION		
(main)	1000	1155
(secondary)	2000	2000

Status: Production has been completed for the Canadian and Dutch armies but can be resumed if further orders are received.

Manufacturer: FMC Corporation, Ordnance Division, 1105 Coleman Avenue, San Jose, California 95108, USA.

Chrysler MAC-1 Armoured Car

Development

The Chrysler MAC-1 (Medium Armoured Car) was developed as a private venture by the Defense Group of the Chrysler Corporation in the early 1960s. Wherever possible standard automotive components were used. A small quantity, believed to be 15, was delivered to Mexico between 1963 and 1964. The vehicle is no longer in production and no longer offered by Chrysler.

Chrysler also proposed a further development of the MAC-1 called the MAC-11, which had the same wheelbase as the earlier vehicle but was heavier, powered by a 276 hp engine and would have been fully amphibious being propelled in the water by its wheels at a speed of 6.43 km/h. The MAC-11 was never built even as a prototype. Chrysler also designed an 8 × 8 vehicle called the SWAT (Special Warfare Armoured Transporter), but it never progressed beyond the mock-up stage and is no longer being offered.

Description

The hull of the MAC-1 is made of all-welded steel with the driver and commander at the front, turret in the centre and the engine at the rear. The driver is seated in the forward part of the vehicle with the commander to his right, each with a single-piece hatch cover that opens outwards. The driver has two periscopes to his front and the commander has one and both also have a periscope to their left and right respectively. The turret is armed with a 20 mm Hispano Suiza cannon and has a single-piece hatch cover that opens forwards. Turret traverse and gun elevation are manual. Immediately behind the turret are two periscopes which give observation to the rear of the vehicle. There are no entry doors in the sides of the hull although two firing ports are provided in each side.

The MAC-1 has no amphibious capability, no NBC system and no night vision equipment.

Chrysler MAC-1 armoured car armed with turret mounted 20 mm cannon

SPECIFICATIONS					
CREW	4	WHEELBASE	2.845 m	TRANSMISSION	Chrysler A727 automatic with torque converter, 3 forward and 1 reverse gears
CONFIGURATION	4 × 4	ANGLE OF APPROACH/ DEPARTURE	58°/53°		
COMBAT WEIGHT	6136 kg	MAX ROAD SPEED	104 km/h	TRANSFER CASE	2-speed
UNLOADED WEIGHT	5681 kg	FUEL CAPACITY	151.4 litres	STEERING	power assisted
POWER-TO-WEIGHT		MAX CRUISING RANGE	483 km	SUSPENSION	semi-elliptical springs
RATIO	29.33 hp/tonne	FORDING	0.914 m	TYRES	11.00 × 20
GROUND PRESSURE	0.95 kg/cm²	GRADIENT	60%	ARMAMENT	1 × 20 mm
LENGTH	5.258 m	VERTICAL OBSTACLE	0.508 m	AMMUNITION	300
WIDTH	2.438 m	TURNING RADIUS		TURRET POWER	
HEIGHT		(left)	7.6 m	CONTROL	manual
(to turret top)	2.108 m	(right)	9.4 m	GUN STABILISER	
GROUND CLEARANCE		ENGINE	Chrysler model HT361 petrol,	(vertical)	no
(hull)	0.457 m		180 hp at 3600 rpm	(horizontal)	no

Status: Production complete. In service only with Mexico.

Manufacturer: Chrysler Corporation Defense Group, 6000 E 17 Mile Road, Sterling Heights, Michigan 48070, USA (now General Dynamics, Land Systems Division).

Cadillac Gage Commando Scout

Development

The Commando Scout (4 × 4) has been designed as a private venture by the Cadillac Gage Company, manufacturer of the well-known Commando range of multi-mission vehicles. The vehicle was first announced in October 1977 at the Association of the United States Army meeting in Washington DC. The basic role of the Commando Scout is reconnaissance and security but it can also be fitted as a command or anti-tank vehicle. In 1983 it was reported that Indonesia had placed an order for a quantity of Commando Scout vehicles as well as Commando Ranger armoured personnel carriers.

Description

The welded hull of the vehicle is made of special hardness armour plate which will defeat at a minimum 7.62 mm armour-piercing rounds. The front, sides and rear of the hull are well sloped to afford maximum protection within the weight of the vehicle.

The front of the Commando Scout is sloped at an angle of 76 degrees to the top of the driver's hatch to the nose. In addition to providing ballistic protection it allows the vehicle to push its way through underbrush.

The driver is seated on the left side of the hull with the engine to his right and is provided with an adjustable seat and a single-piece hatch cover that slides to the front of the

Commando Scout with 1-metre turret

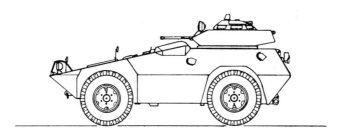

Cadillac Gage Commando Scout fitted with command pod and 7.62 mm pintle-mounted machine gun

182

Cadillac Gage Commando Scout armed with twin 7.62 mm MGs in 1-metre turret

vehicle when he is driving with his head out. There is a vision block in the front part of the hatch for when the vehicle is being driven closed down.

The fuel tank is at the front of the hull between the wheels. The power plant is coupled to an Allison four-speed automatic transmission via a Cadillac Gage power transfer unit. The complete powerpack, consisting of the engine, transfer unit, transmission and cooling system, can be removed and replaced in two hours. Access to the engine is by a large hatch in the right side of the hull through which all fluid levels (coolant, lubricant, brake fluids etc) can be checked.

The turret or pod is at the rear of the vehicle and access is by a two-part hatch in the rear of the hull with the bottom part folding downwards and the top part opening to the right.

The front axle is solid and sprung by a parallel arm arrangement attached to coil springs. The split rear axle is tied to a heavy duty coil spring suspension. Cone-shaped passages in the rear of the hull allow for high individual vertical road wheel travel. Both axles are fitted with positive locking differentials which provide improved traction by preventing one wheel spin-out.

The integral hydraulic power steering is powered by a gear-driven pump working directly off the engine. This approach has eliminated the requirement for belt drives which slip or break and steering cylinders that require maintenance. The independent front and rear brake systems function through a split master cylinder and a back-up system supports them in the event of an engine failure. The back-up system consists of an electric motor which supplies pressure to the master cylinder. The tyres are of the run-flat type. Standard equipment includes two hand-held fire extinguishers stowed inside the vehicle, pioneer tool set, breaker bar and lug wrench, first aid kit, vehicle tool kit, and an air compressor with 15.24-metre hose.

The Commando Scout is not fitted with an NBC system, has no night vision equipment and is not amphibious. Optional equipment includes a siren/public address system, radio installations, weapon stowage, water and petrol can, slave cable, 15.24 metre auxiliary cable, camouflage net, smoke grenade system and fragmentation grenade system.

Variants

Twin/Combination Machine Gun (1-metre) Turret

This turret is manually/electrically rotated by a Power Assist Traverse system and can be armed with twin 7.62 mm, twin 0.30 calibre or twin 0.50 calibre machine guns, or a combination of 0.30/0.50 or 7.62 mm/0.50 calibre machine guns, which can be elevated from −10 to +55 degrees, manually traversed rate with PAT is a maximum of 45 degrees per second. The amount of ammunition depends on the armament installed but if twin 7.62 mm or 0.30 calibre weapons are fitted each gun is provided with 200 rounds of ready-use ammunition and 2200 rounds stowed in the vehicle. If twin 0.50 calibre weapons are fitted, each weapon has 100 rounds of ready-use ammunition and 1000 rounds stowed in the hull. It can also mount a 7.62 mm MG and a 40 mm Mark 19 grenade launcher with 100 ready rounds and 200 rounds stowed in the vehicle. The turret is also provided with eight vision blocks, an M28C sight with a magnification of ×1.5 (×5 magnification optional) and a 500 000 candlepower spotlight mounted coaxially with the weapons.

Cadillac Gage Commando Scout fitted with command pod armed with 12.7 mm MG

Twin Machine Gun (1-metre) Turret

This is armed with twin 7.62 mm machine guns which can be fired singly or together and 400 rounds of ready use ammunition are carried with a further 2200 rounds stowed in the vehicle. It has manual traverse and elevation and the weapons can be elevated from −10 to +55 degrees. The turret is provided with eight vision blocks, and an M28C sight with a magnification of ×1.5 (×5 magnification optional); a 500 000 candlepower spotlight is mounted co-axially with the weapons.

Command Pod

This model has a three-man crew, commander, radio operator and driver and has a pod mounted on top of the hull in each side of which is a firing port and a vision block. A circular hatch cover is provided on which a 7.62 mm machine gun and shield can be mounted. 2000 rounds of 7.62 mm ammunition are carried. When fitted with radios the antennas are mounted at the rear of the hull.

Anti-tank armed with TOW

This model has a crew of three and is fitted with a Hughes TOW ATGW launcher which has a traverse of 120 degrees and can be elevated from −10 to +30 degrees. Two TOW ATGWs are carried inside the hull with provision for carrying a further four missiles outside. A standard TOW ground mount is carried inside the vehicle which enables the TOW system to be deployed away from the vehicle. Two positions

Cadillac Gage Commando Scout armed with 12.7 mm and 7.62 mm MGs in 1-metre turret

for mounting one 7.62 mm machine gun are also provided with 2000 rounds of ammunition being carried for this weapon.

Anti-tank armed with 106 mm Recoilless Rifle

This has a modified pod with opening doors with the 106 mm M40 recoilless rifle pivot-mounted forward of the pod. The recoilless rifle has a traverse of 150 degrees and can be elevated from −10 to +10 degrees. Fifteen rounds of 106 mm ammunition are carried plus 100 rounds of 12.7 mm (0.50) ammunition for the spotting rifle.

Cadillac Gage Commando Scout fitted with Hughes TOW ATGW system

---

SPECIFICATIONS

CREW (depending on role)	1 + 1 or 1 + 2
CONFIGURATION	4 × 4
COMBAT WEIGHT (with twin 7.62 mm MG turret)	6577 kg
POWER-TO-WEIGHT RATIO	24.33 hp/tonne
LENGTH	4.699 m
WIDTH	2.057 m
HEIGHT (with 1-metre turret)	2.235 m
TRACK	1.651 m
WHEELBASE	2.667 m
MAX SPEED (road)	88.5 km/h
FUEL CAPACITY	208 litres
MAX RANGE (road)	800 km
FORDING	1.168 m
GRADIENT	60%
SIDE SLOPE	30%
VERTICAL OBSTACLE	0.609 m
TURNING RADIUS	7.925 m
ENGINE	Cummins V-6 diesel developing 149 hp at 3300 rpm
TRANSMISSION	Allison automatic with 4 forward and 1 reverse speeds
TRANSFER CASE	2-speed with spline engagement clutch for front-axle drive
STEERING	integral hydraulic
SUSPENSION (front)	swing-mounted solid front axle
(rear)	independent rear axle with coil springs for each wheel
TYRES	15.50 × 21
BRAKES (main)	dual power 4-wheel hydraulic, pump driven emergency electrical back up
(parking)	drum and shoe, hand operated
ELECTRICAL SYSTEM	24 V
BATTERIES	2 × 12 V, 100 Ah

NOTE: Height and weight is for vehicle with 1-metre turret and twin 7.62 mm MGs.

Status: In production. On order for Indonesia.

Manufacturer: Cadillac Gage Company, Post Office Box 1027, Warren, Michigan 48090, USA.

Abbreviations

AA anti-aircraft
AAG anti-aircraft gun
ACVT Armored Combat Vehicle Technology Programme
ADATS Air Defence Anti-Tank System
AFV armoured fighting vehicle
Ah ampère hour
AIFV armoured infantry fighting vehicle
AML Automitrailleuse Légère (light armoured car)
AMR Auto Mitrailleuse de Reconnaissance
AMX Atelier de Construction d'Issy-les-Moulineaux
AP armour-piercing
APC armoured personnel carrier
APC armour-piercing capped
APC-T armour-piercing capped tracer
APDS armour-piercing discarding sabot
APDS-T armour-piercing discarding sabot tracer
APE Amphibisches Pionier-Erkundungsfahrzeug (amphibious pioneer reconnaissance vehicle)
APERS anti-personnel
APERS-T anti-personnel tracer
APFSDS armour-piercing fin-stabilised discarding sabot
APFSDS(P) armour-piercing fin-stabilised discarding sabot (practice)
APFSDS-T armour-piercing fin-stabilised discarding sabot tracer
APG Aberdeen Proving Ground
APHE armour-piercing high explosive
API armour-piercing incendiary
APIT armour-piercing incendiary tracer
APT armour-piercing tracer
APU auxiliary power unit
APV armoured patrol vehicle
AR/AAV Armored Reconnaissance/Airborne Assault Vehicle
ARE Atelier de Construction Roanne
ARMSCOR Armament Manufacturing Corporation (South Africa)
ARMVAL Anti-Armor Vehicle Evaluation

AT anti-tank
ATGW anti-tank guided weapon
ATS Atelier de Construction de Tarbes
AVGP armoured vehicle general purpose
AVR armored vehicle reconnaisance

BAOR British Army of the Rhine
BD base detonating
BE base ejection
bhp brake horsepower
BL blank
BLR Blindado Ligero de Ruedas (light wheeled armoured vehicle)
BL-T blank tracer
BMR Blindado Medio de Ruedas (medium wheeled armoured vehicle)

CAF Canadian Armed Forces
CCV Close Combat Vehicle
CFV Cavalry Fighting Vehicle
Comp.B composition B
COTAC Conduite de Tir Automatique pour Char
CP concrete-piercing
CRR Carro de Reconhecimento Sobre Rodas (wheeled reconnaissance vehicle)
CTRA Carro de Transporte Sobre Rodas Anfibo (amphibious wheeled transport vehicle)
CVR(T) Combat Vehicle Reconnaissance (Tracked)
CVR(W) Combat Vehicle Reconnaissance (Wheeled)

DARPA Defense Advanced Projects Agency
DIA Defense Intelligence Agency
DOD Department of Defense
DS/T practice descarding sabot/tracer
DTAT Direction Technique des Armements Terrestres
DU depleted uranium

EBR Engin Blindé de Reconnaissance
EFAB Etablissement d'Etudes et de Fabrications d'Armement de Bourges
ELKE Elevated Kinetic Energy Weapon
EMC Engin Blindé Mortier Cannon
EMG externally mounted gun
ENGESA Engesa Engeheiros Especializados

ERC Engin de Reconnaissance Cannon
ESD Électronique Serge Dassault
ESRS electro slag refined steel
EWK Eisenwerke Kaiserslautern Göppner

FLIR forward looking infra-red
FMC Food Machinery Corporation
FMS Foreign Military Sales
FN Fabrique Nationale
FOV Field of View
FRAG Fragmentation
FV fighting vehicle
FVRDE Fighting Vehicles Research and Development Establishment
FVS Fighting Vehicle System
FY Fiscal Year

GIAT Groupement Industriel des Armements Terrestres
GLS Gesellschaft für Logistischen Service
GMC General Motors Corporation
GPMG general purpose machine gun
GW guided weapon

HB heavy barrel
HE high explosive
HE-APERS-FRAG high-explosive anti-personnel fragmentation
HEAT high-explosive anti-tank
HEAT-MP high-explosive anti-tank multi-purpose
HEAT-MP(P) high-explosive anti-tank multi-purpose (practice)
HEAT-T high-explosive anti-tank tracer
HEAT-T-HVY high-explosive anti-tank tracer heavy
HEAT-T-MP high-explosive anti-tank tracer multi-purpose
HEAT-TP-T high-explosive anti-tank target practice tracer
HEDP high-explosive dual purpose
HE-FRAG high-explosive fragmentation
HEI high-explosive incendiary
HEIT high-explosive incendiary tracer
HEP high-explosive plastic
HE-PR high-explosive practice
HEP-T high-explosive practice tracer
HESH high-explosive squash head
HESH-T high-explosive squash head tracer

HIMAG High-Mobility Agility Test Vehicle

hp horsepower

HSTV(L) High Survivability Test Vehicle (Lightweight)

HVAP high-velocity armour-piercing

HVAPDS-T high-velocity armour-piercing discarding sabot tracer

HVAPFSDS high-velocity armour-piercing fin stabilised discarding sabot

HVAP-T high-velocity armour-piercing tracer

IAFV infantry armoured fighting vehicle

IFV infantry fighting vehicle

ILL illuminating

IMI Israel Military Industries

IOC initial operational capability

IR infra-red

IS internal security

ITV Improved TOW Vehicle

JGSDF Japanese Ground Self-Defence Force

JPO Joint Project Office

KE kinetic energy

LAV Light Armored Vehicle

LAV Light Assault Vehicle

LLLTV low-light level television

LMG light machine gun

MAC Medium Armoured Car

MAP Military Aid Programme

MBT main battle tank

MG machine gun

MICV mechanised infantry combat vehicle

MILAN Missile d'Infanterie Léger Antichar

MoD Ministry of Defence

MPGS Mobile Protected Gun System

MPWS Mobile Protected Weapon System

MV muzzle velocity

MVEE Military Vehicles and Engineering Establishment

NATO North Atlantic Treaty Organisation

NBC nuclear, biological, chemical

PAT power assisted traverse

PRAC practice

PRAC-T practice tracer

PTO power take off

RARDE Royal Armament Research and Development Establishment

RDF/LT Rapid Deployment Force Light Tank

RMG ranging machine gun

ROF Royal Ordnance Factory; rate of fire

RSAF Royal Small Arms Factory

RUC Royal Ulster Constabulary

SAM surface-to-air missile

SAMM Société d'Applications des Machines Motrices

SAPI semi-armour piercing incendiary

SH/PRAC squash head practice

SLR Super Low Recoil

Smoke BE smoke base ejection

Smoke WP smoke white phosporus

SPAAG self-propelled anti-aircraft gun

TACOM Tank Automotive Command

TOW Tube-launched, Optically tracked, Wire-guided

TP target practice

TP-T target practice tracer

TTS tank thermal sight

USMC United States Marine Corps

VAB Véhicule de l'Avant Blindé (front-armoured car)

VAE Vehiculo Armado Exploración (armoured reconnaissance car)

VAPE Vehiculo Apoyo y Exploración (support and reconnaissance vehicle)

VBC Véhicule Blindé Combat (armoured combat vehicle)

VBL Véhicule Blindé Léger (light armoured car)

VCR véhicule de Combat à Roues (wheeled combat vehicle); variable compression ratio

VLC Véhicule Léger de Combat (light armoured car)

VRL Véhicule Reconnaissance Léger (light reconnaissance vehicle)

WAPC Wheeled Armoured Personnel Carrier

WFSV Wheeled Fire Support Vehicle

WMRV Wheeled Maintenance and Recovery Vehicle

WP white phosphorus

WP-T white phosphorus tracer

Index

Light Tanks and Tracked AFVs and their variants in alphabetical order of countries

Note: Type designations in bold print indicate principal models; page numbers in bold print relate to detailed descriptions.

Armoured Cars and other Wheeled AFVs and their variants in alphabetical order of countries